ROBOT HOUSE

Instrumentation Representation Fabrication

PETER TESTA

Forewords by Greg Lynn and Eric Owen Moss

with over 1,600 illustrations

Thames & Hudson

First published in the United Kingdom in 2017 by
Thames & Hudson Ltd, 181A High Holborn, London
WC1V 7QX

This paperback edition 2018

Cover image courtesy Testa & Weiser Inc.

Designed by Omnivore
omnivorous.org

British Library Cataloguing-in-Publication Data
A catalogue record for this book is available from the British Library

ISBN 978-0-500-29344-7

Printed and bound in China by Reliance Printing (Shenzhen) Co. Ltd

CROSS-REFERENCES
Throughout the book, the numbers beside the images refer to the page number of the project or technique with which the image is associated.

Peter Testa is founding partner of Testa & Weiser, an architecture studio known for conceptual and technical breakthroughs, and is a senior design faculty member of SCI-Arc (Southern California Institute of Architecture). Author of three books, he has lectured extensively in the United States and Europe, and is the recipient of numerous awards, including the MIT Innovation in Teaching Award and the Design Arts Award of the National Endowment for the Arts. His work is in the permanent collection of the Canadian Centre for Architecture, and is exhibited at museums worldwide.

Greg Lynn is founder of the design practice FORM, and pioneered the fabrication and manufacture of complex functional and ergonomic forms using CNC machinery. He has been named one of the world's ten most influential living architects by *Forbes* magazine and is recipient of the Golden Lion Award at Venice Biennale of Architecture. His work is in the permanent collections of the Canadian Centre for Architecture and the Museum of Modern Arts, among other international institutions.

Eric Owen Moss, principal of Eric Owen Moss Architects, was director of SCI-Arc between 2002 and 2015. He has received numerous awards and prizes in the field of architecture, including, most recently, the Austrian Decoration of Honor for Science and Art.

1–TECHNIQUES

2–PROJECTS

3—PLATFORM

2.01

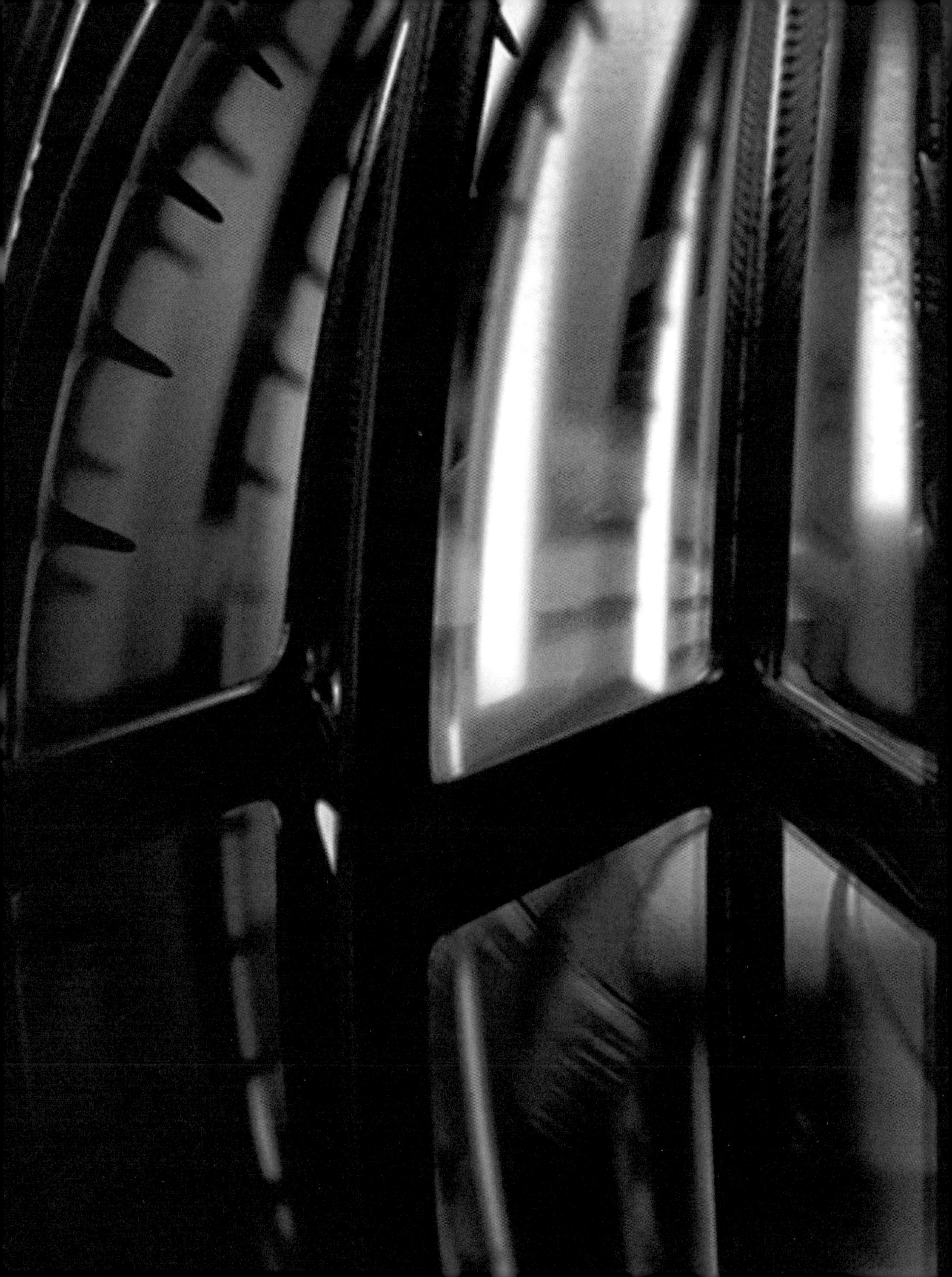

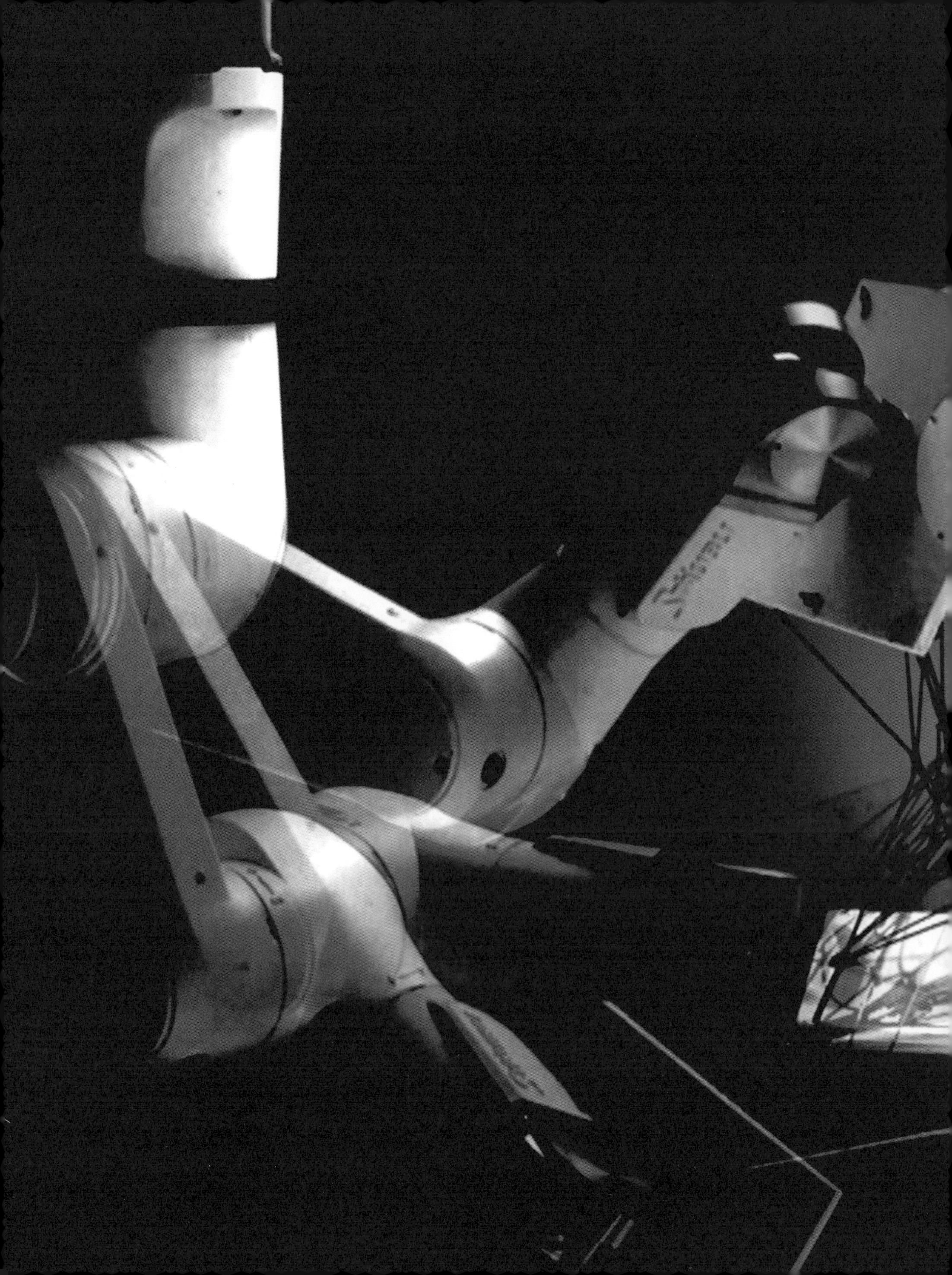

FOREWORD GREG LYNN

Robot House, led by Peter Testa and Devyn Weiser, is a fundamental study of coordinated robotic motion and its possibilities for architecture and design. When it comes to robots, their work is exceptional in a field myopically dedicated to CNC machining. Discovering their work on robotics is reminiscent of the John Travolta and Uma Thurman dance scene at the center of *Pulp Fiction*, or akin to finding a ballet company performing at a convention of carpenters: It is an exception that makes you reevaluate business as usual.

Experimentation with robotics by architects at universities directly followed the use of animation software for design, in near lock-step. First with the use of a IRIX command window that was readily accessible to users of Wavefront, Alias and SoftImage on Silicon Graphics Workstations, and later with AutoLISP and Maya MEL Script Editor tools, a move was made from keyframe animation to scripting. With the shift from keyframing, moving elements to the use of scripting tools for procedural modeling came a focus on form generation and digital fabrication, rather than the choreography of bodies in motion. Speaking for myself, I jumped immediately to stereolithography, then several years later, employed CNC routers for my Embryological House project.

The most cogent theoretical treatise of these methods, that I'm aware of, was written by Bernard Cache, who pioneered the use of design algorithms for direct-to-machine fabrication that generations of architects continue to do the mop-up work on today. Robotics had little to contribute to questions of animation and movement as it instantaneously became merely a tool for fabrication by machine rather than drawing. Design tools unlocked new potential in fabrication as CNC systems were already in place at the steel, glass, metal cladding, concrete and cabinetry fabricators' shops. At UCLA, ETH Zurich and the Angewandte in Vienna, institutions where this became pedagogy fifteen years ago, robotics were merely a precise non-modular facilitating tool for complex methods of construction. Among other facets, Robot House explores methods of digital construction as well.

Recently, the activities of Robot House have cultivated additional interests in animation, which are even more relevant today, when CNC manufacturing is meeting with a resounding lack of interest. I had the pleasure of visiting the Robot House for its first-year review and was astonished. Peter managed to keep the robots out of the school's general shop, and instead conducted fundamental research on the dynamic principles of robotics relevant to architecture beyond the vocational concerns of CNC manufacture.

In a short time a broad spectrum of techniques has been developed, all involving linked robotic motion, which includes: projectors and screens; cameras and sensors; deforming skins under constant tension; time-lapse capture of virtual volumes in space; luminous trails defining surfaces and volumes—all involving between two and five robots working together spatially.

This publication marks a return to the first principles that were sadly neglected in the early rush towards whittling with robots. But this welcome record of the possibilities is better late than never. I will be the first to admit what a lost opportunity it has been not to look at the coordination of machines as a source of inspiration and innovation of the built environment. I offer my thanks to Robot House for pointing out what we should have been thinking about all along.

WHAT'S A ROBOT? ERIC OWEN MOSS

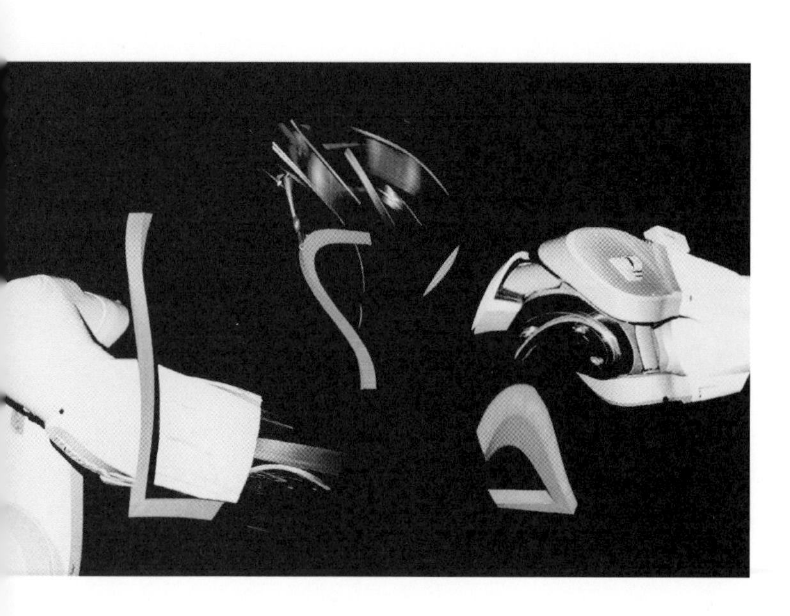

Here's how the TV ad runs: two well-dressed professionals, a man and a woman, are seated in an airport lounge discussing future software prospects. "Do you guys have XYZ software?" she queries. "Are you kidding? Of course. Had it for months," he responds. She leaves to board her plane. He grabs his phone and shouts a directive to his office personnel on the other end: "Get out there immediately, and purchase XYZ," he commands.

The culture would like to shame us if we're not "up to date."

The architecture profession shares that apprehension.

Architects have an intrinsic weakness for what purports to be next.

Schools of architecture teach the aspiration to welcome what might be coming around the corner.

That is, the contemporary education of young architects continues to suggest that a lack of technical capacity is likely to be synonymous with falling behind (presumably behind those who possess that capability).

SCI-Arc has no such intrinsic vulnerability, thanks to its enduring interest in accessing the capacity of new technologies as they arrive, and evaluating how new tools might redefine design, engineering, fabrication, and the construction processes.

SCI-Arc is not ipso facto a technology aficionado, nor a technology chaser.

We're irreverent, but we're curious.

We're interrogators.

SCI-Arc's interest in a particular technical prospect is never to simply validate a current conception of the value or use of a particular piece of equipment, but rather to purchase the equipment for exploratory purposes.

SCI-Arc's job is to interrogate the machine, not to genuflect before it—
a combination of optimism in our ability to evaluate, mixed with some skepticism regarding conventional technical cheerleading.

We might ask—
for a precise accounting of what the "tool" is,
for what purposes it was originally intended,
who are the designers and what are their histories,
how it might be used other than originally intended,

how it might be modified to achieve different purposes,
and finally, whether the prospective new tool has the capacity
to change the architecture discourse.

In other words, if it's new, how is it new?
Four years ago Peter Testa and Devyn Weiser came to me with a curious directive: Let's purchase six Stäubli robots for SCI-Arc.

"Hey guys—what's a robot?"

And so began the discourse.

We want the robot scrutiny to teach us something we don't already know. We want to avoid repeating the a priori caricatures and value judgments. We want to understand whether the tool is mutable. That is, might it allow us to imagine new prospects?

We want to hear what we haven't yet heard.

So the robots must be less a standardized production venue to be exploited (faster/cheaper/more precisely, for instance), and more a learning venue suggesting possible new design and production opportunities.

There are several conventional images that are associated with robots: R2-D2 traversing a movie set was readily dispensed with.

But a sequence of robot-driven operations in the assembly of an automobile, for instance, and by analogy, perhaps, in the construction of a building, might be applicable to the robot adventure at SCI-Arc.

The analogy: First the crank shaft, then the doors, the engine, the tires, and so on. The model of a predictable chronology of operations handled by robots, step by step, over and over again.

That application suggested an expedited efficiency and precision quotient, performing known operations more quickly and accurately: The automobile assembly line example—robots as surrogates of the people who once inhabited that assembly line.

Or were there other possibilities, which would allow us to reimagine the robots' applicability to the inventing of new architecture?

If the analogy was the generic person in the generic assembly line, might the human capacity argument extend beyond a repetitive sequence of predictable operations?

The human prospect suggests the potential for an evolving design conception: We begin to imagine; we draw and model; the conception evolves; we begin to see what originally we didn't see; and in the end, we conclude with what we couldn't have foreseen at the outset.

Could the robots, by analogy, redefine their intentions in the midst of a developing design process? Could the robots revise and reprogram as a consequence of newly perceived data that changes the original conception?

In other words, can robots "change their minds"?

SCI-Arc bought the robots to inculcate unpredictability.

The assembly line conception also suggested a series of specified operations produced one operation at a time. Could we choreograph a varying sequence of integrated operations utilizing multiple robots simultaneously, with that evolving conception of design image and purpose?

In other words, could the robots dance together?

SCI-Arc bought the robots to explore the choreography prospect.

And finally, aside from the predictable history of mechanized operations, could we imagine the robots used, not so much in a pre-programmed or post-programmed chronology of operations, but instead, to invent? Could the robots originate?

In other words, could the robots sketch?

SCI-Arc bought the robots to teach them to draw.

Peter and Devyn's robot-mind-changing, robot-choreography, and robot-inventing discourse is on-going at SCI-Arc.

PREFACE
PETER TESTA

Robot House is an interactive robotics program that is shaping the discourse of post-digital design culture. Inspired by vital Los Angeles antecedents, from Gehry Technologies to Disney Imagineering and from Google's Alphabet to SpaceX, this initiative opens a new chapter in the evolution of design in architecture and its allied fields. Based at SCI-Arc (the Southern California Institute of Architecture), Robot House is a platform for investigating a unique interface that enables and encourages architects, artists, designers, and directors to bridge digital and physical worlds. Without reducing the digital to the physical, this speculative initiative builds a flexible new apparatus and infrastructure. Robot House is conceived of as a construction that takes robotics as its model but that in itself is not about robotics in the technical sense. Robotics become a "theoretical installation," a conduit to explore a new discourse on spatial perception and representation. By rethinking architecture's instrumentation, this apparatus is arguably the first significant reimagining of design protocol since the introduction of animated 3D digital modeling and algorithmic design over a decade ago.

The body of work produced in Robot House turns inwards, towards first principles, tied to a history of instrumentation and experimentation with techniques of representation in architecture; and outwards, towards a rapidly transforming material culture. Continuing a line of development that extends from Leon Battista Alberti's window to Ivan Sutherland's Sketchpad (the program that inaugurated the interfaces and tools of the digital revolution), Robot House transforms architectural practice from within by working on its instrumentation and modelization. Moving beyond now familiar tropes of "digital design," this new space of speculation is open to the incursions and possibilities of new media. With first-hand knowledge of technologies from artificial intelligence (AI) to machine vision (MV) that are coming to dominate the cultural landscape, projects emerging from Robot House's experimentation can be redeployed and form the basis for alternative design practices.

A measure of success is the capacity to renew the field and the ability of designers to apply these approaches to the transformation of architectural representation, theory, and practice—to think differently and lead new enterprises. In just a few years Robot House has engendered thinking about the analogue and the digital not as separate, but as a continuum. Robot House has been influential globally in structuring other initiatives in academia and architectural research but also across a wide range of art practices and industries, including cinema, product design, and mobility design, in addition to architecture and construction. The aesthetics of the apparatus itself has captured the imagination of leading film and art directors, as evidenced in numerous film projects and popular media that exploit the digital–physical interface of Robot House.

The book is structured in three parts, beginning with texts identifying major themes and positioning Robot House as an apparatus of speculative design. This is followed by a thematic survey of projects—organized in relation to the triad Instrumentation, Representation, Fabrication—that imagine what design after the digital might look like, and is concluded with a section documenting the apparatus and interfaces specific to Robot House and a glossary of terms providing a conceptual reference to ideas and techniques. The layout of the book is envisioned as a mapping of ideas, images, and information that may be assimilated as part of a larger debate on architectural theory, practice and education.

ON THE HOUSE
PETER TESTA

FROM FABRICATION TO NON-FABRICATION

Fabrication, particularly since the advent of the digital, claims precedence of the performative over the abstract and speculative. While groundbreaking work in digital fabrication is being carried out, Robot House proposes another position that no longer privileges fabrication and its technological focus, which might be called "non-fabrication." Non-fabrication is not the simple absence of fabrication, but a withdrawal or suspension of the primacy of fabrication in order to undertake a new practice that instead creates a kind of artistic fiction. No longer limited to the physical creation of what has been digitally envisioned, the focus on modelization, virtualization, and fictionalization yields another "idea of fabrication," as Marcel Duchamp explored in *3 Standard Stoppages*.[1] Although opening models up to material agency (the way in which inanimate objects or technology can influence actions), this proposition acknowledges that reality cannot be reduced to causal relations of material interaction (cause and effect).

Paradoxically, while Robot House remains focused on abstract design protocols, breakthroughs in fabrication have resulted from misreading, picking up the wrong information, or contingent (chance) arrangements of the apparatus. These contingent models of non-fabrication harness the discrepancy, or non-correlation, between digital and physical processes to create new workflows. This methodology may be seen as a "post-facture," as opposed to "manufacture," as it is often not possible to discern how images and artifacts were made.[2] The robot is not used as an instance that needs to maintain its trace (that is, the robot's involvement does not need to be obvious) but rather as a part of a more complex superposition that lies outside the duality of artisanal and mechanical, or digital and analog. Non-fabrication is not intended to supplant, or substitute fabrication but to demonstrate that it is possible to define design without perpetuating the schism between digital and physical realms. The conflation of digital and analog challenges the repetition and continuities that have become the hallmark of algorithm-driven design as the most prevalent strain of digital practice.

FROM BINARY CODE TO GENERIC MATRIX

A new vision of the design interface as a whole is proposed in which digital and physical workspaces are cloned. These two different modalities are not synthesized or opposed but run alongside each other in superposition. This apparatus challenges the naturalized and automated synthesis of "computational descriptions" and "physical descriptions" within the interfaces and technical systems with which architects and designers increasingly work.[3] By interrupting and corrupting the computer's capacity for synthesis, connection, and communication, Robot House takes up residence between these two antithetical descriptions—computational and physical—without resolution or linear correlation. Under the regime of what media theorist Lev Manovich calls "softwarization"—the process by which all aspects of conception and materialization become encapsulated in software—constructing non-unitary versions of the digital/physical interface (that is, interfaces that are not based on reducing one type of information, representation, or data structure to the other) becomes a creative act in itself.[4] This new type of design interface is not to restore earlier analog systems of representation or to reflect on automation, but to see the conventional hierarchy of image, object, and matter as artificial and not determining in the first place.

Borrowing from French philosopher François Laruelle's idea of the computer, Robot House may be best understood as a "generic matrix or collider, producer, detector of new thought particles rather than devoted to formal calculation."[5] Unlike the homogeneity of the digital computer, the non-correlated parts of Robot House's "generic matrix" can interoperate despite their differences. In the construction of this apparatus the robot is just one object among others—an element in a retooled digital/physical design interface. Withdrawn from its industrial context, the robot is taken offline and broken by subversion of its technical representation and control model that strive for perfection and objectivity. The robot arm is reprogrammed as an improvisational technology—an underdetermined (unexplored, little understood, and open to interpretation) generic object.

FROM HOMOGENEOUS SPACE TO HETEROGENEOUS SPACE

Robot House problematizes a whole series of assumptions regarding the homogeneous space of digitality. Multiple human and nonhuman viewpoints, and participation in the space of action, have everything to do with this apparatus that mobilizes space and time differently. Most significant is the enactment of an immanentist viewpoint—that is, the viewpoint is placed within the motion/material construct. In this way, a unique field of thought is created at the cutting edge of theory—"to think not about motion but according to motion."

When working with multiple synchronous and asynchronous robot systems, a series of innovations in kinematics and nonlinear time-based and event-based motion control grants reciprocal determination between digital and physical modalities. The apparatus is configured in such a way as to not overwhelm the subject of inquiry or to force technological performance, but with the ambition to enlarge our understanding of performance beyond the quantifiable.

Robot House offers a reconfigurable spatial model that acts within a coordinate system whose axes are composed in an orbital, synchronistic, and combinatory manner.[6] Neither Euclidean nor directly mechanical, this model, and its paired geometrical thinking, turns attention towards radical abstraction and a type of non-homogeneous spatiality that Peter Sloterdijk has written about. The spherical and vectorial geometries of Robot House introduce a new game beyond Cartesian grid logic and Euclidean space—the 2,000-year-old model recapitulated in the flattened space of the digital computer. By enabling both non-Euclidean and non-Newtonian mutations, the apparatus offers a wider range of possible mappings than previous instrumentation in architecture. This challenges the linear rationality of the grid logic but also conventional representational thinking by opening design up to other forms of modelization and virtualization. In questioning the assumed correlation of matter and geometry, the objective is not to reassert a pre-digital or purely analog materialism but a paradigm in which the actual and the virtual always exist together.

FROM INSTRUMENT TO APPARATUS

As theorist Alexander Galloway writes, "the computer and the digital have become the central mitigating factor in society and we cannot conceive a world outside this matrix."[7] Neither "art machine" nor "desiring machine,"[8] this project sees in automation the opportunity for another kind of thought. Robot House is not a machine but a new object of theoretical thinking, a mode of thought and sensibility rather than a web of technological events. Paradoxically, rather than accelerating automation, this apparatus makes more explicit the processes by which objects make objects. In a lineage extending from Albrecht Dürer's picturing machines to Philibert de l'Orme's use of projective geometry in the sixteenth century, the apparatus is that which produces a part of the real—phenomena are the product of different apparatuses.[9] As an experimental apparatus of superposition, Robot House offers new interpretive frameworks—transforming architectural practice from within by working on its models and techniques of representation. The sensibility plays with the increasing overlap in today's visual culture between the fictive and the actual and what is generated by mediated vision and image-processing software and rendered in physical form.

FROM REALIZATION TO FICTIONALIZATION

Just as in the twenty-first century nonrepresentational aesthetics abandons reference to an original, so many observers of contemporary scientific practice and visualization note that resemblance is not the dominant requirement any more.[10] The functionalities of images now "range from resemblance to design, to visions that mobilize."[11] This post-representational understanding argues that today the world is mediated by technological imagery in which traditional concepts of truth, reality, authorship, original, and copy are no longer categorical.

As a multifaceted experiment, Robot House aims to free theories of representation from definitions that see geometry as a double of the world. A form of modeling is developed that allows designers to construct novel methodologies that emphasize the contingent aspects of computation. This shift towards the practice of modelization and simulation is taking place in parallel with other developments in imaging and post-processing that can draw on an increasingly sophisticated series of techniques to render and manipulate images. As an apparatus of visual thinking, Robot House investigates succession and simultaneity, events occurring over time and events occurring at a single point in time, and speed as well as slowness as key features of the image and a speculative aesthetics.[12] These fictions play with multiple narratives and structures simultaneously and point to the inadequacy of singular technique(s). In this way work in Robot House challenges the "binary thought images" that the discipline of architecture traditionally works with, such as the oppositions between the "phantastic" and the "real" that, as Peter Sloterdijk notes, keep architecture trapped in modernity.[13]

FROM REPRESENTATION TO REPRESENTATIONAL OBJECT

Surpassing default protocols of digital modeling and rendering, work on this platform explores shifting hierarchies of geometry, image, and matter as part of a contemporary image discourse.[14] A focus on visual thinking reintroduces the paradox of representation, dimensionality, and ways of seeing. Working with evolving genres of vision yields a mutation between depicting "what is out there" and the practices of mapping. Pattern recognition, image processing, multiple and simultaneous projections collide with orthographic projections and geometric mappings to produce new classes of images and processes that inventively conflate two- and three-dimensional representations as well as digital and physical.

Robot House encompasses machine vision and techniques of representation that were not part of the original canon of transcription of static objects (such as linear perspective and orthographic projection). As real-time or near real-time imaging disrupts established conventions of representation and production in architecture, it allows for superposition of the orthographic and the tomographic, multiple 2D projections, and real-time projection mapping. These types of visualization expand the space and time of design thinking to form a creative and unstable dynamic. The layering of processes produces its own resistances, accidents, and opportunities. The hardware/software architectures enable kinetic models based on active analytical processing of design information—choosing categories for instigating, processing, and reacting to design problems in real-time. Such abstract, iterative, or generative representations have long been a source of innovation and formal invention in architecture and these are expanded and made more mobile and complex by this image-inducing apparatus.[15]

FROM HUMAN-CENTERED VISION TO MACHINE VISION

Machine vision is about to fundamentally transform not only what we see and how we see but also the role of techniques and logistics in architecture. Without attempting to naturalize "machine perception," computational visual systems are understood both in continuity with and divergence from a history of instrumentation and an architecture of seeing that cuts across twentieth-century art practices. The ambition to remove the human perceiver from the equation is common to post-humanism, since "the human is considered to be a limiting factor vis-à-vis what may be known about the real."[16] As Benjamin Bratton notes, "the machinic visual subject sees differently, it is not something that possesses humanlike or human-level perceptual and aesthetic capabilities, but rather something that is uncanny." The aesthetics of machine vision in Robot House is coherent with Bratton's argument that "the human visual subject—should be situated adjacent to machinic user subjects, instead of above them or before them."[17]

In Robot House, machine vision tied to robotics becomes a retooled technology of design—a different gesture towards the real that does not simply displace or supersede but disturbs and disorders conventions of representation. This decentering of human vision leads to a different vocabulary. Defamiliarizing the ways in which images and objects are constructed and perceived, these "inhuman" optical regimes have the potential to provoke new aesthetics and themes for architecture and art practice.

1—The "idea of fabrication" is a neologism coined by Marcel Duchamp in 3 Standard Stoppages (1913).

2—See Benjamin Buchloh, "From Faktura to Factography," October 30, 1984, 82–119.

3—See Eric Winsberg, Science in the Age of Computer Simulation (Chicago: University of Chicago Press, 2010), 67. Winsberg writes: "Conflating these two asymmetrical sets of descriptions (physical and computational) results in an inflated metaphysics of computation ultimately leading to different forms of pan computationalism, a view according to which everything can be furnished with a computational description. On the other extreme eliminating the possibility of mediation between these two descriptive sets by privileging the physical description leads to unsound ontological and epistemic claims about the limits of constructability and knowledge eventually reinscribing ineffability in new guises."

4—See Lev Manovich, Software Takes Command (London: Bloomsbury Academic, 2013).

5—See François Laruelle, "L'ordinateur transcendantale: Une utopie non-philosophique," in Homo ex machina (Paris: L'Harmattan, 2015), 13.

6—See Vera Bühlmann, Peter Sloterdijk's Phantastic Philosophy—taking the concept of the differential as a relational measure (2007). Accessed October 10, 2016. http://www.caad.arch.ethz.ch.

7—See Alexander R. Galloway, Laruelle: Against the Digital (Minneapolis: University of Minnesota Press, 2014).

8—The concept of "machine" is not central to this project—"technical machines" are undermined without recourse to the cliché of "broken tools," Deleuze and Guattari's "desiring-machine," or attributing human agency and creativity to machines.

9—See McKenzie Wark, Molecular Red: Theory for the Anthropocene (London/New York: Verso, 2015).

10—See Catelijne Coopmans, Janet Vertesi, Michael E. Lynch, Steve Woolgar, Representation in Scientific Practice Revisited (Cambridge: MIT Press, 2014).

11—See Martin Ruivenkamp and Arie Rip, "Nanoimages as Hybrid Monsters," in Representation in Scientific Practice Revisited, ed. Catelijne Coopmans et al. (Cambridge: MIT Press, 2014),193.

12—These are some of the vectors of what Jacques Rancière calls "the future of the image."

13—See Willem Schinkel and Liesbeth Noordegraaf-Eelens, eds, In Medias Res (Amsterdam University Press, 2001).

14—See Tristan Garcia, "In Defense of Representation," in Realism Materialism Art, ed. C. Cox, J. Jaskey, and S. Malik (Berlin: Sternberg Press, 2015), 245–51.

15—Experimental cinema is employing similar robot ecologies. Alfonso Cuarón's Gravity demonstrates the uncanny potential of virtualization and physical intensification that this apparatus affords within the cinematic space.

16—See Galloway, op. cit., xxi.

17—See Benjamin Bratton, "Machine Vision," dismagazine.com/discussion/73272/benjamin-bratton-machine-vision/ (accessed December 20, 2015).

1— TECH-NIQUES

Digital/Physical Interfaces
Animated Motion Control
Object-Oriented Programming
Visual Programming

Synchronous Robotics
Multi-Robot Choreography
Real-Time
Rigging and Kinematics

Effectors
End Effectors
Physical Computing

Digital/Physical Interfaces
Animated Motion Control
Object-Oriented Programming
Visual Programming
Synchronous Robotics
Multi-Robot Choreography
Real-Time
Rigging and Kinematics
Effectors
End Effectors
Physical Computing
Imaging
Image Processing
Machine Vision
Fictioning
Object Animation
Physical Rendering
Robotic Cinematography
Augmented Fabrication
Free-Form Fabrication
Image-Based Fabrication
Multiresolution Fabrication
Computational Materials
Scaffolds and Templates
Transitive Materials

Digital/Physical Interfaces
Animated Motion Control
Object-Oriented Programming
Visual Programming

Multi-robot motion control interfaces are reinvented with designer-friendly animation (Maya) and visual programming (Grasshopper and Python) toolsets. Unlike conventional computer interfaces, the cloning of workspaces (digital/physical/robotic), by which workspaces operate in parallel and simultaneously or all at once, offers an alternative path to simple representation. In contrast to conventional assumptions about robotics associated with automation and repetition, this contingent space has no default settings, and breaks the boredom and predictability of a homogeneous digital practice. Working within this reimagined interface, designers propose and create workflows that bridge the digital and the physical. The interplay of information and physical processes is an integral part of projects via techniques of animated motion control, object-oriented programming, and visual programming.

Animated Motion Control

The first-generation motion control interface

esperant.0 is a plug-in for Autodesk Maya that bridges

2.
02

2.
02

2.
01

the gap between designers and industrial robots.

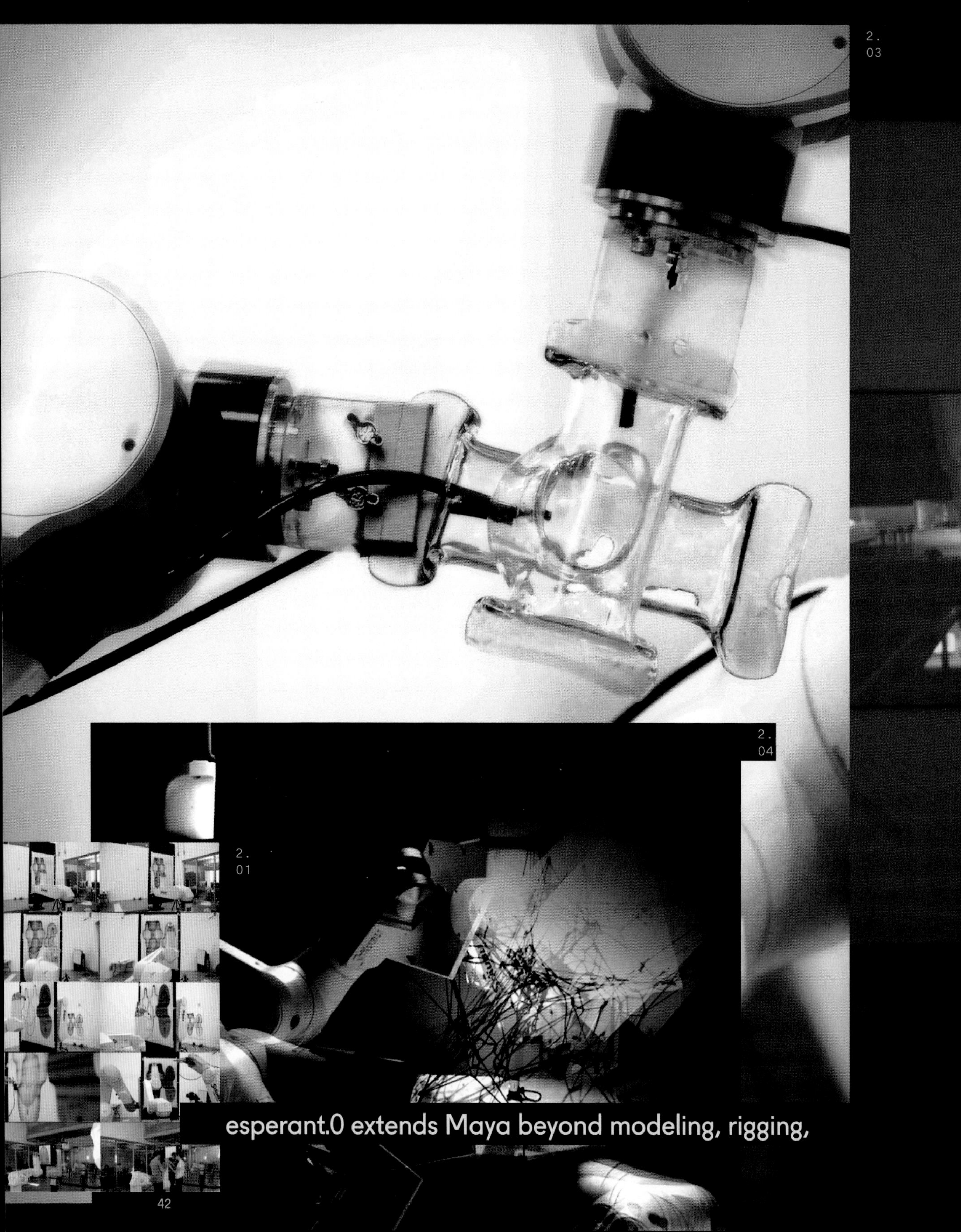

2.
03

2.
04

2.
01

esperant.0 extends Maya beyond modeling, rigging,

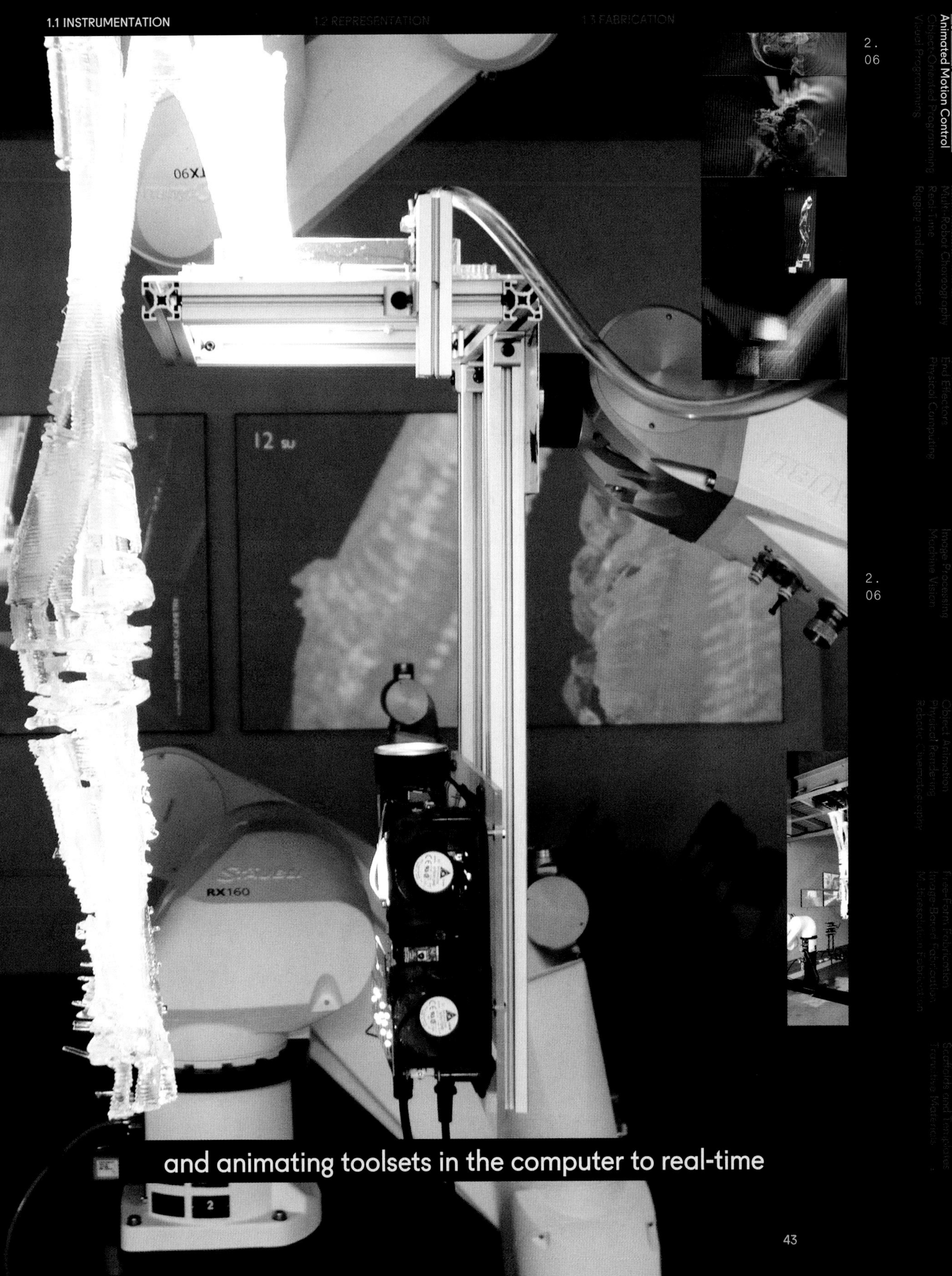

and animating toolsets in the computer to real-time

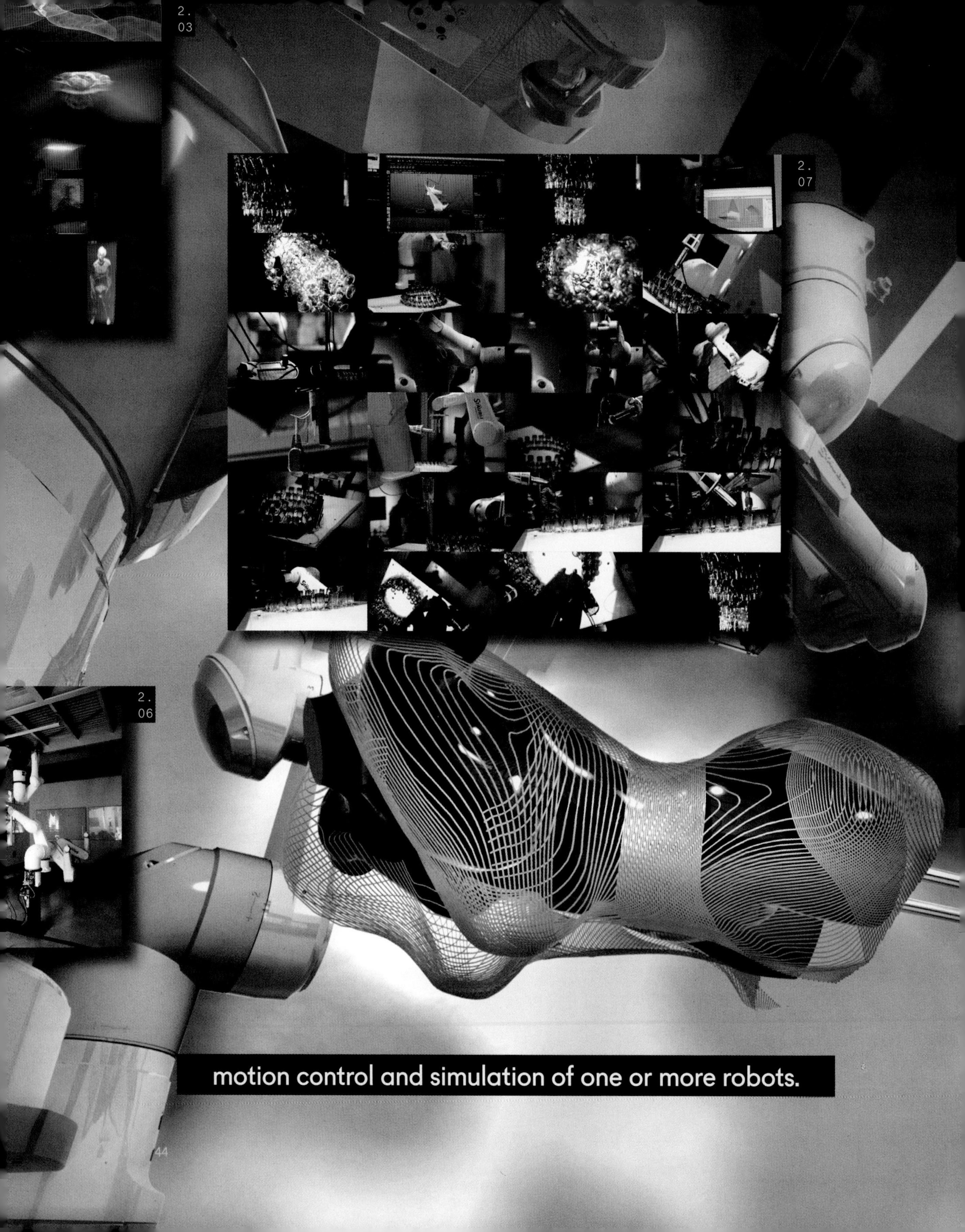

motion control and simulation of one or more robots.

2.
05

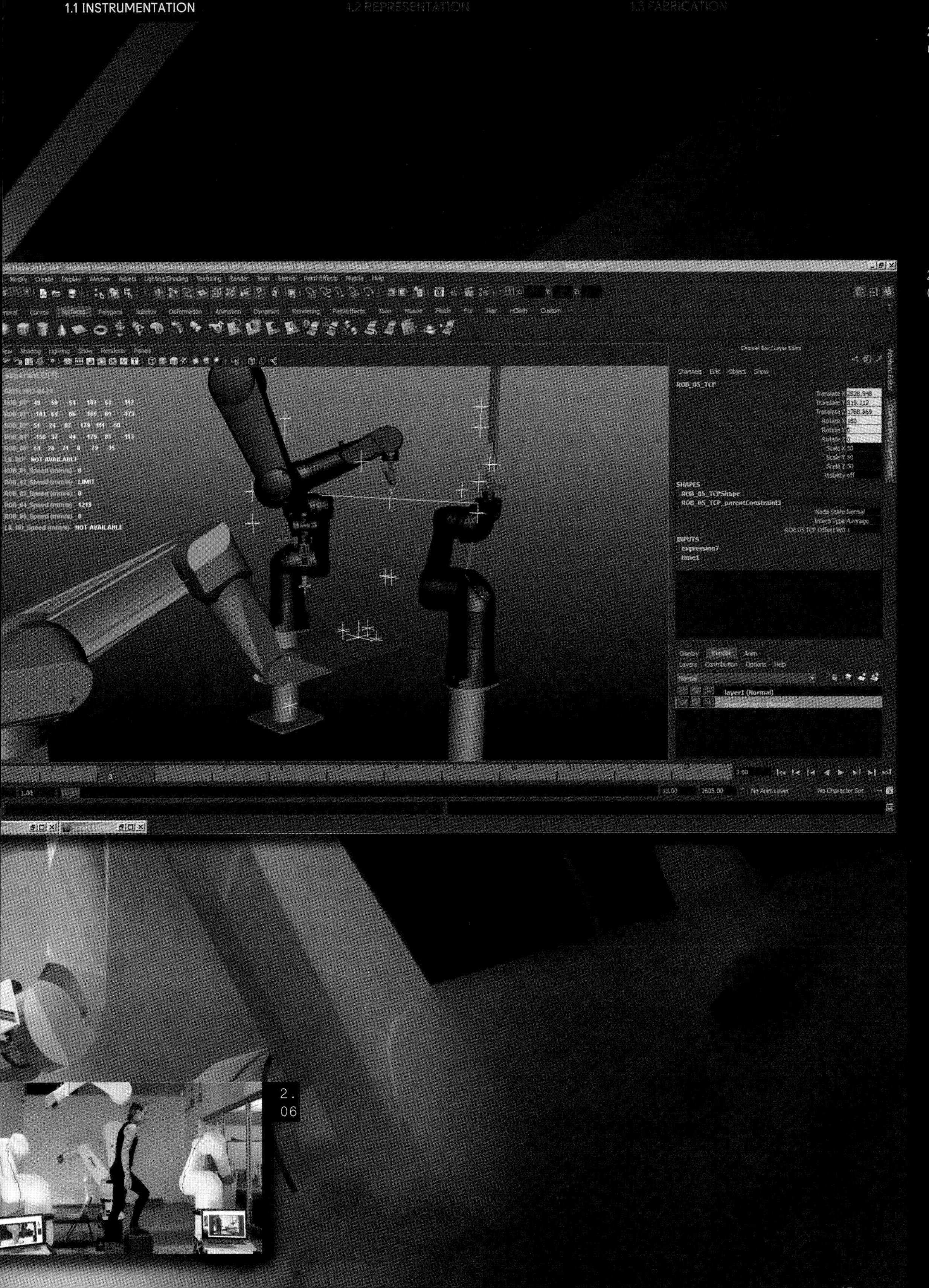

2.
02

2.
06

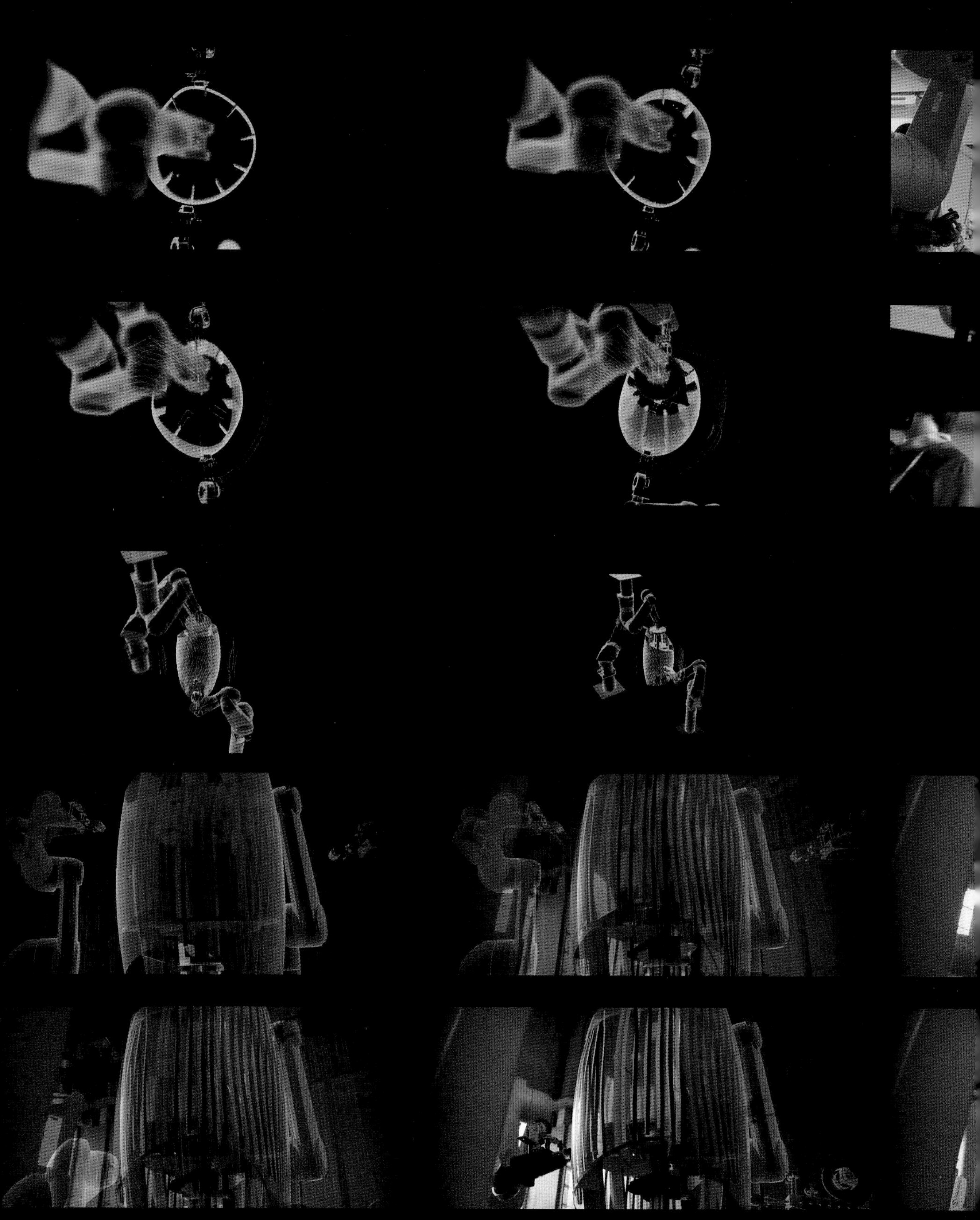

2.
07

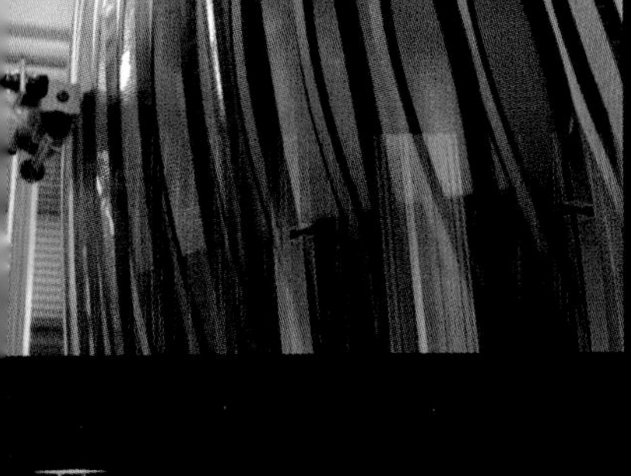

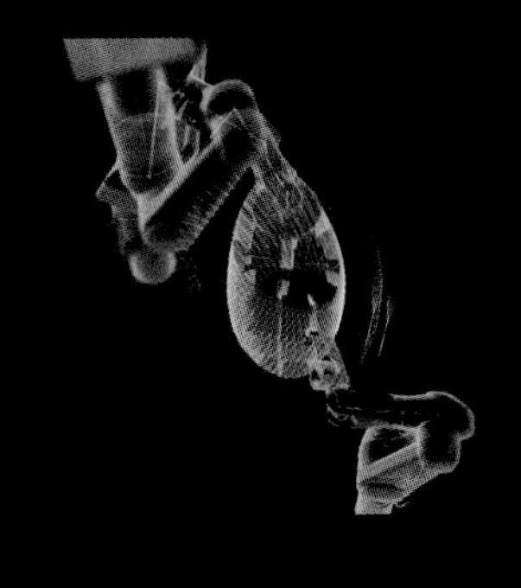

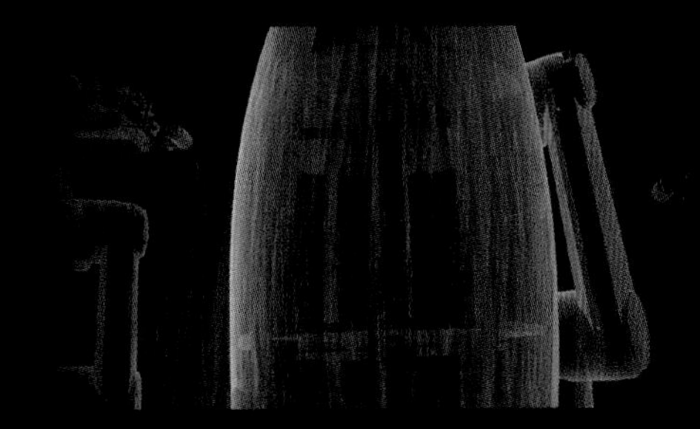

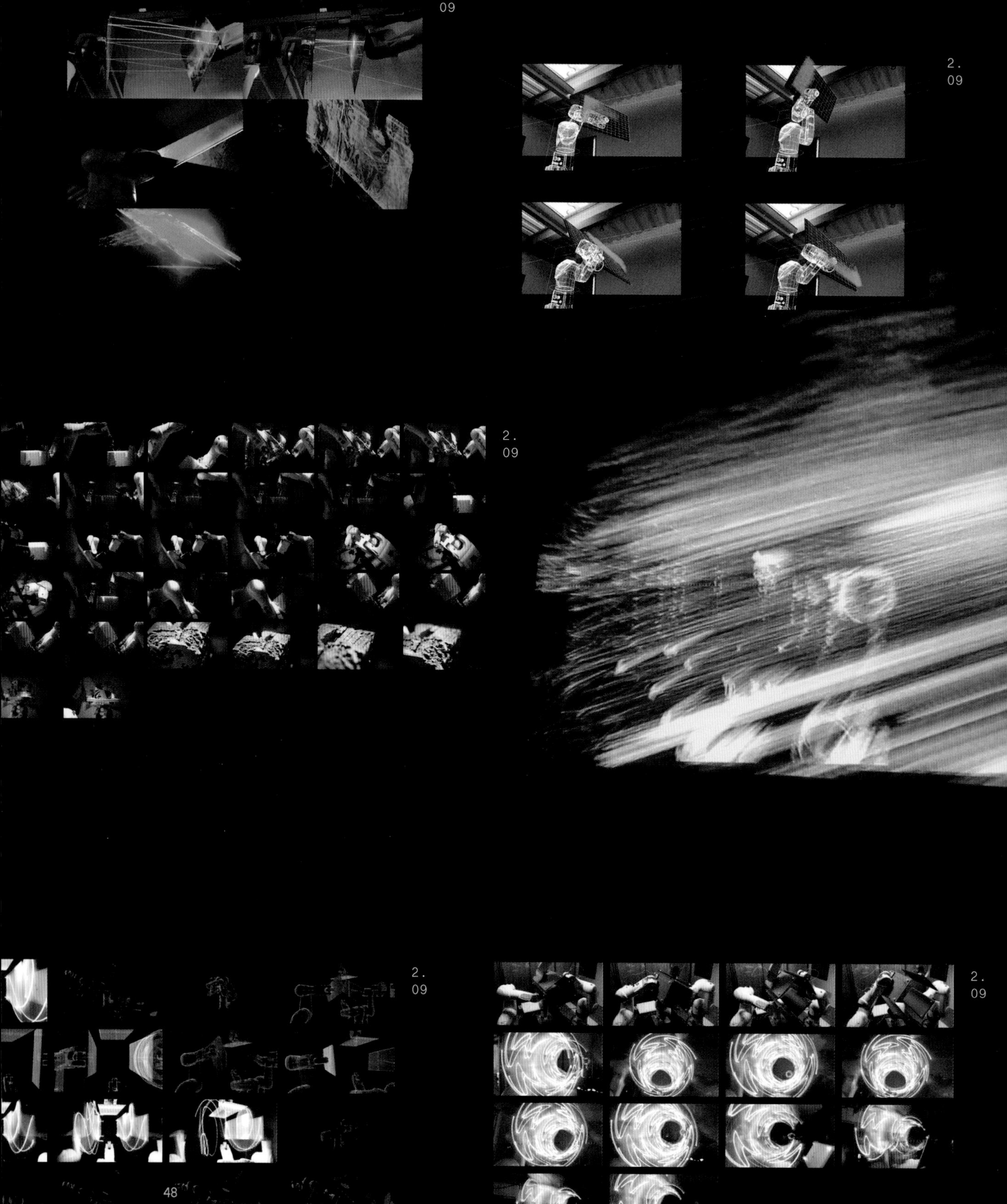
09
2.
09
2.
09
2.
09

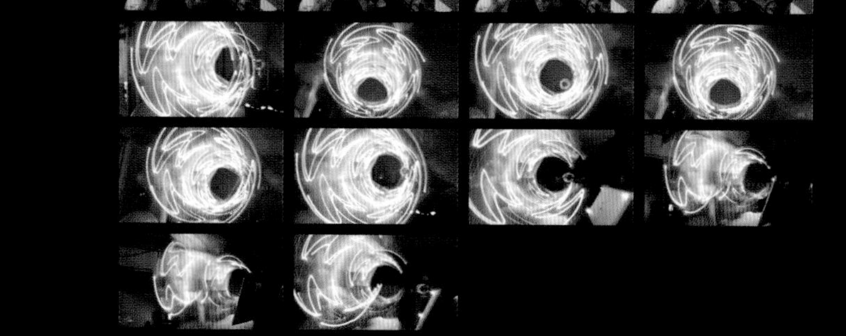
2.
09

2.
10
2.
09
ÄUBLI
NIMATION

2.
02

Digital/Physical Interfaces
Animated Motion Control

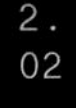
2.
02

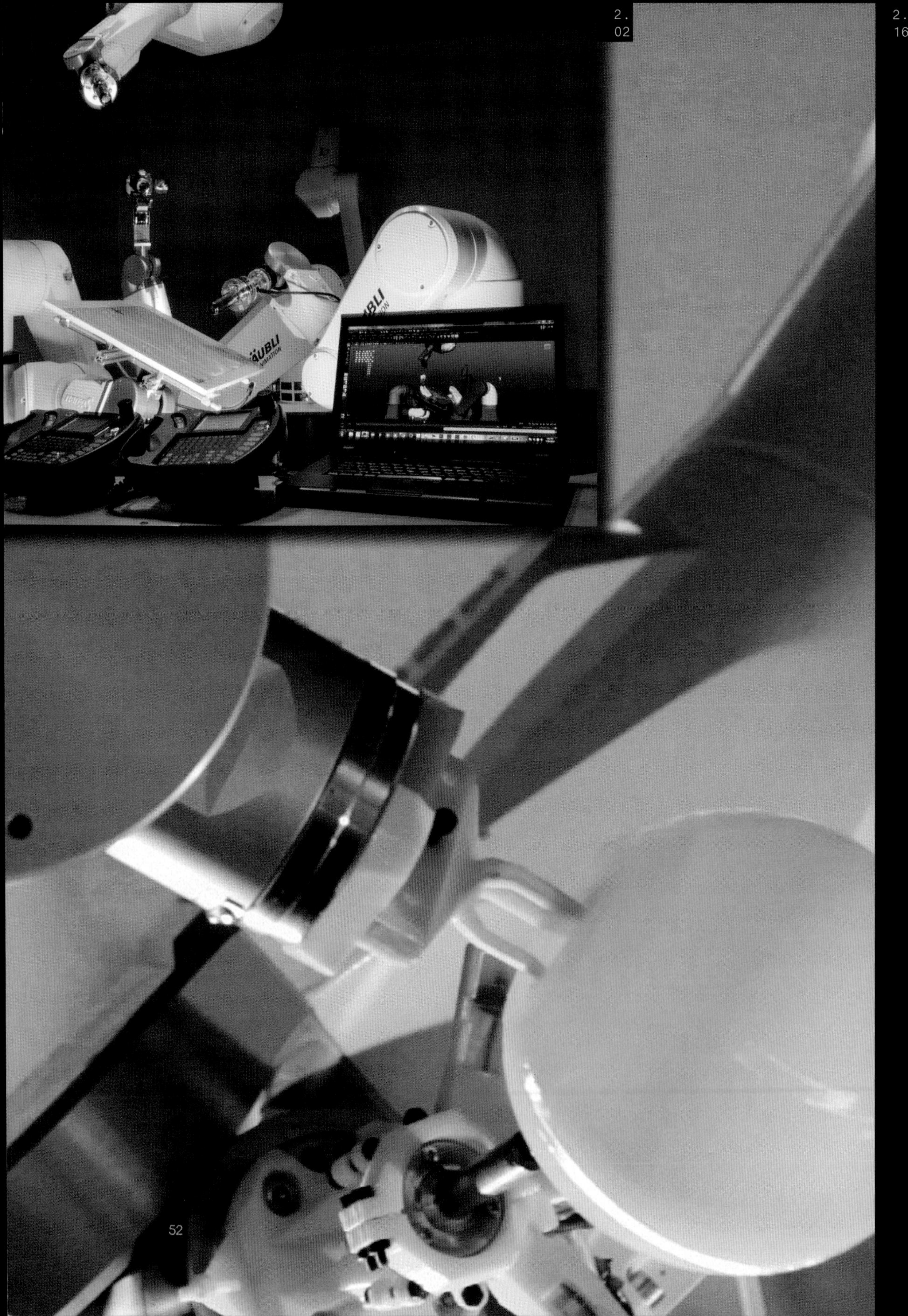

2.
02

2.
16

Object-Oriented Programming

2.
09

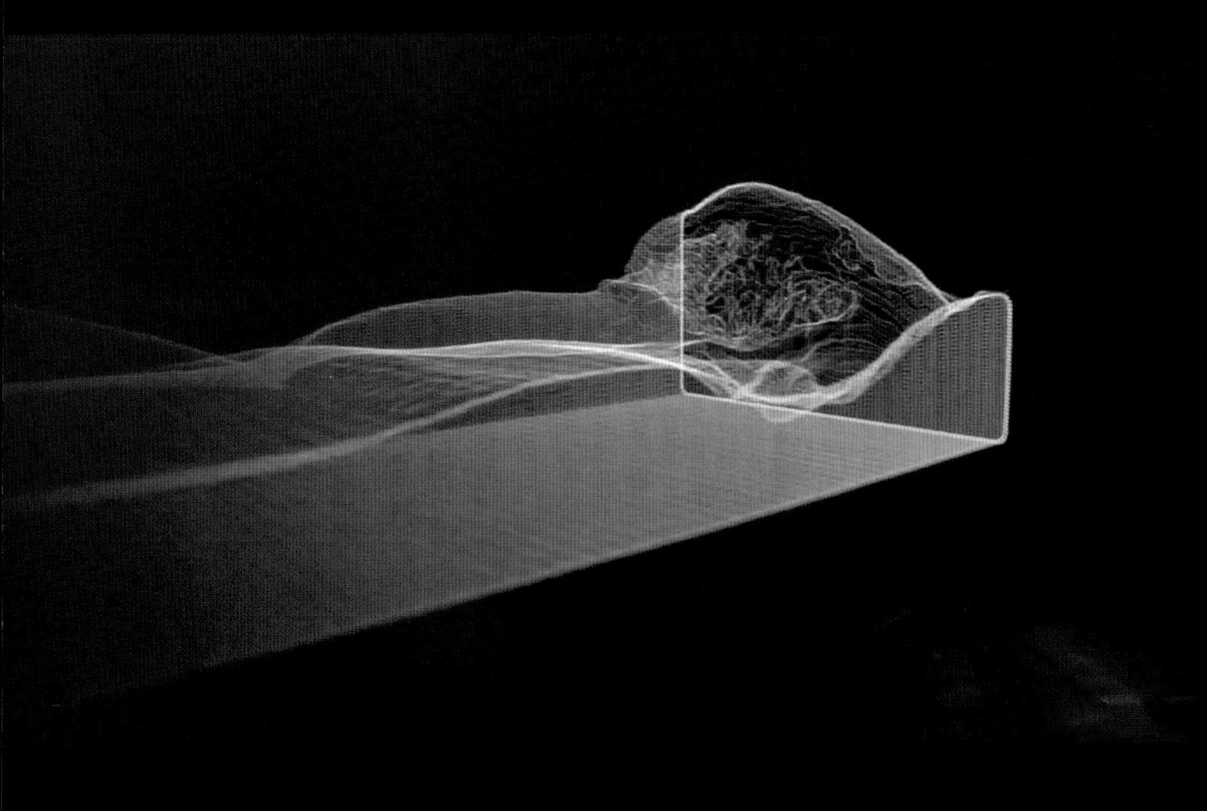

Leap Motion, Quad V, Touch Designer, and other

digital/physical interfaces support new models of

human–machine interaction as part of the design

2.
09

model. The integration of real-time visualization,

2.09

2.10

inertial sensing, and sensor fusion applies principles

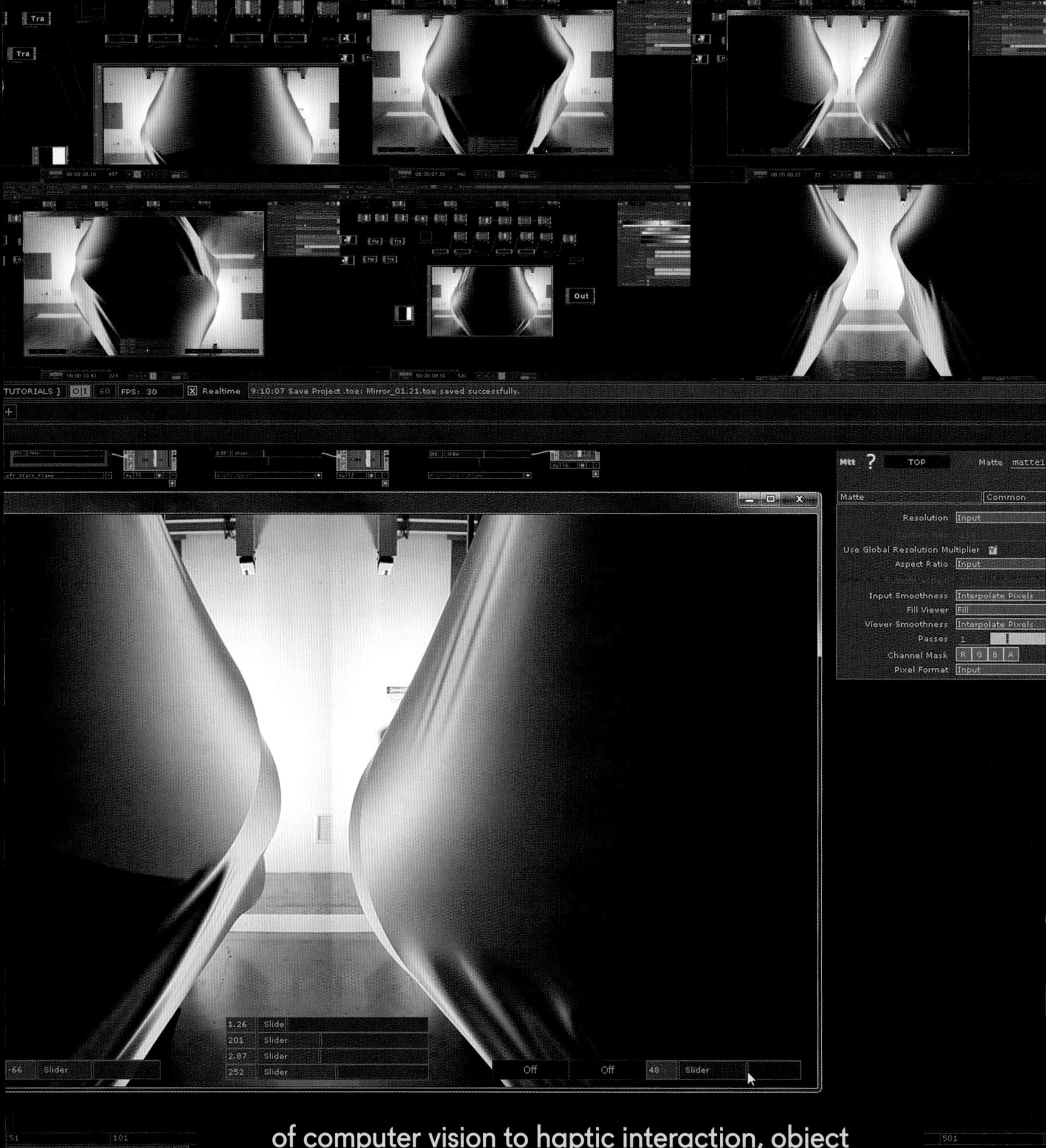

of computer vision to haptic interaction, object

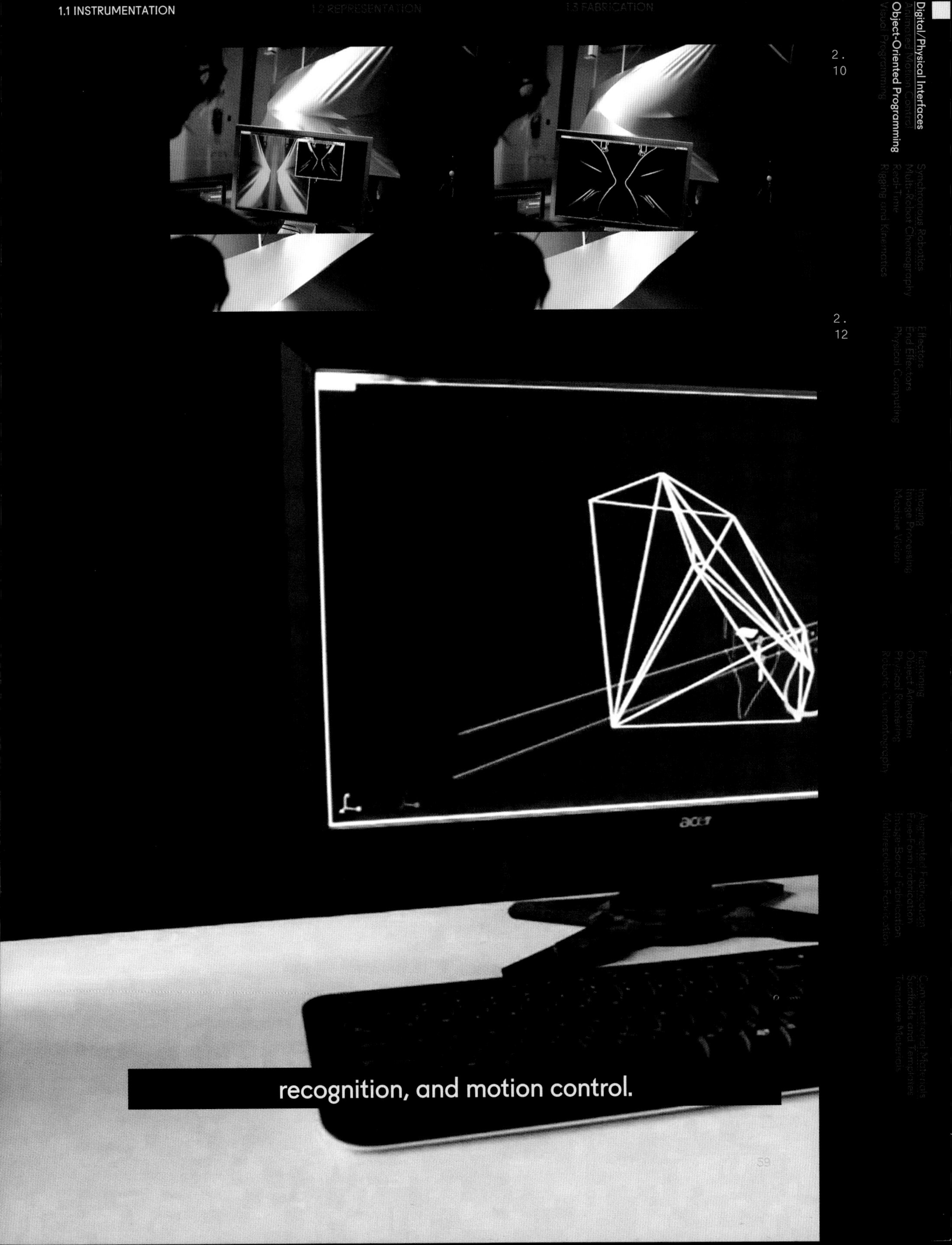

recognition, and motion control.

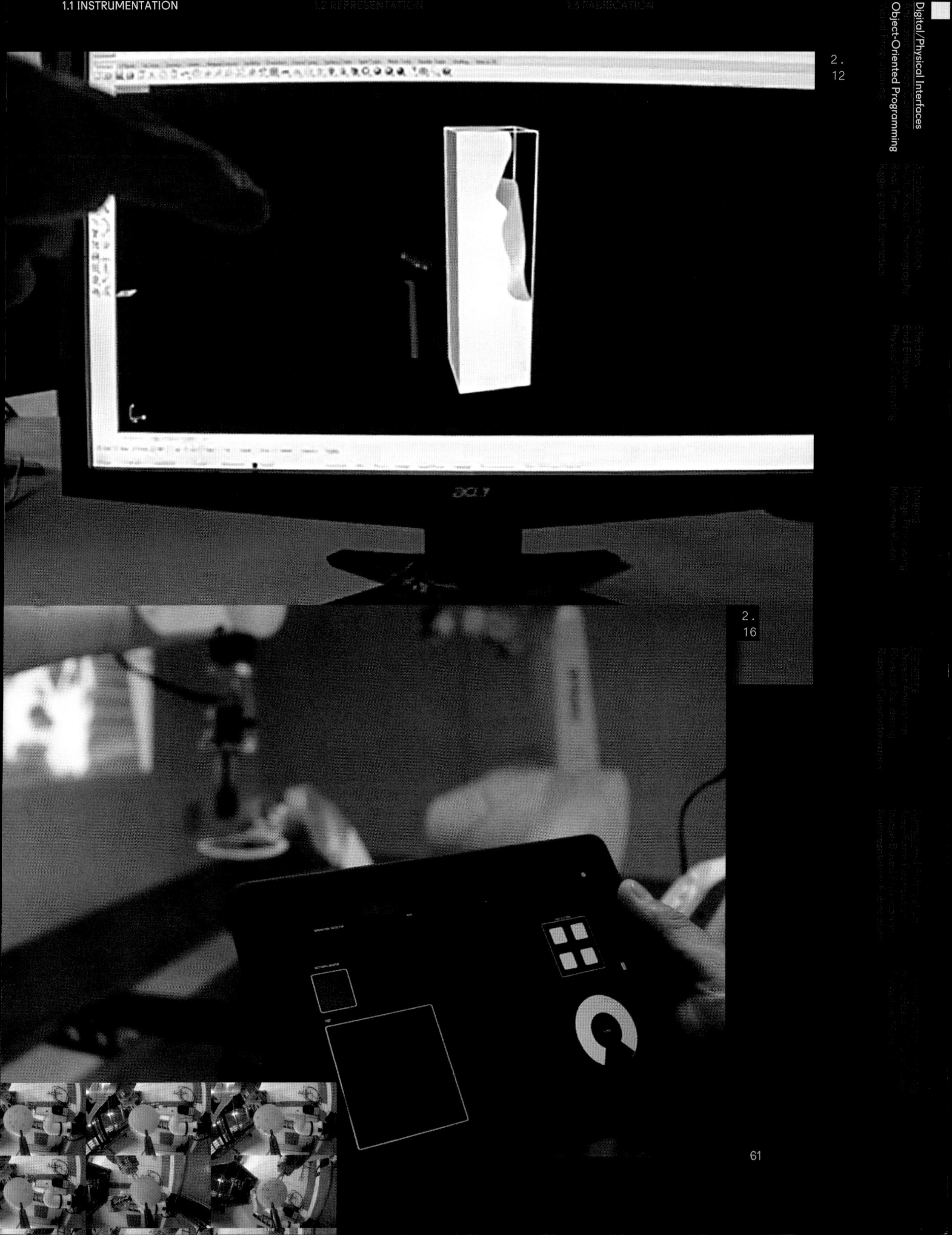

2.12

2.16

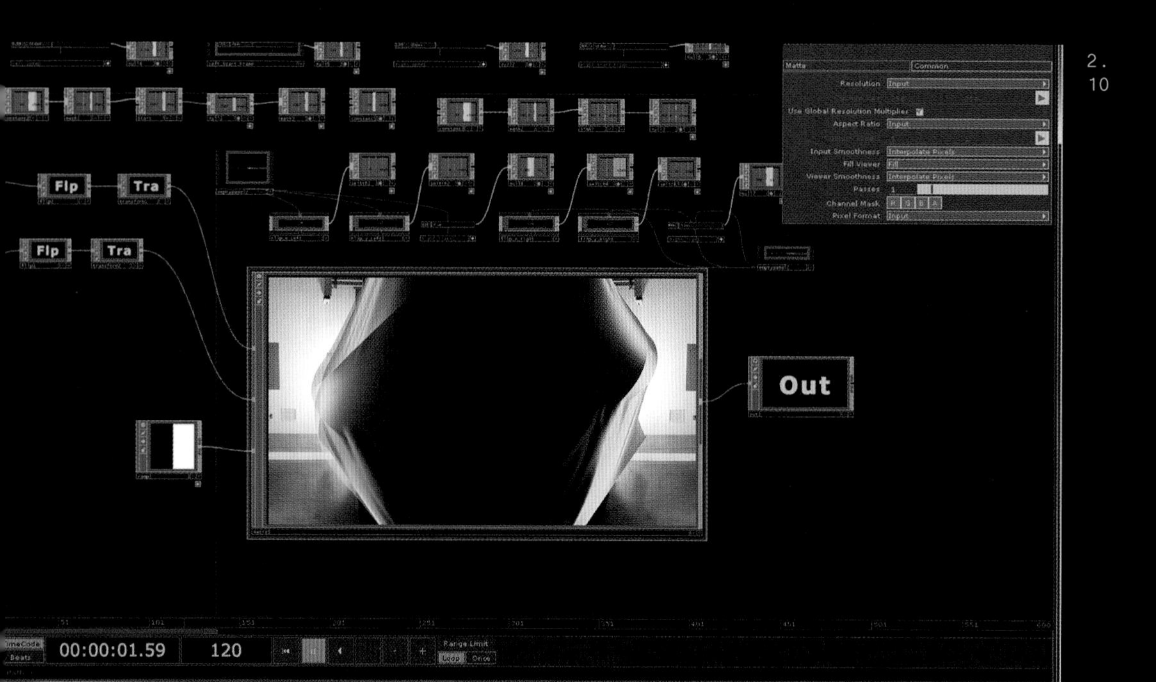

Matte
Common
Resolution
Input
Use Global Resolution Multiplier
Aspect Ratio
Input
Input Smoothness
Interpolate Pixels
Fill Viewer
Fill
Viewer Smoothness
Interpolate Pixels
Passes
1
Channel Mask
Pixel Format
Input
Flp
Tra
Flp
Tra
Out
Beats
00:00:01.59
120
Range Limit
Loop
Once

2.
10

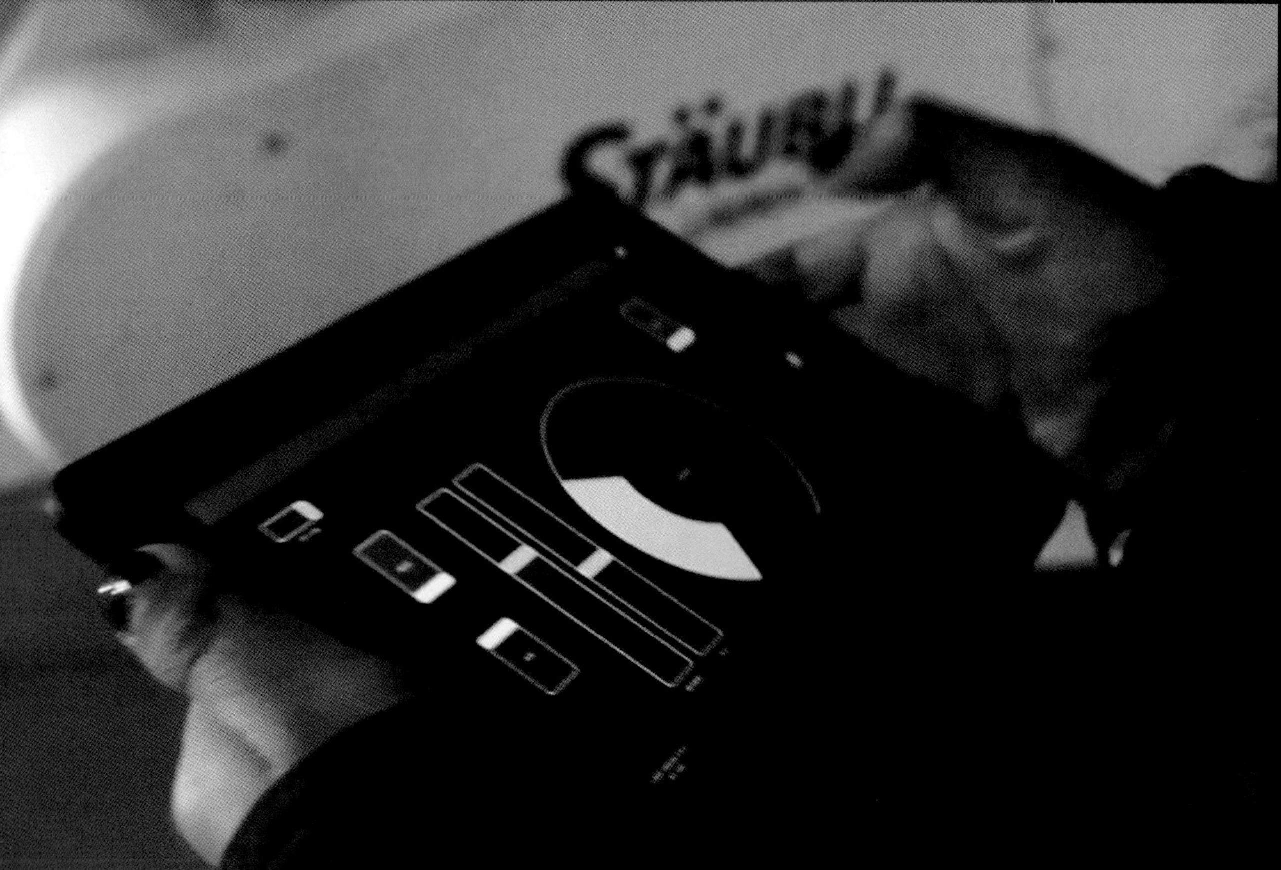

2.
16

Visual Programming

CRANE, developed in-house, is an extensible robot

2.
06

2.
01

2.
01

2.
09

2.
06

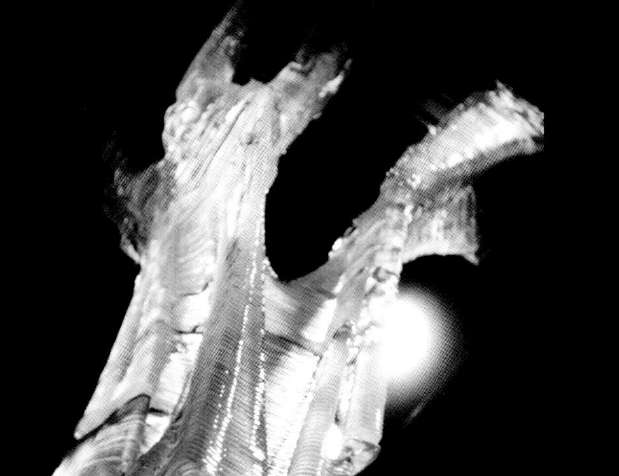

motion control suite for Grasshopper, the parametric

2.
09

2.
19

modeling plug-in for Rhino3D. CRANE provides

IK solving; visualization and diagnostic information,

and one-click file generation for Stäubli articulated

robot arms.

Synchronous Robotics
Multi-Robot Choreography
Real-Time
Rigging and Kinematics

Robot House suspends utilitarian purposes to reinvent choreography of movement and capacity for intercommunication and synchronous behavior. Techniques extend the use of time and motion in new and unexpected ways for architectural representation, form generation, and fabrication. Real-time, synchronous robotics collapses the distance between presentation and representation, as the output or the image is the presentation—the working object of design. Multi-robot choreography, real-time, and rigging and kinematics push beyond the computational revolution of emulation and computer simulations to introduce a logic of cooperation.

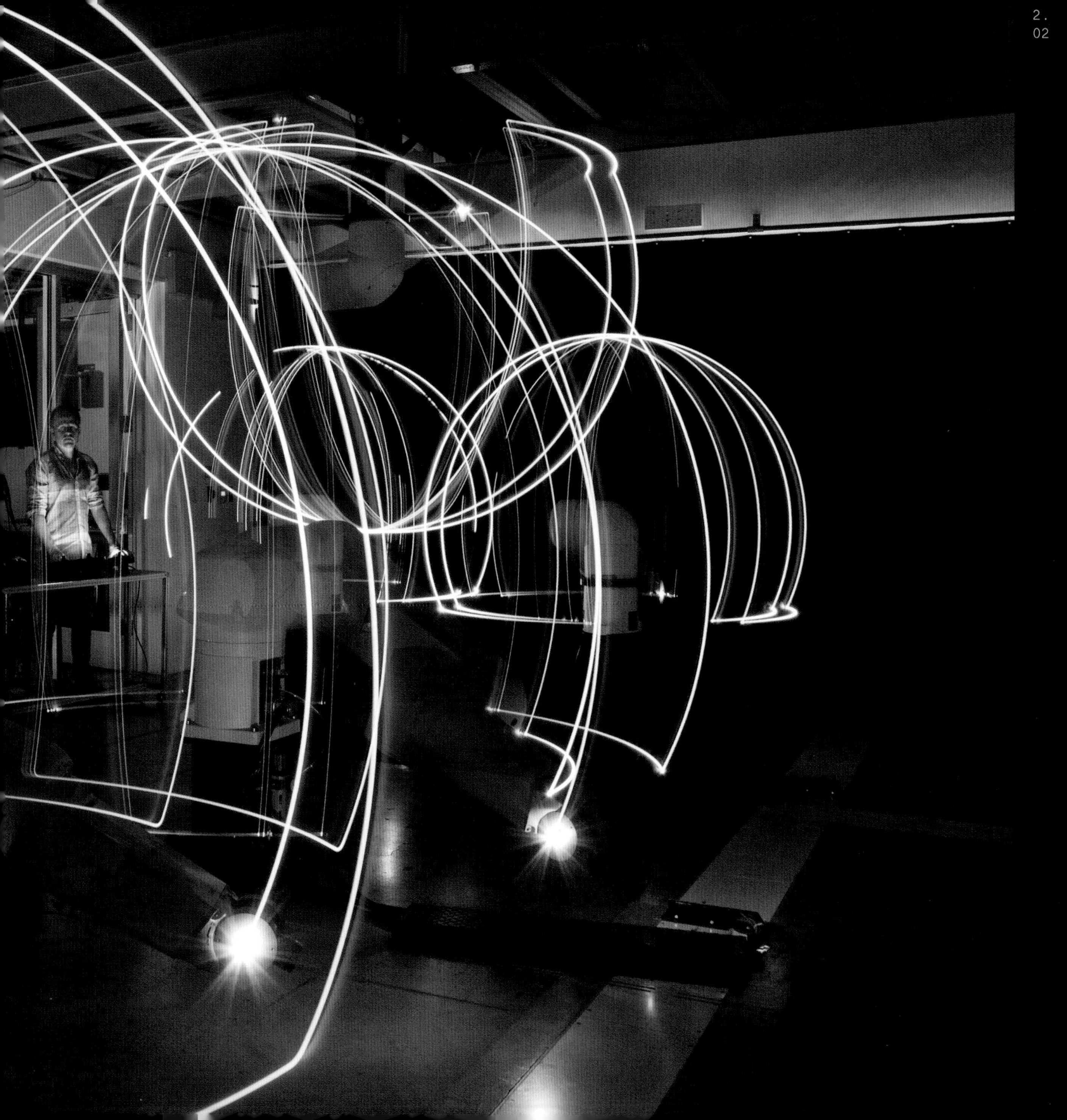

Multi-Robot Choreography

The implementation of multiple robot systems

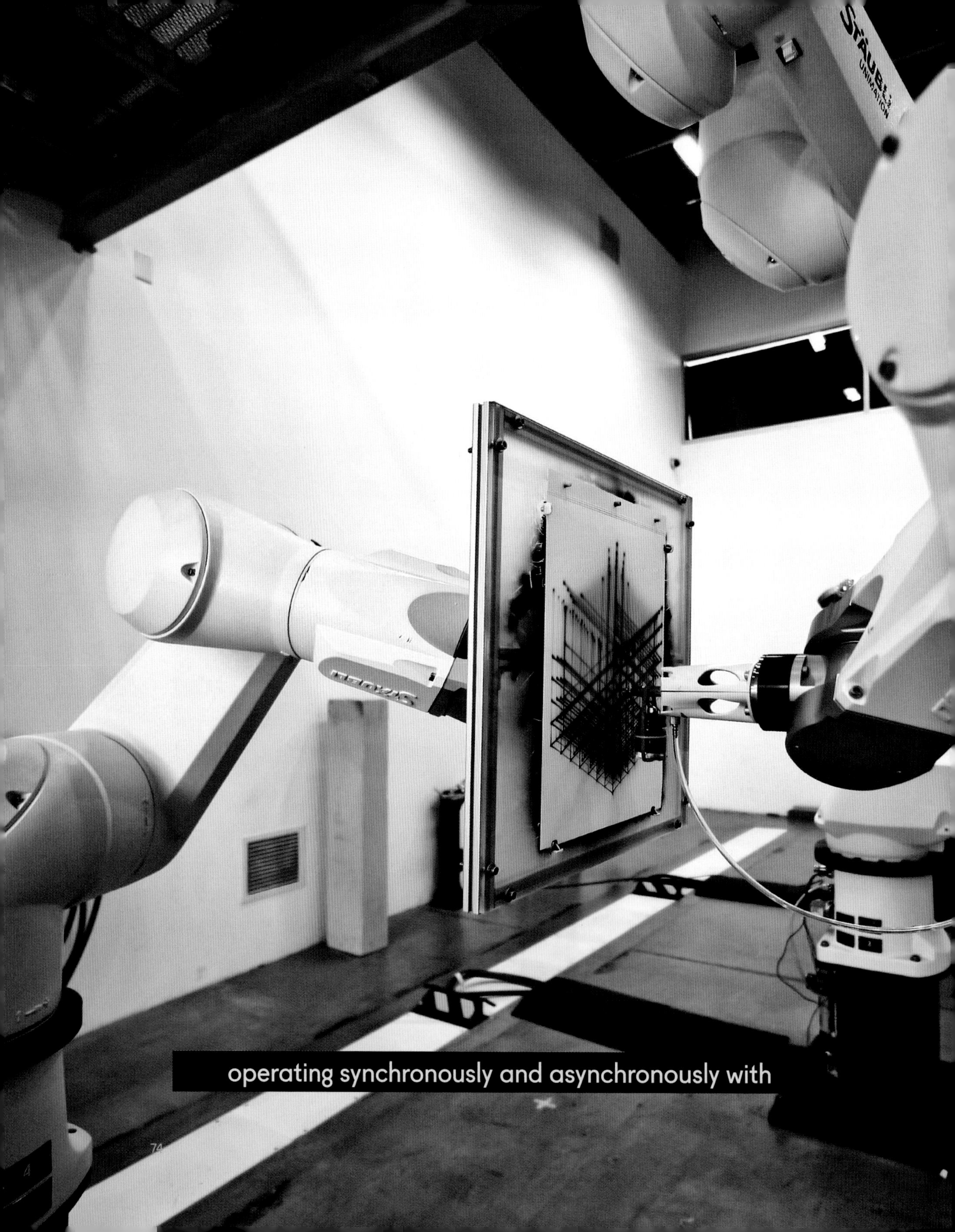

operating synchronously and asynchronously with

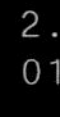
2.
01

2.
02

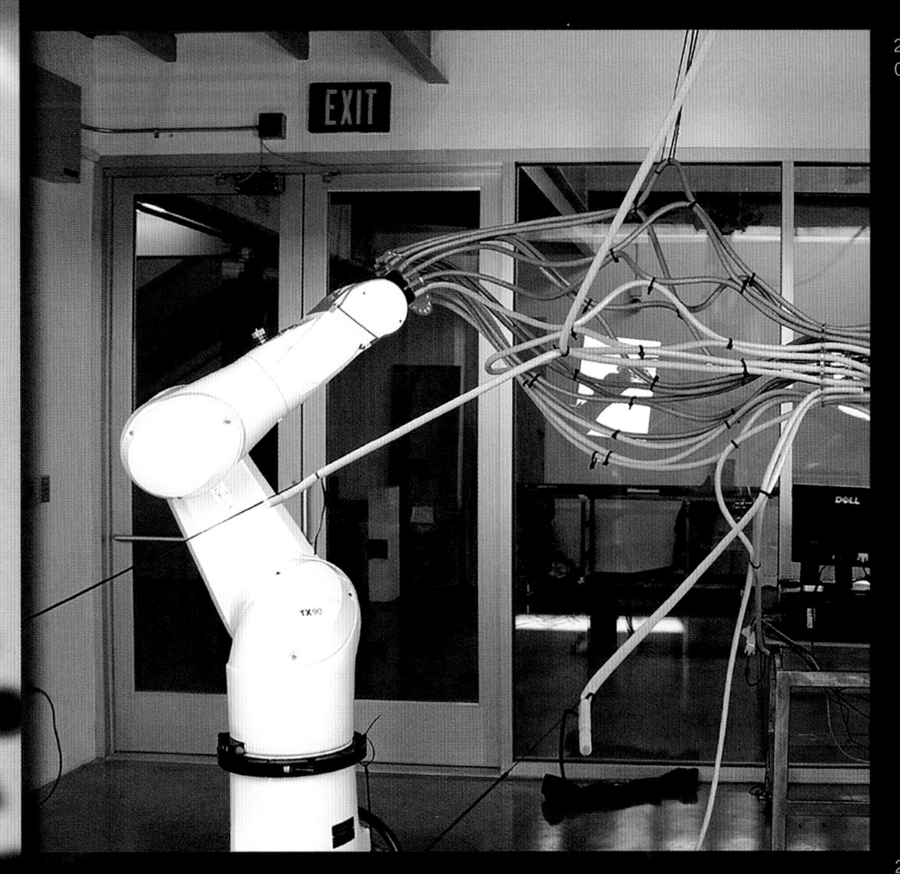

2.
02

intersecting work spheres offers a

new model of multi-robot choreography and

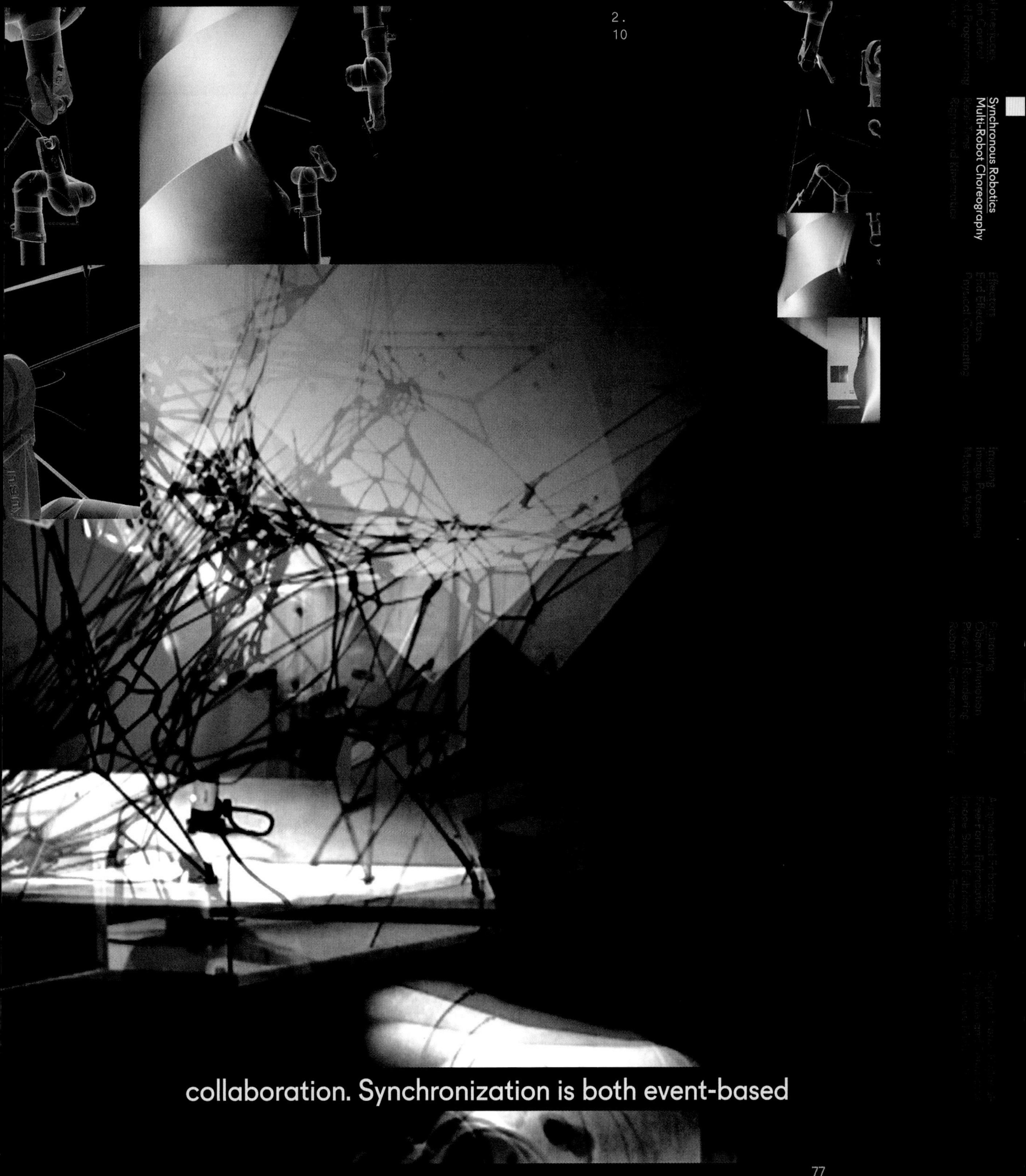

collaboration. Synchronization is both event-based

and time-based, which allows for a communication

system for multi-robot scenarios that can react to

2.
11

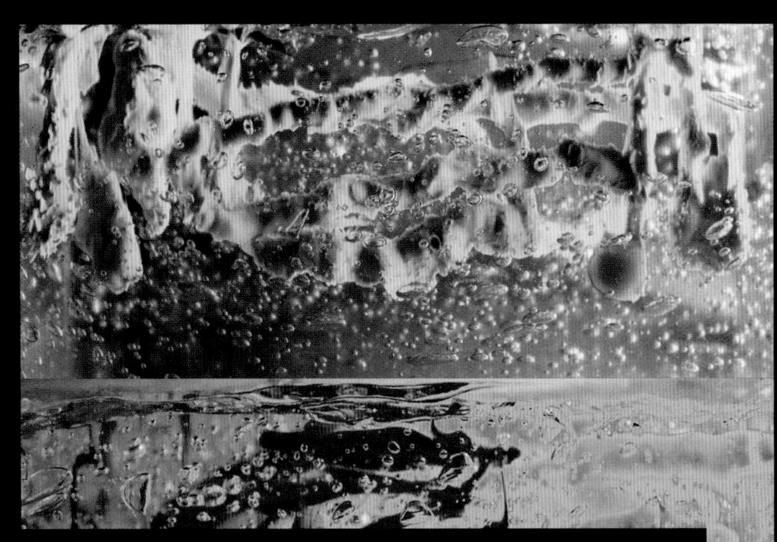

disruptions and alterations in the actual environment.

Real-Time

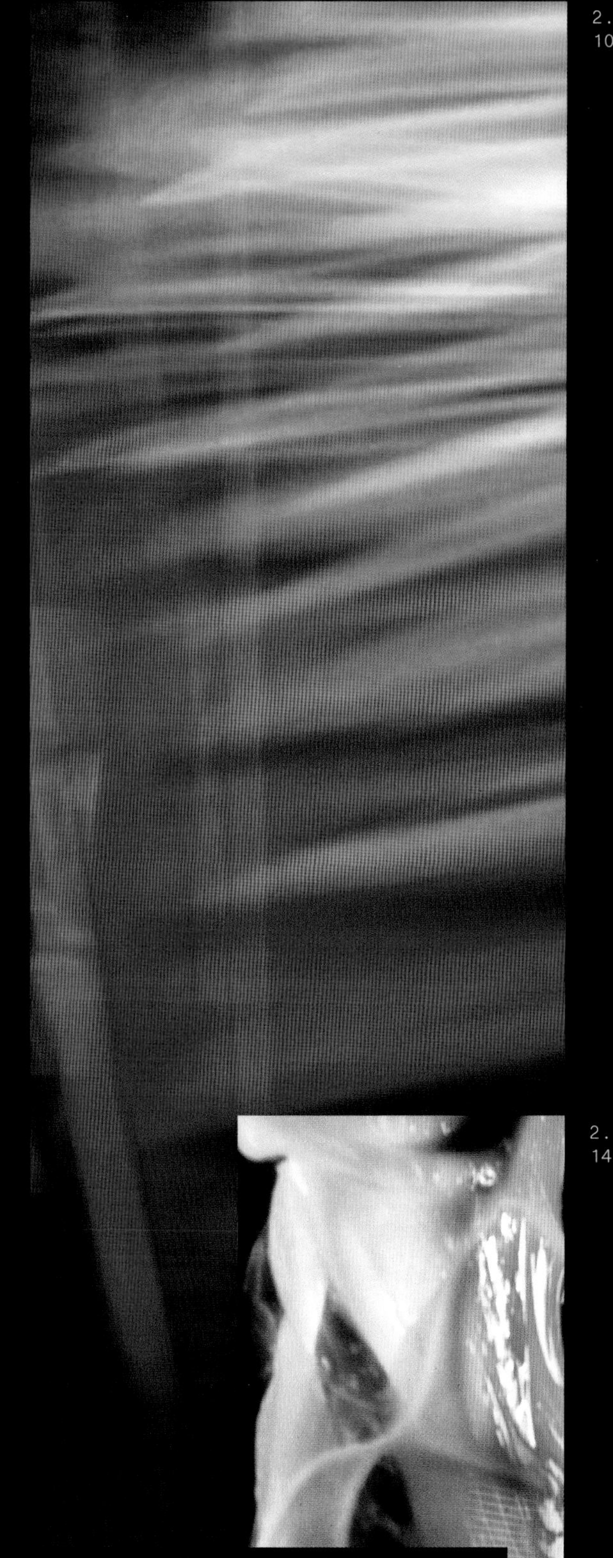

A real-time feedback loop is implemented that

2.
10
2.
14

2.
02

2.
10

2.
03

combines programmed and unprogrammed

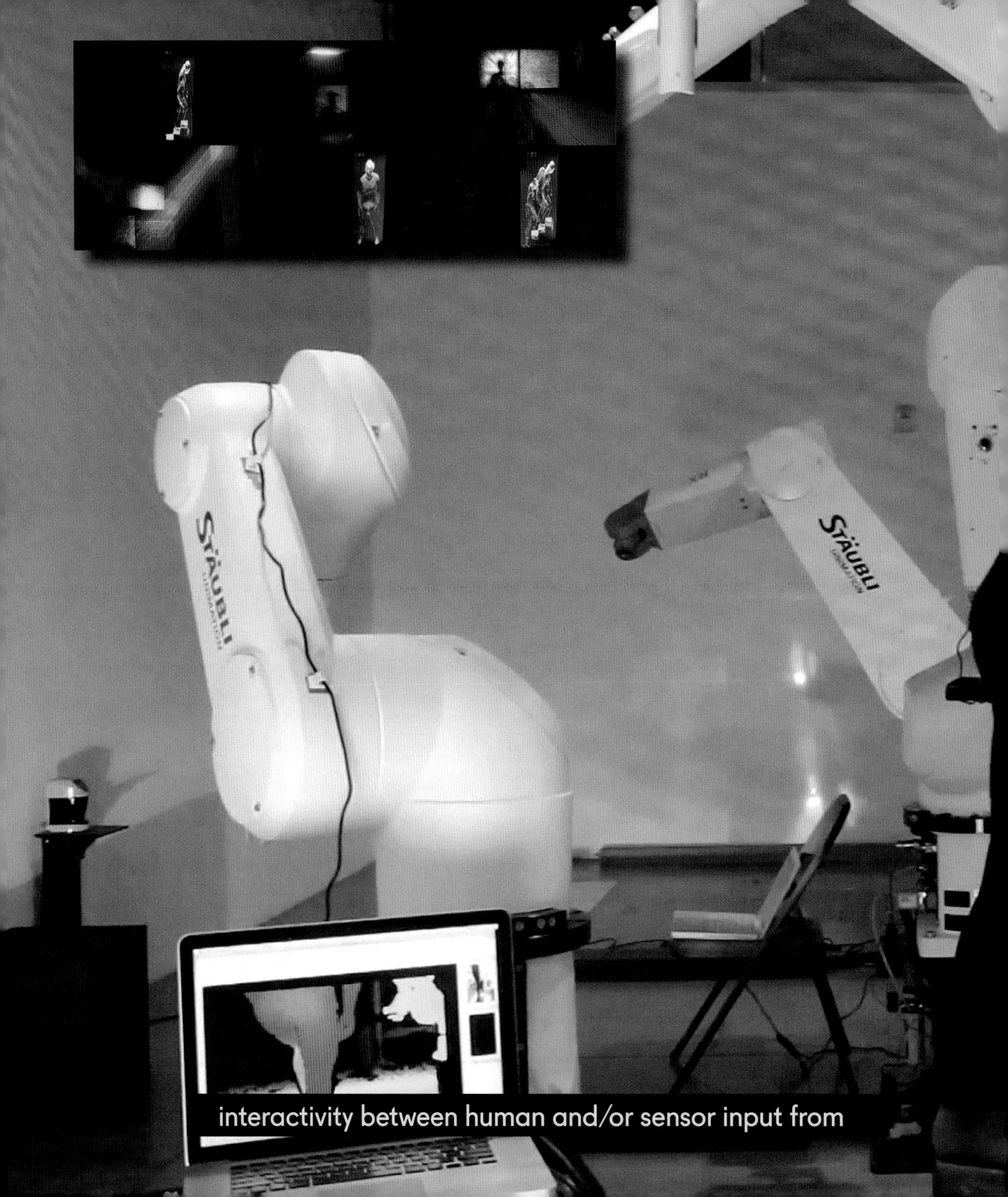

interactivity between human and/or sensor input from

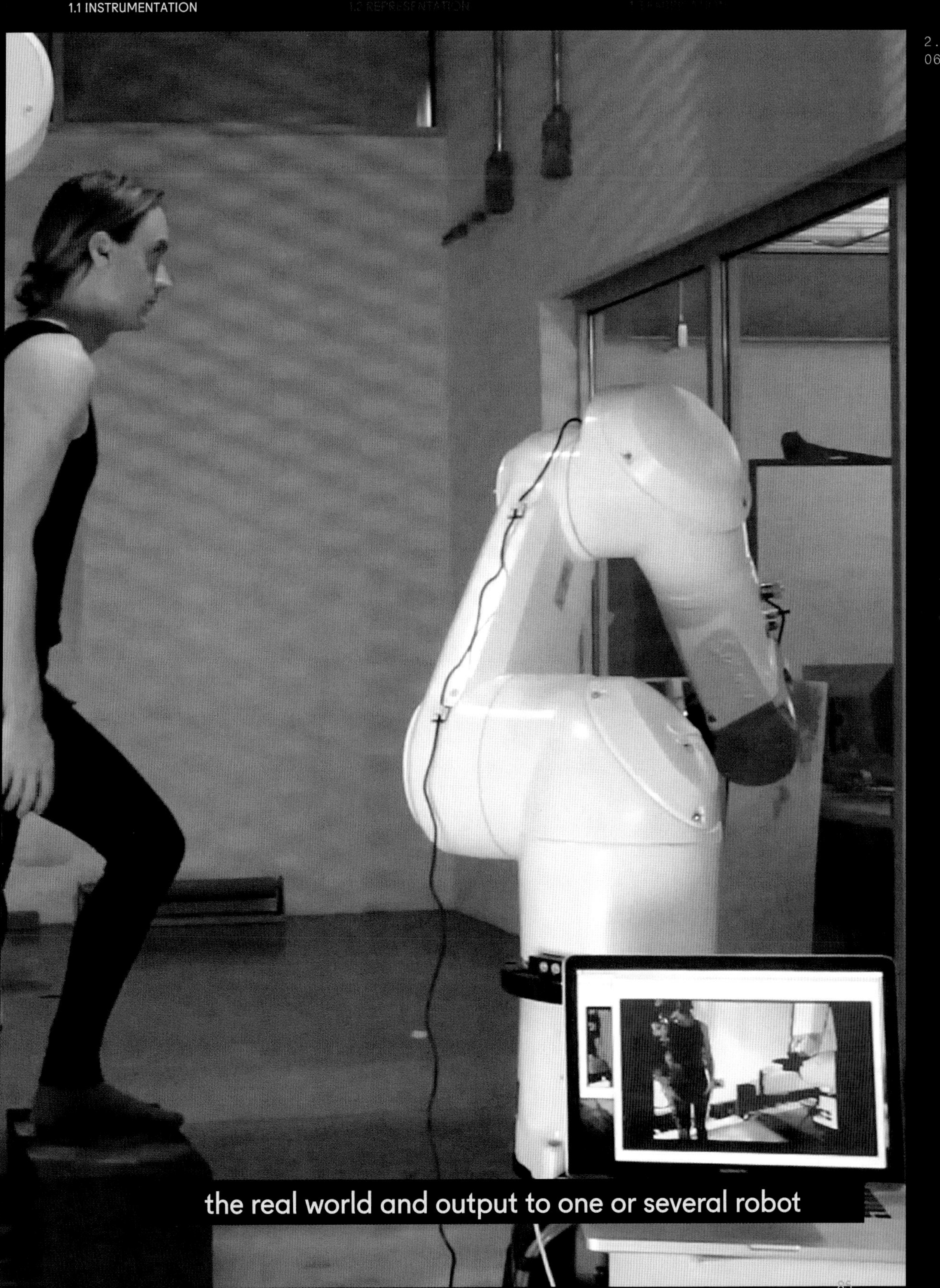
the real world and output to one or several robot

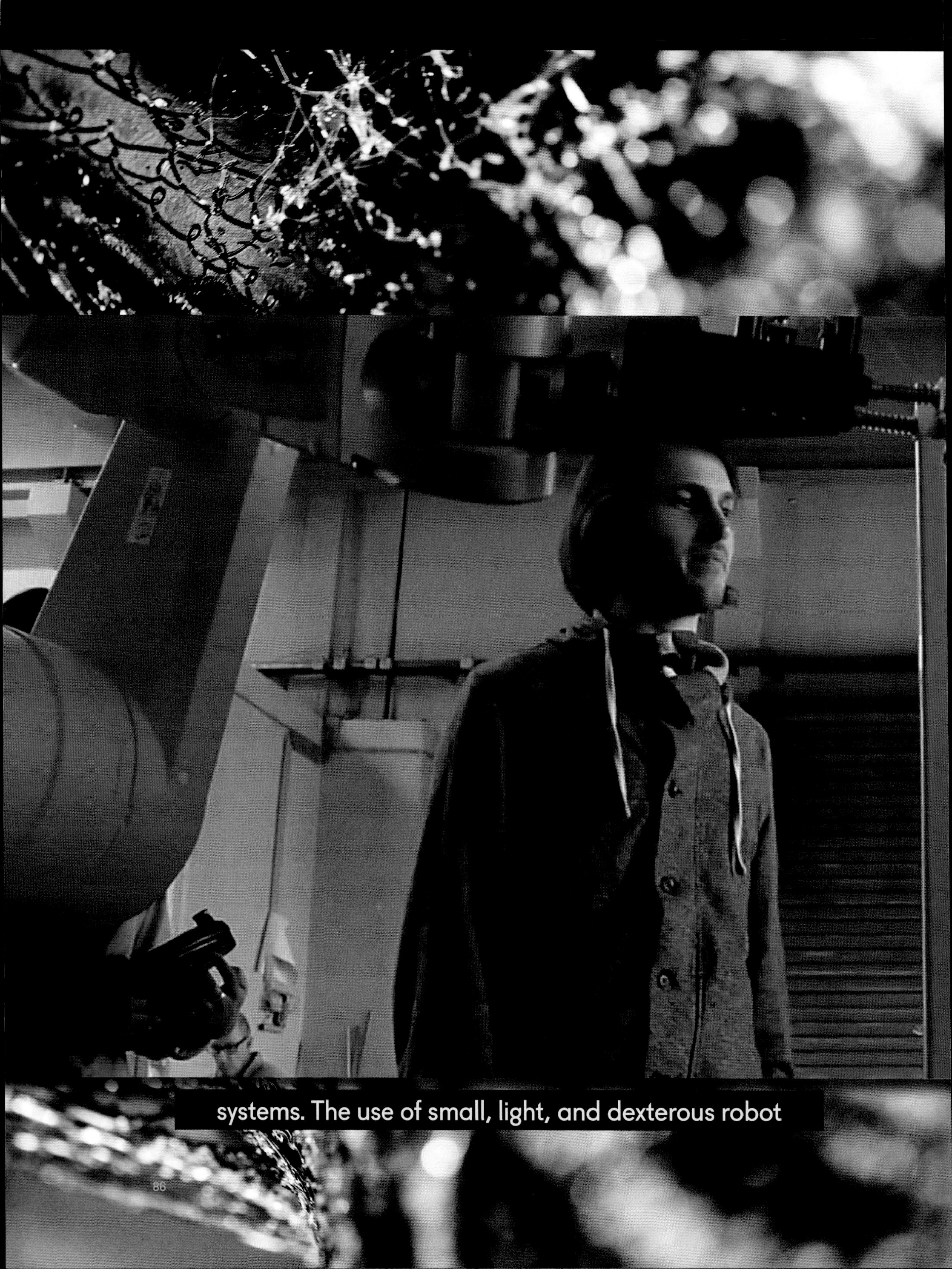

systems. The use of small, light, and dexterous robot

systems invites real-time user interaction.

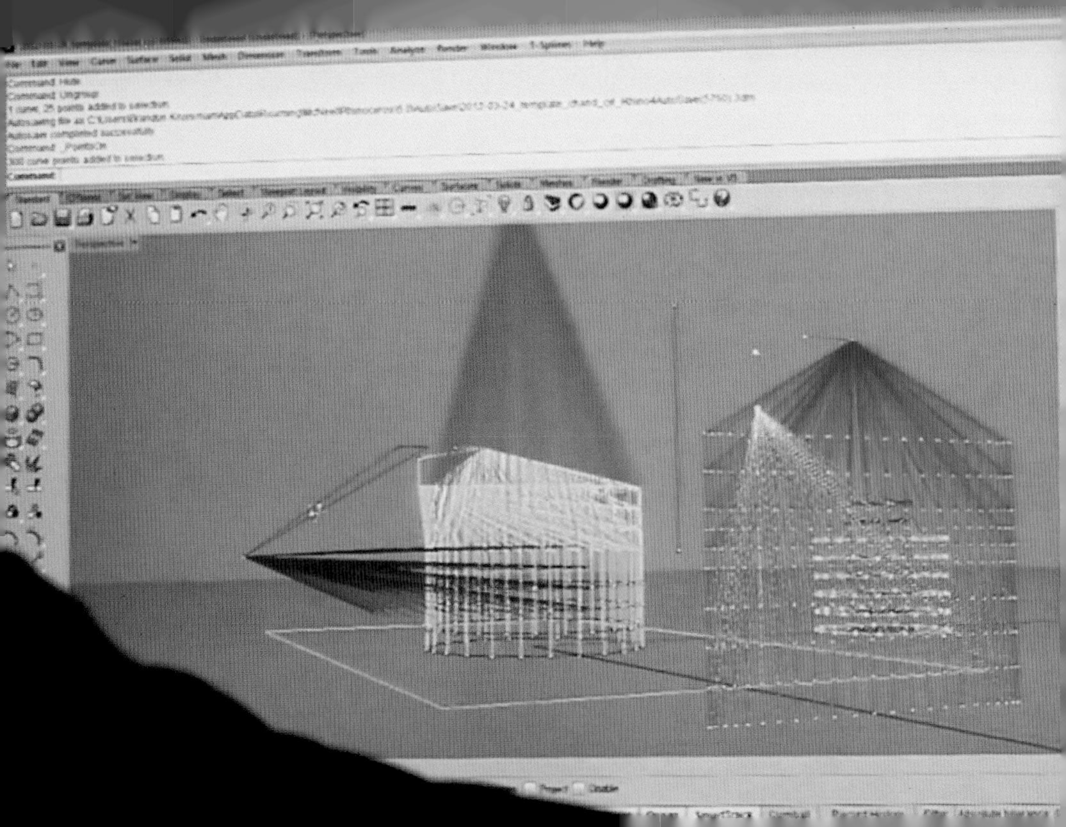
File Edit View Curve Surface Solid Mesh Dimension Transform Tools Analyze Render Window T-Splines Help

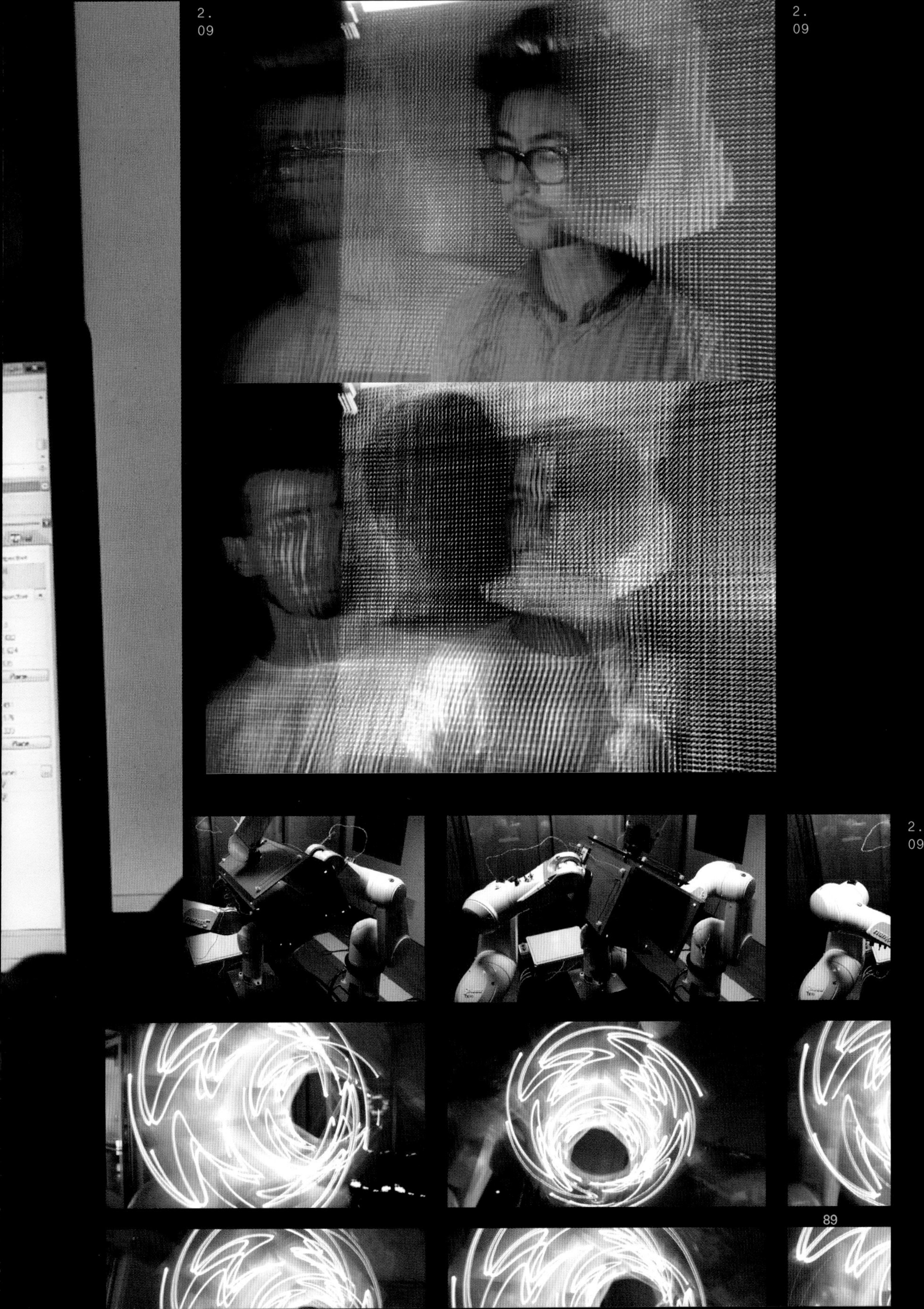

2.
09

2.
09

2.
09

89

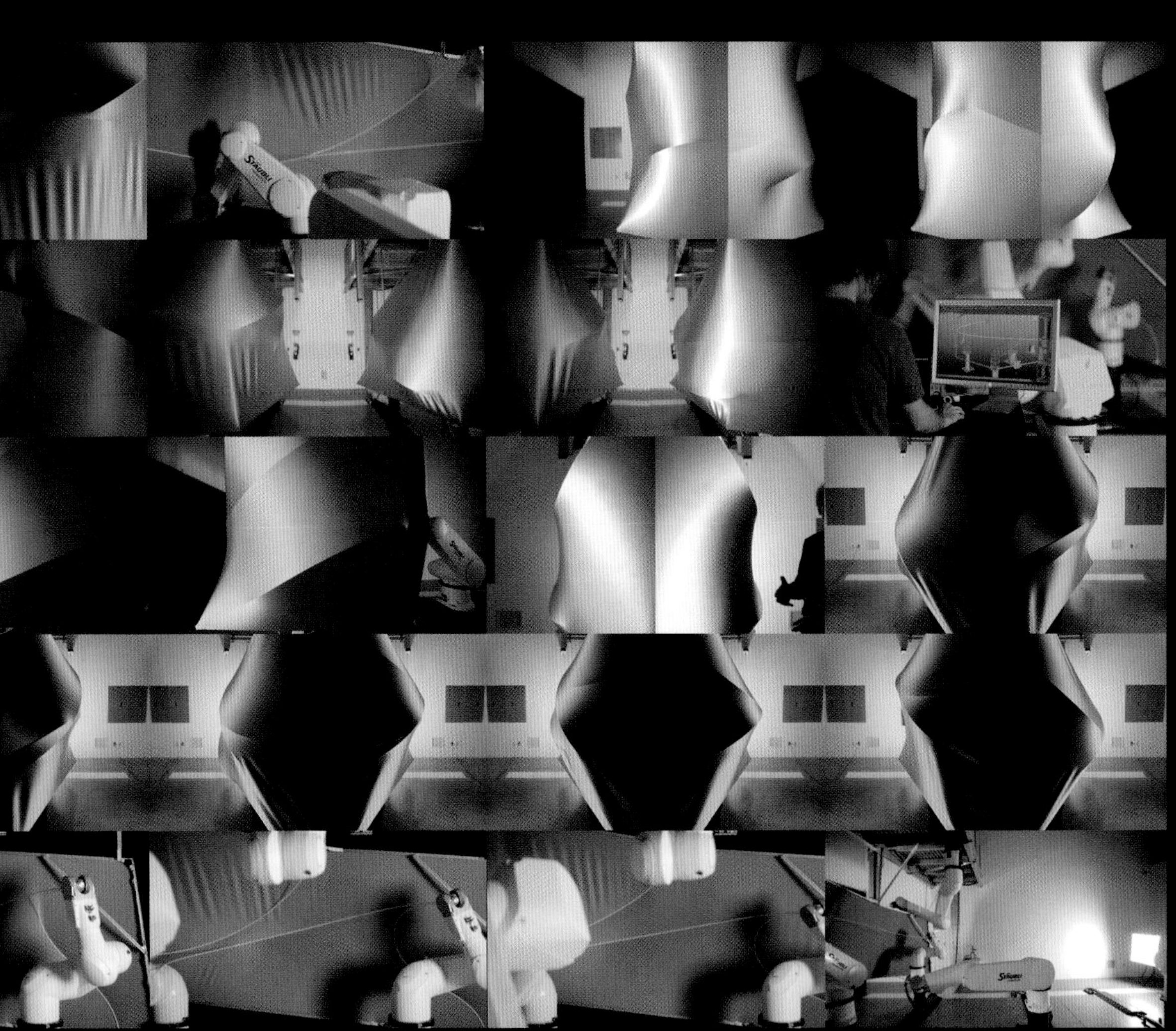

2.
10

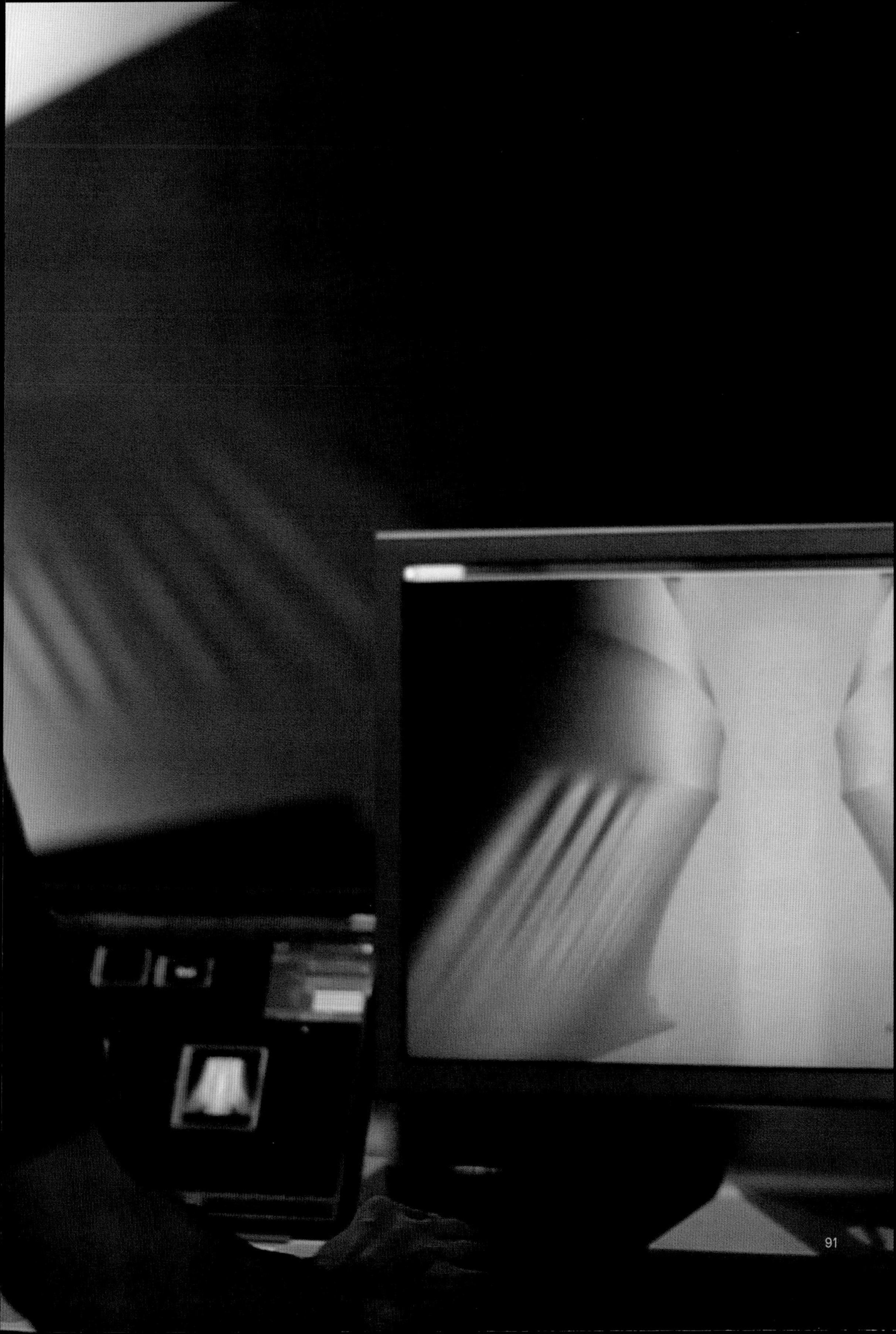

2.
10

Synchronous Robotics

Real-Time

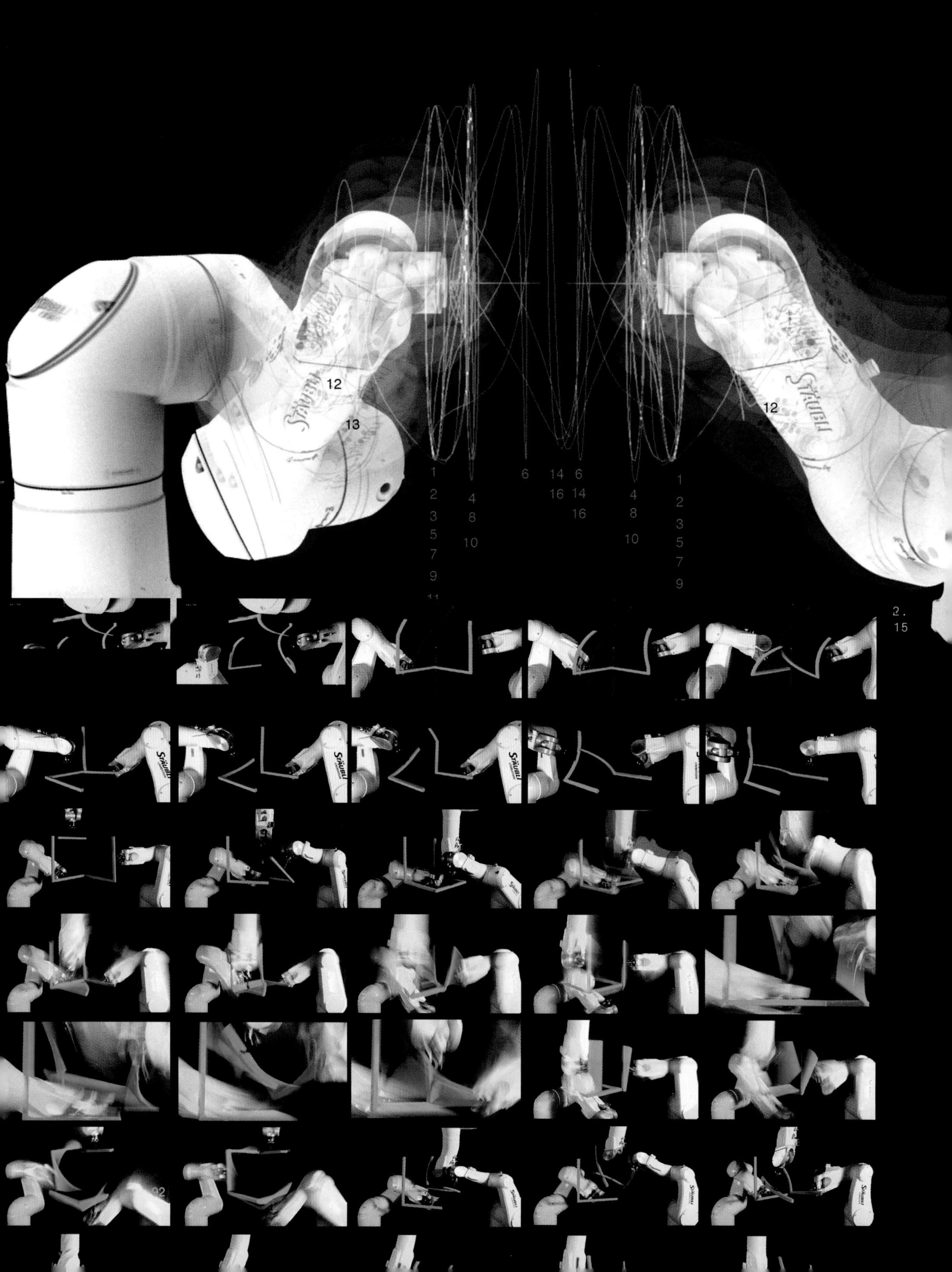
12
13
12
1
2
3
5
7
9
4
8
10
6
14
16
6
14
16
4
8
10
1
2
3
5
7
9
2.
15
92

2.13

2.14

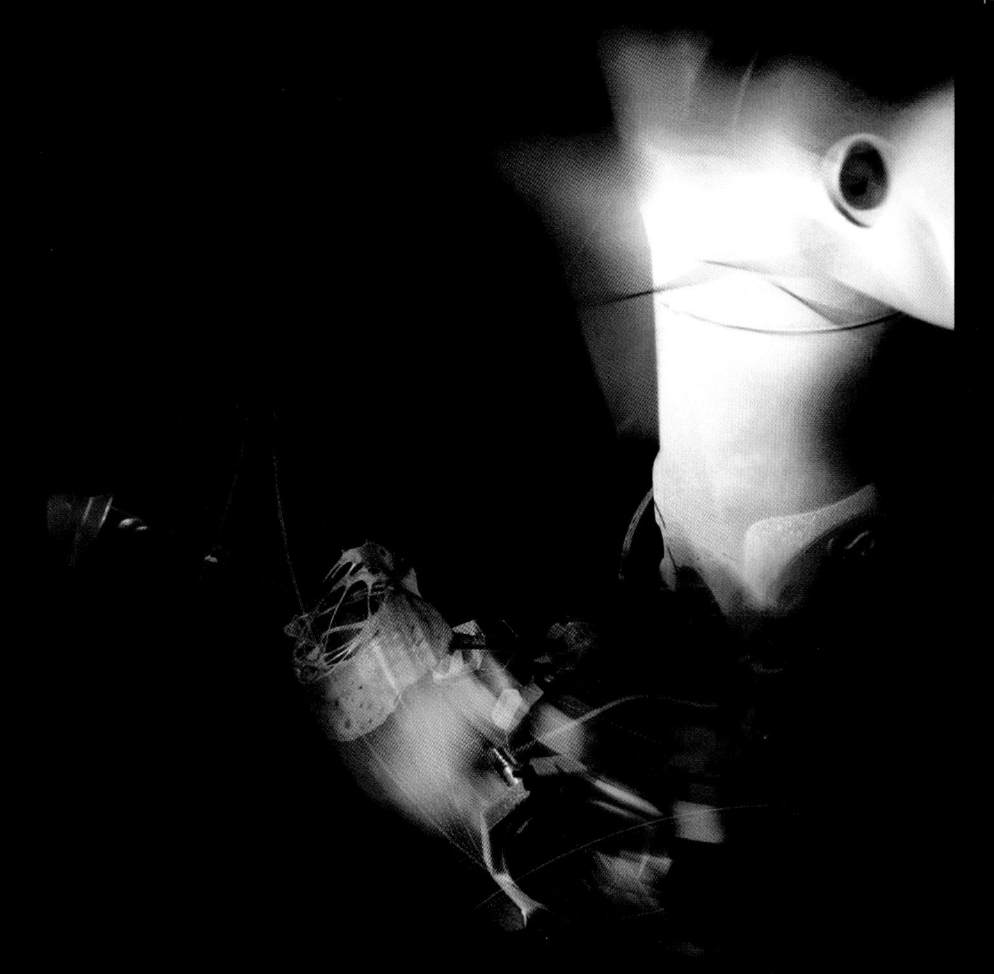

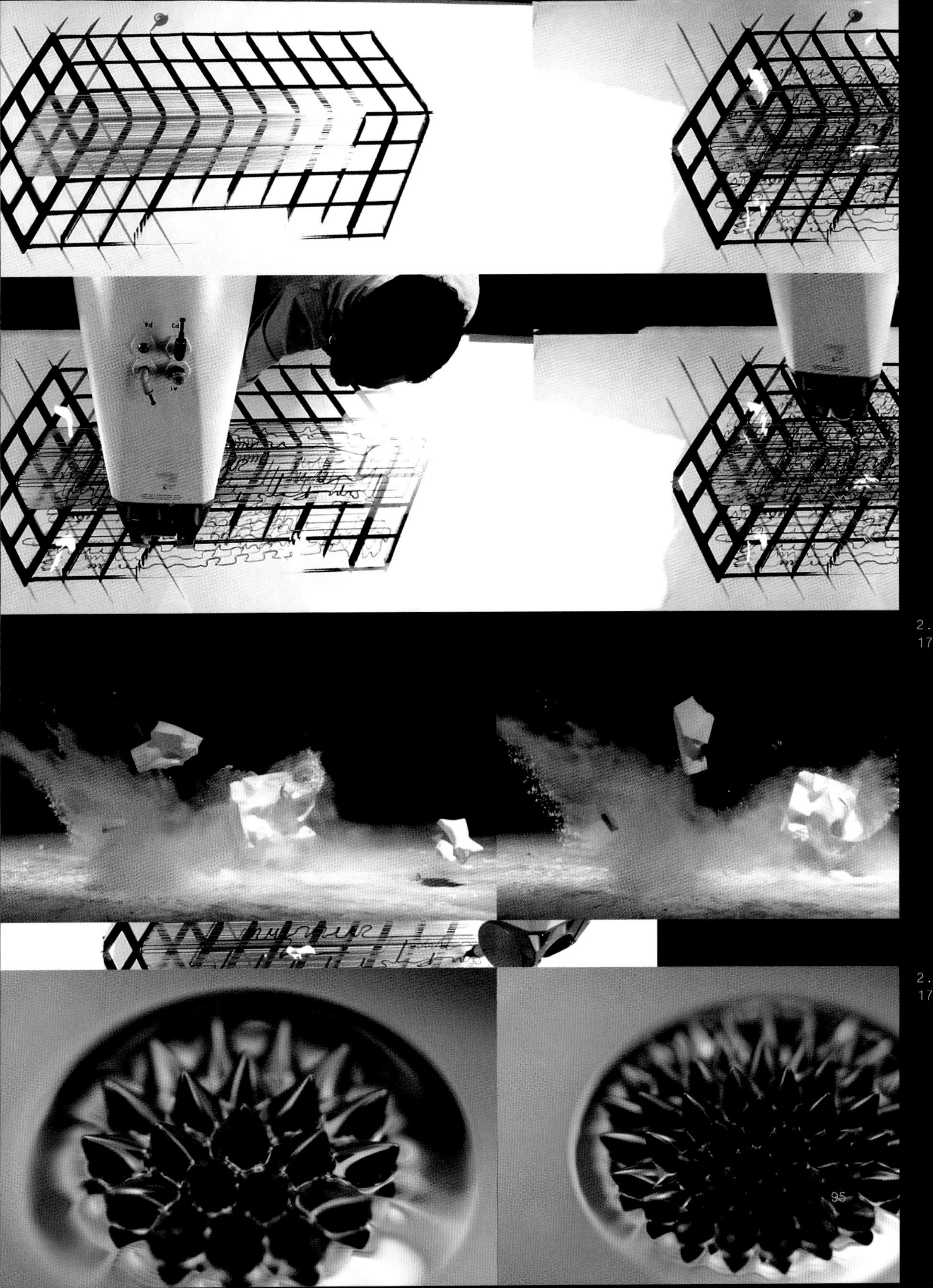

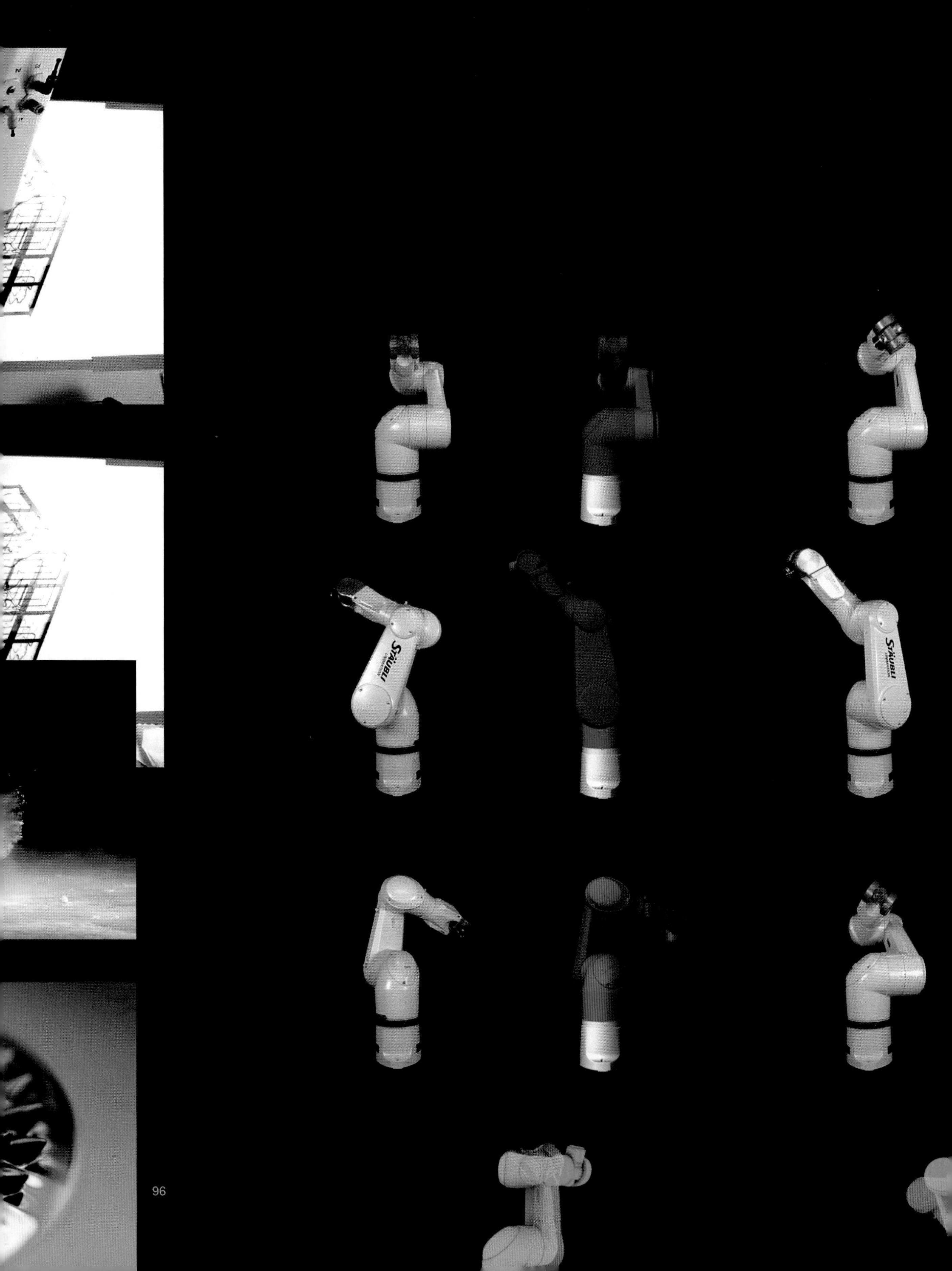
Stäubli
Stäubli

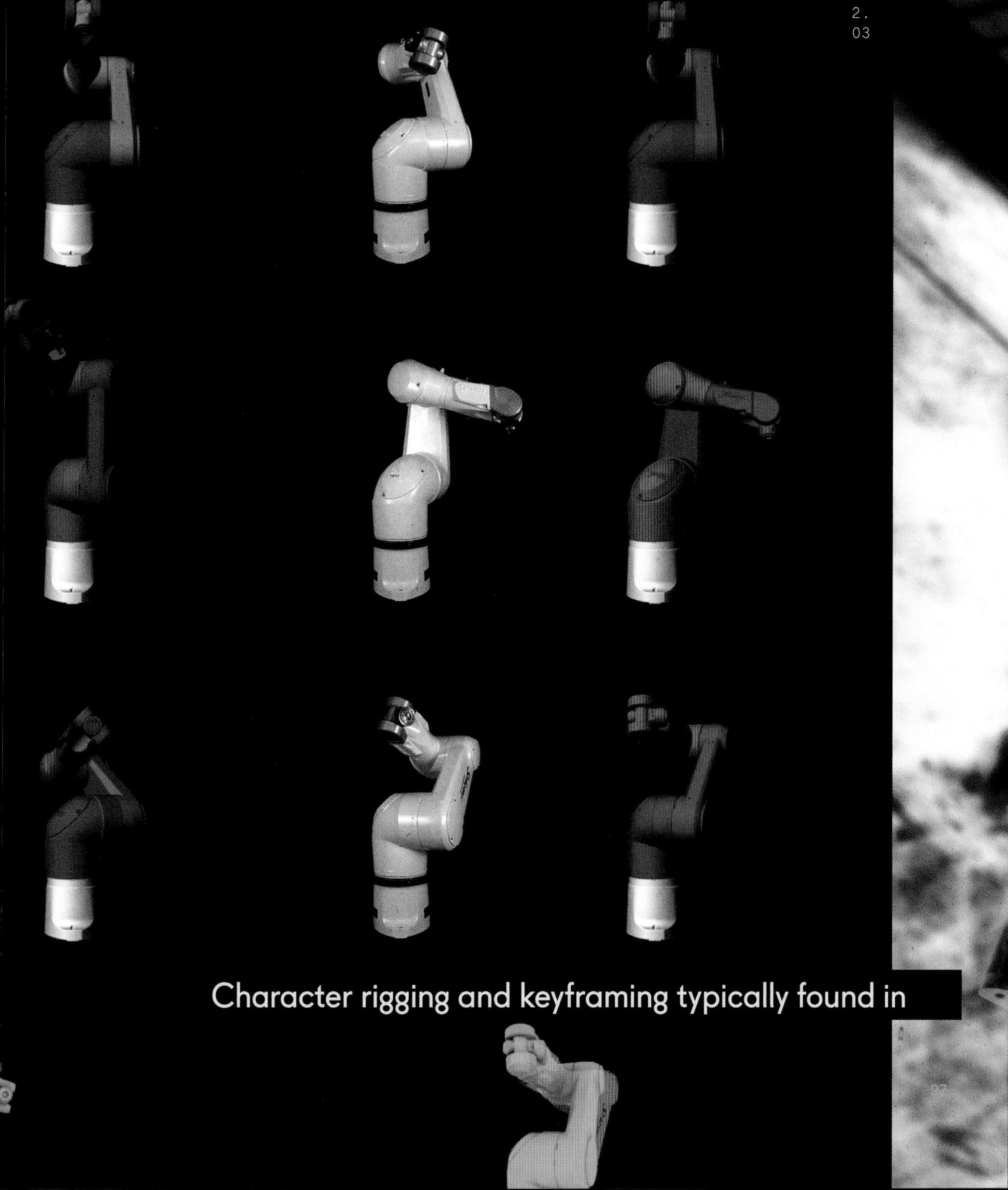

Character rigging and keyframing typically found in

872.211452
1163.096712
786.277614
860.848312
783.01345
630.957607

the animation and film industry are used to emulate

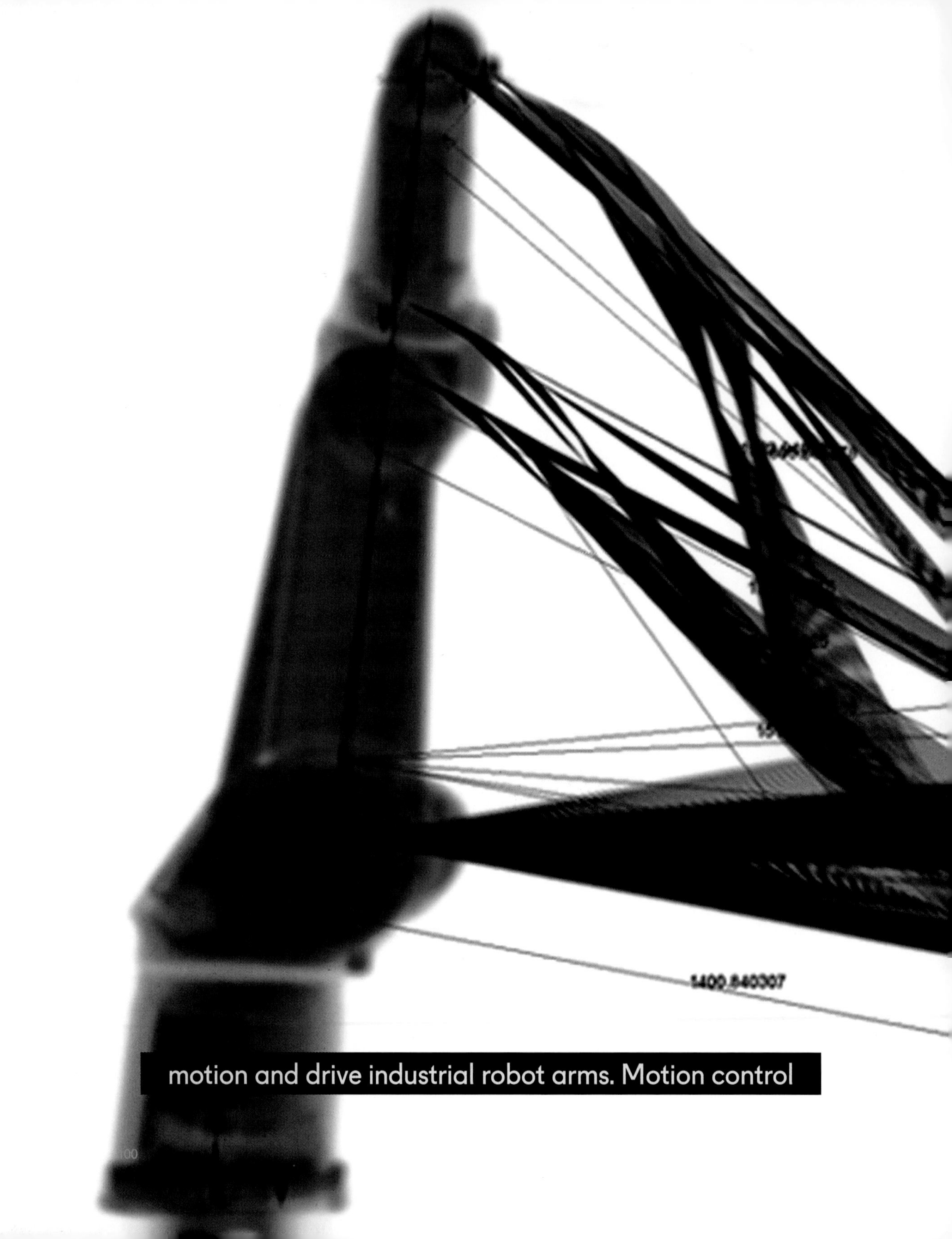

motion and drive industrial robot arms. Motion control

2.
02

2.
10

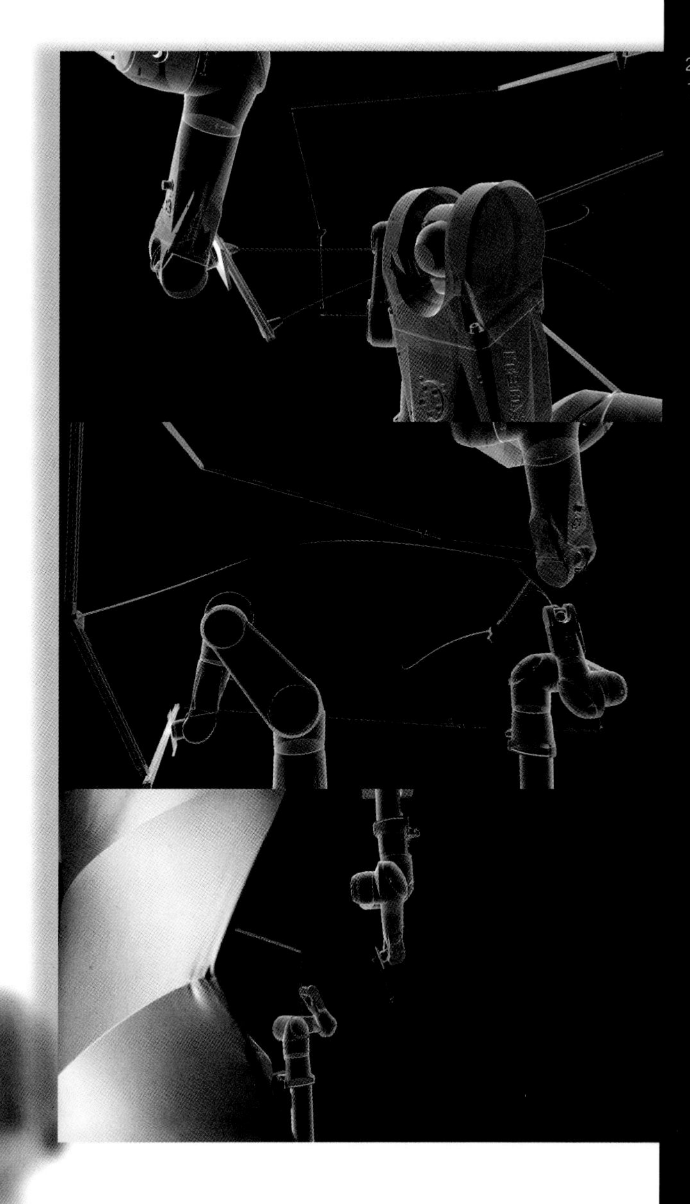

protocols and new workflows, including the creation

STÄUBLI
UNIMATION

of digital simulations linking both forward and inverse

kinematic modeling, tie simulations to actual robotic

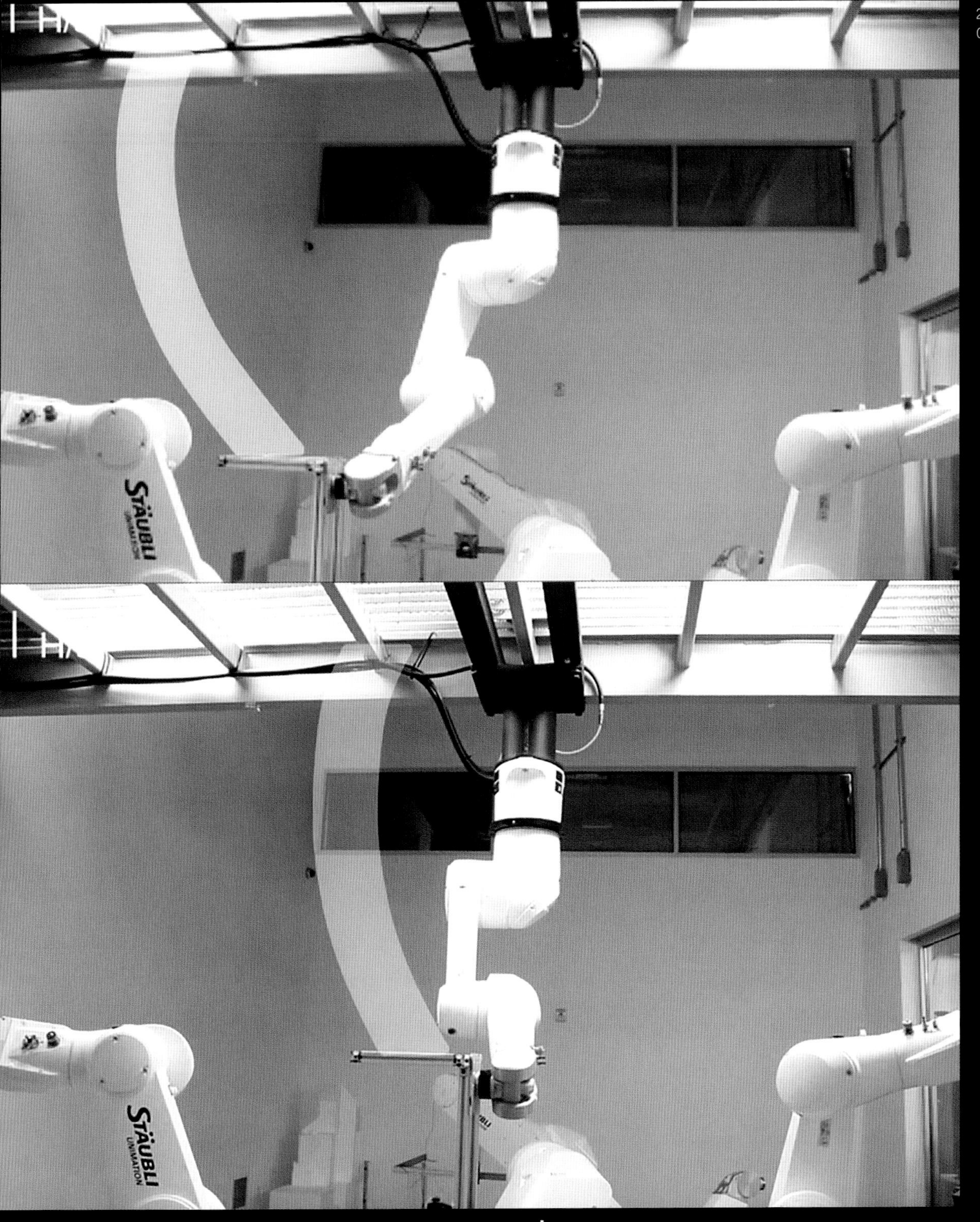

motion in real-time.

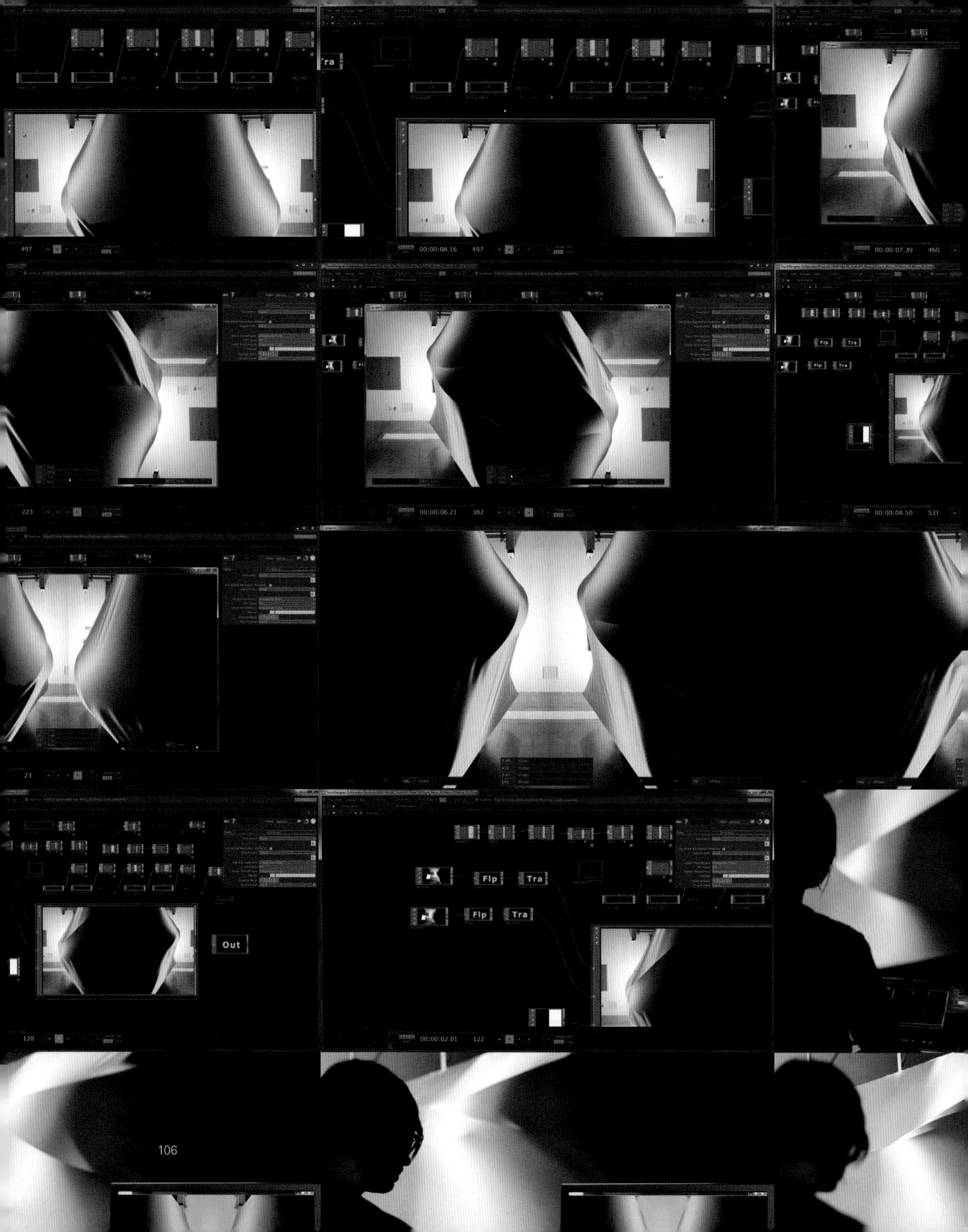

Tra
497
00:00:08.16
497
00:00:07.39
460
Flp
Tra
Flp
Tra
223
00:00:06.21
382
00:00:08.50
531
23
Out
Flp
Tra
Flp
Tra
120
00:00:02.01
122

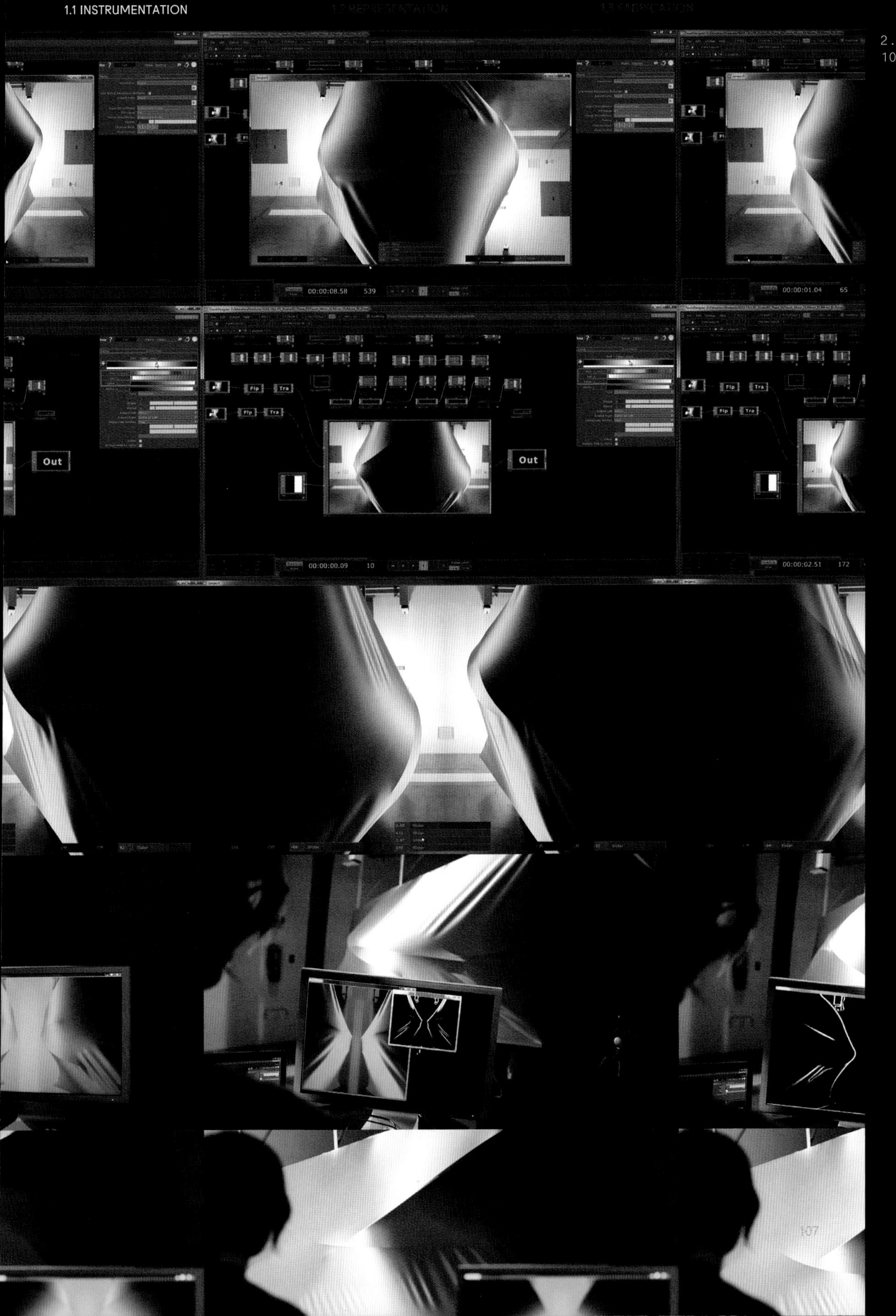
00:00:08.58
539
00:00:01.04
65
Out
Out
00:00:00.09
10
00:00:02.51
172

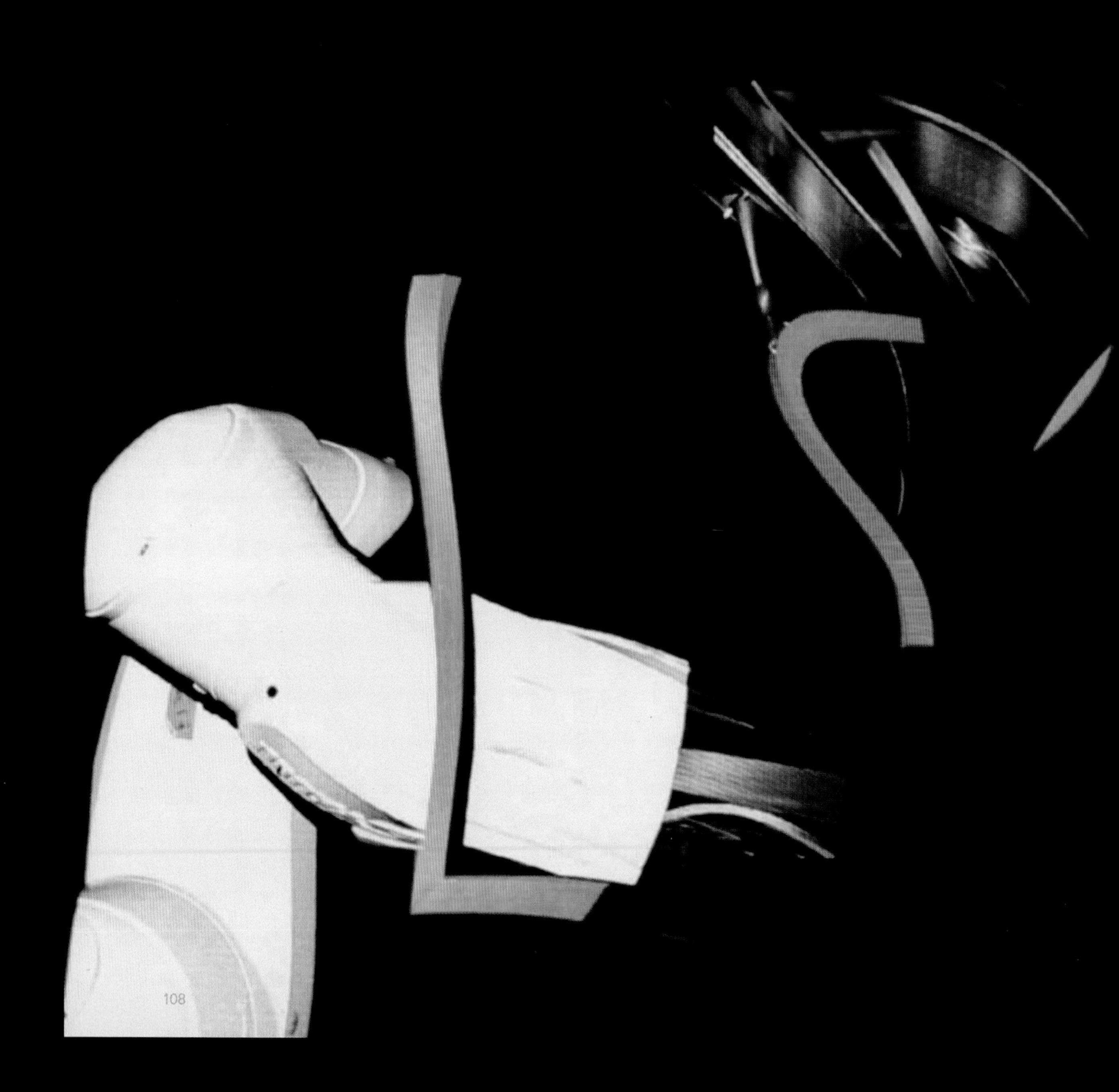

2.
15

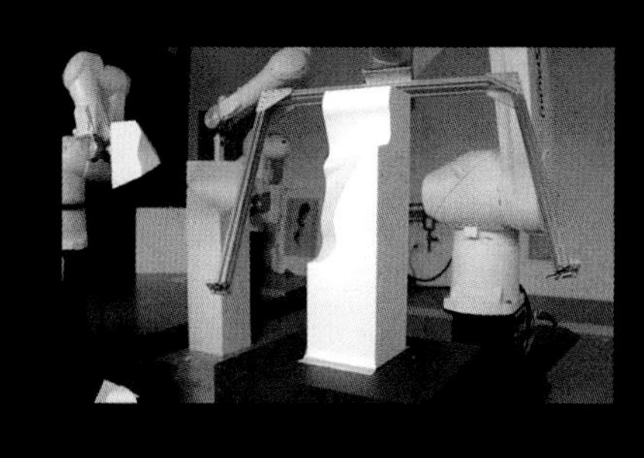

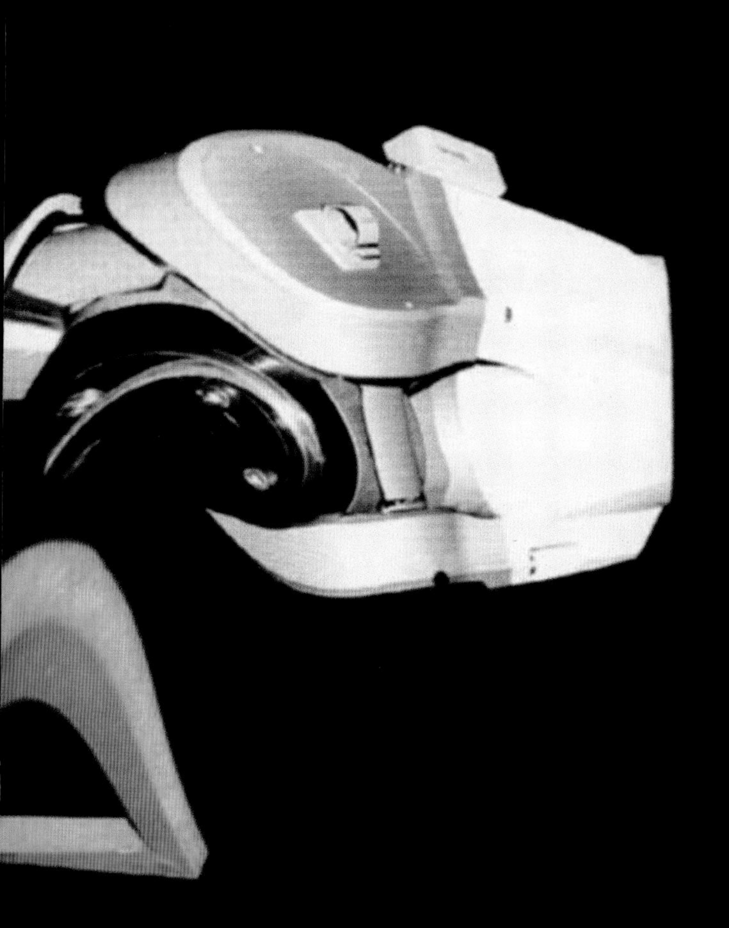

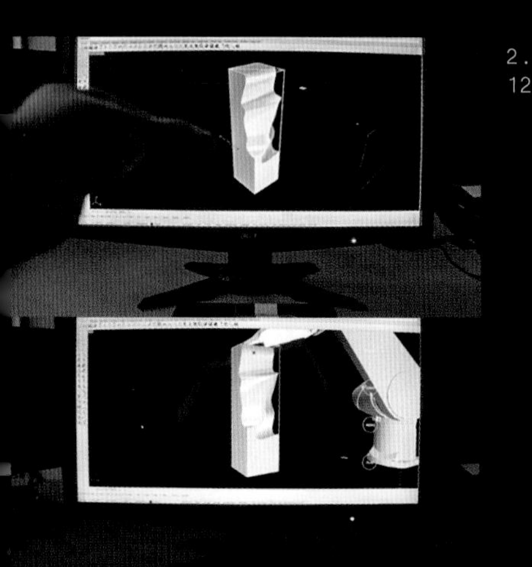

2.
12

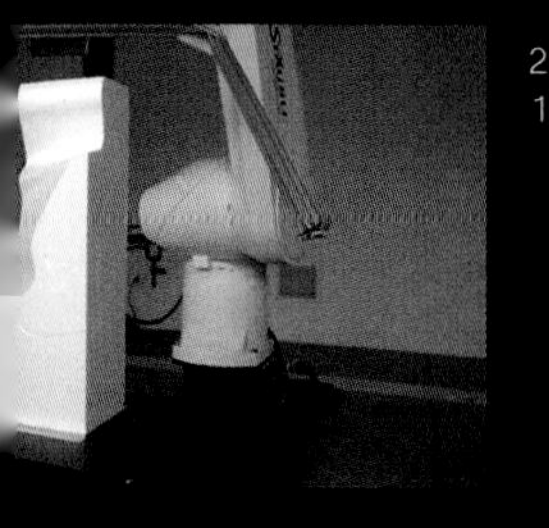

2.
12

Effectors
End Effectors
Physical Computing

Augmented or intelligent hardware attachments implement a wide range of techniques, from mediated vision to dynamic scanning and projection, as well as various forms of additive fabrication. By hacking what were previously closed technological systems, these implements are tied to specific materials and ideas. Combining sensing and actuation, image analysis, pattern recognition, and shape analysis, techniques explore feedback and feedforward protocols across a range of physical and computational media involving intelligent end effectors and physical computing.

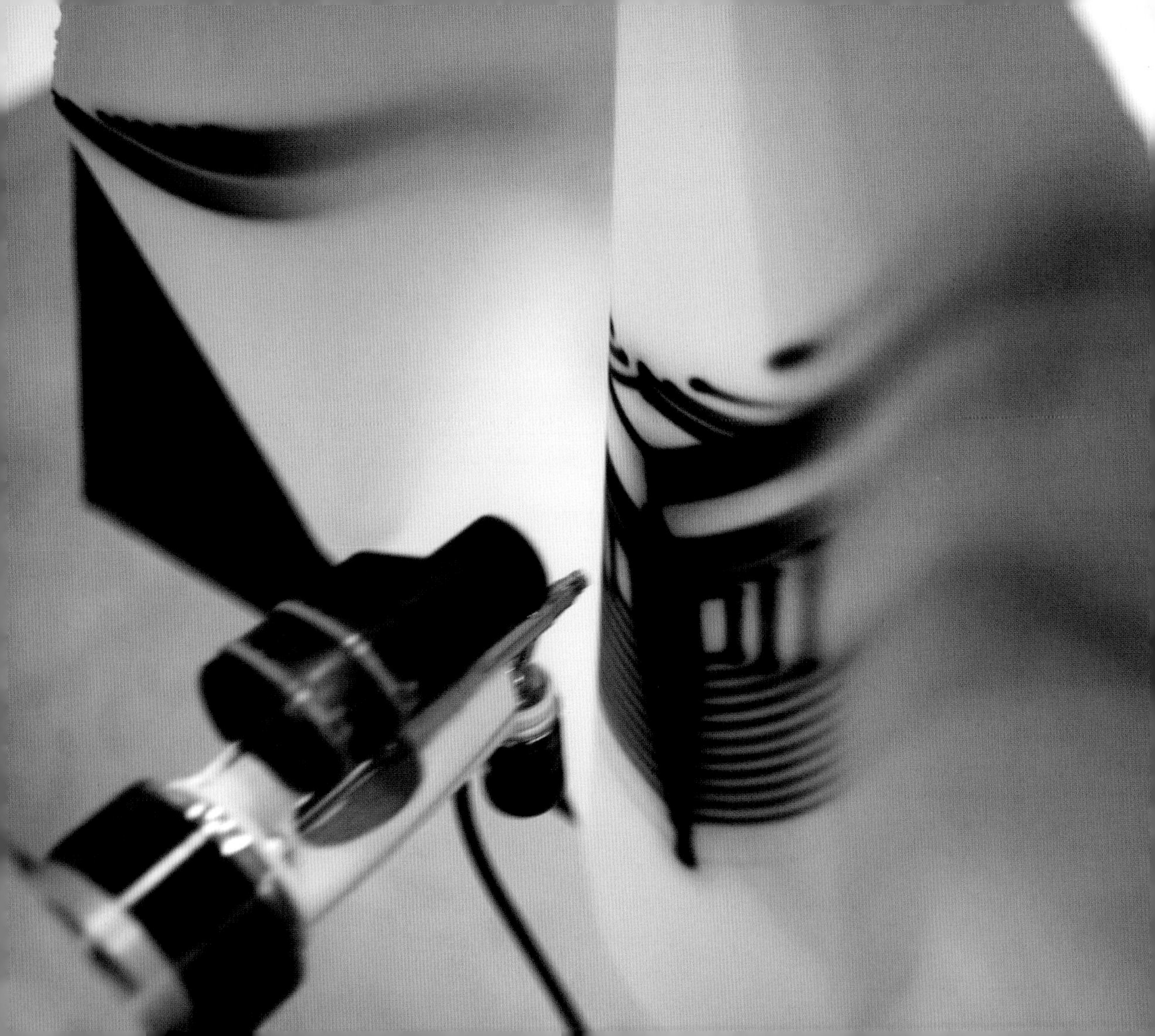

End Effectors

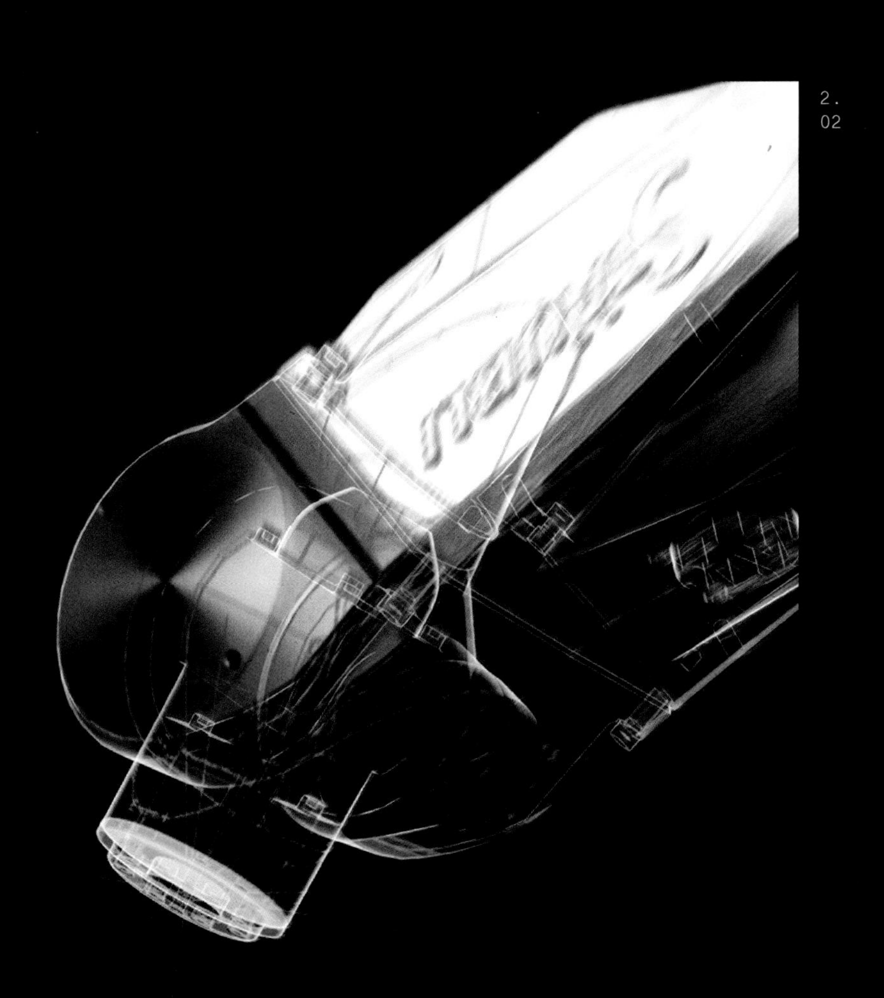

Industrial robot arms interact with users, materials,

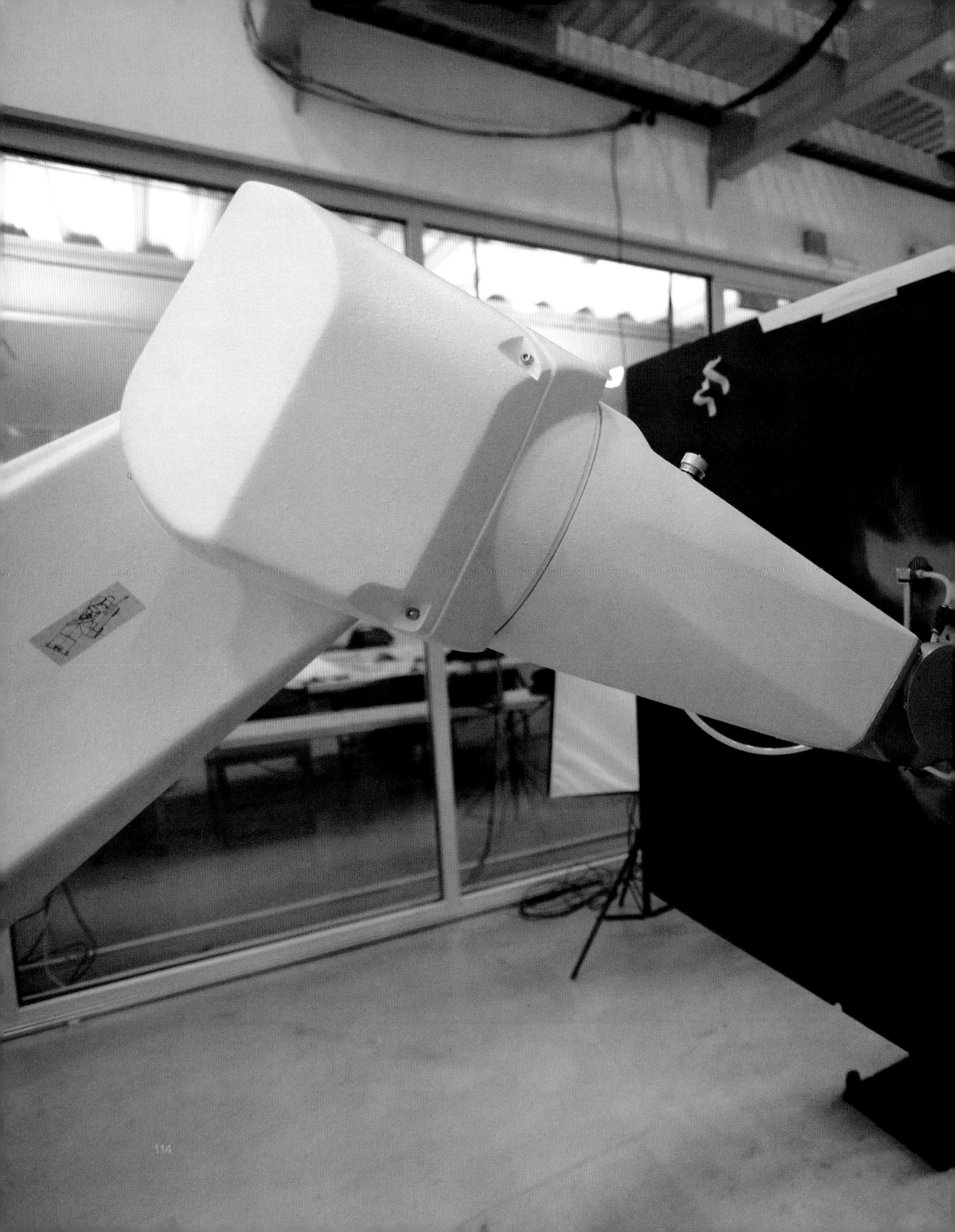

and the environment through the use of end effectors,

2.
14

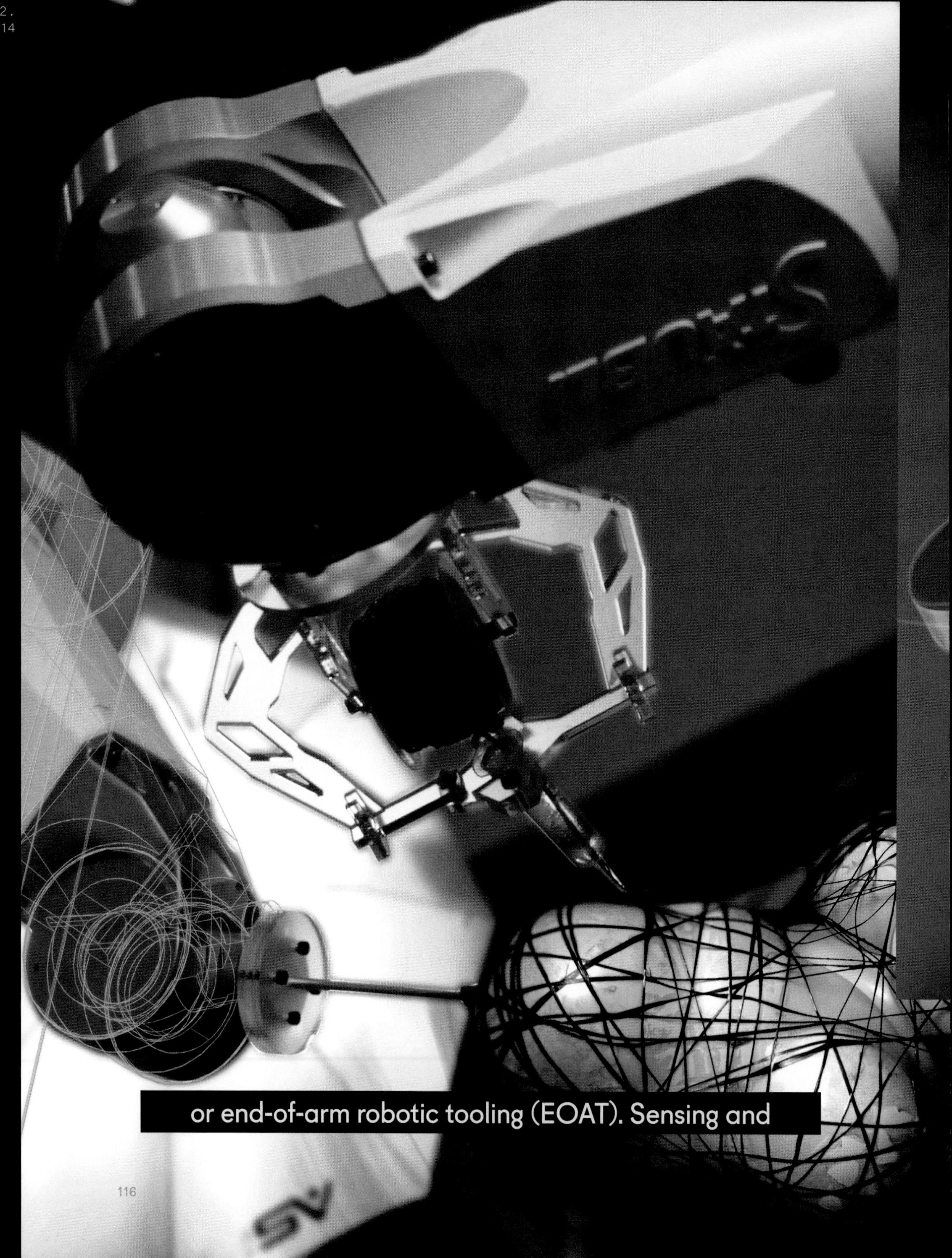

or end-of-arm robotic tooling (EOAT). Sensing and

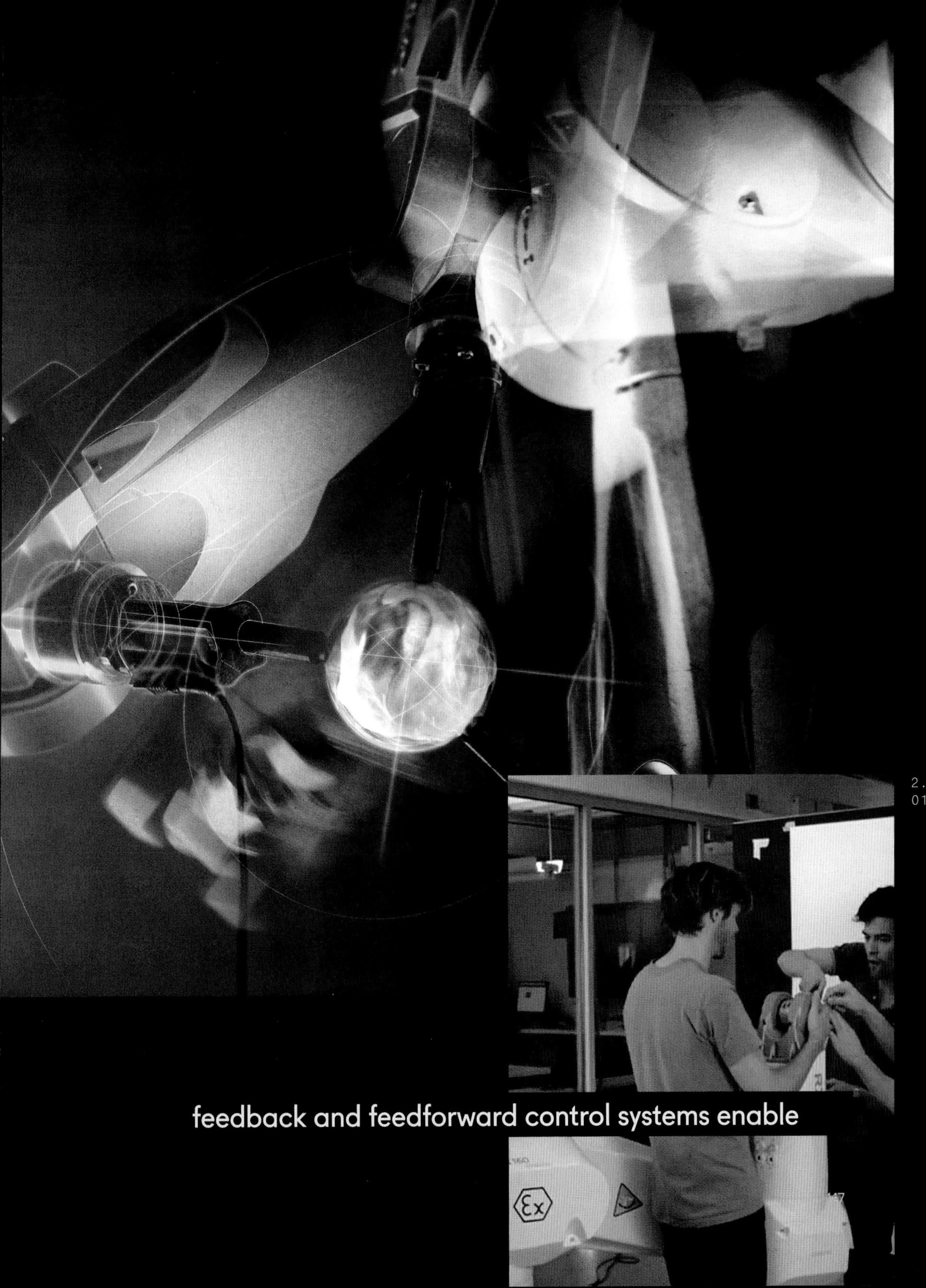

feedback and feedforward control systems enable

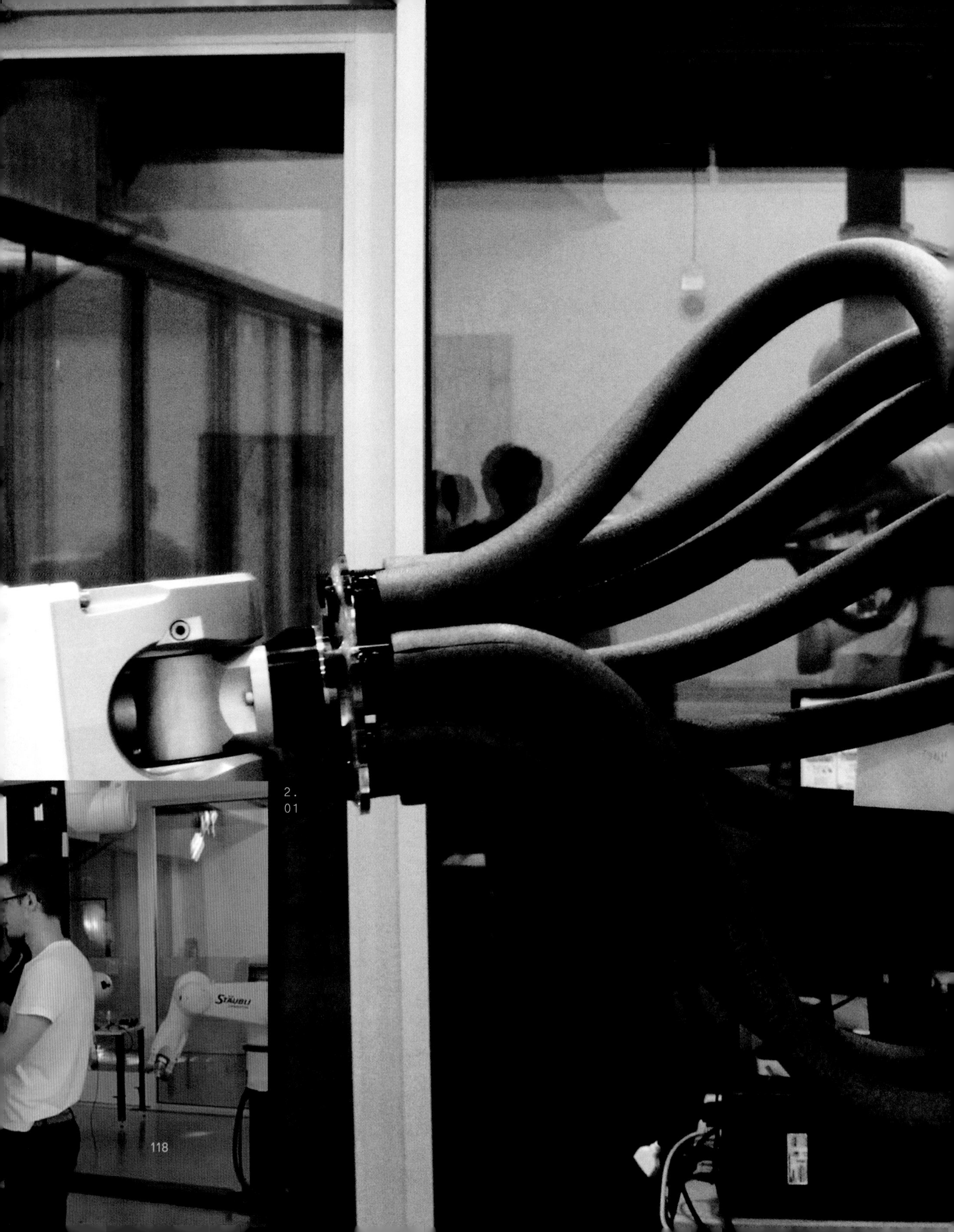

2.
01

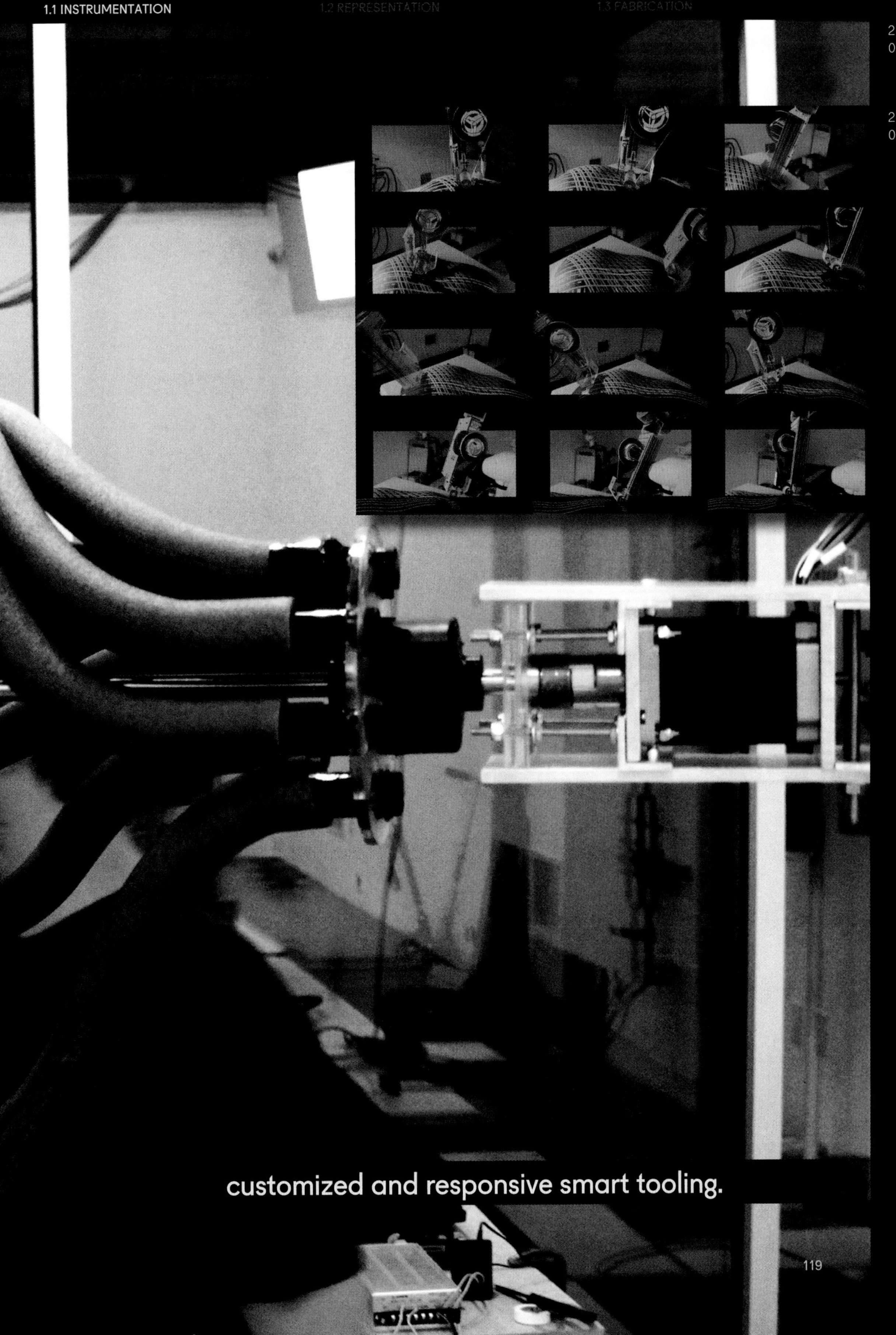

customized and responsive smart tooling.

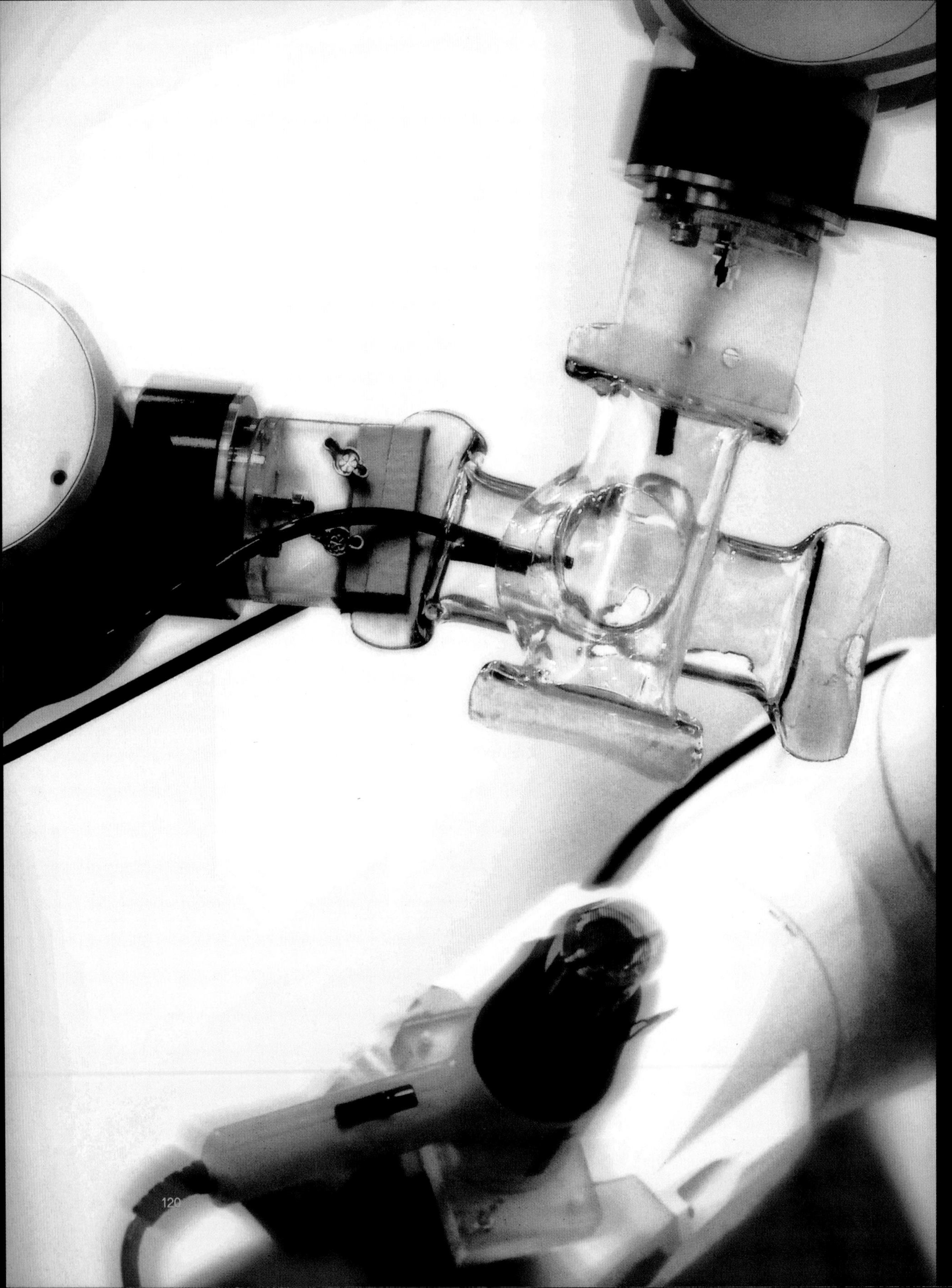

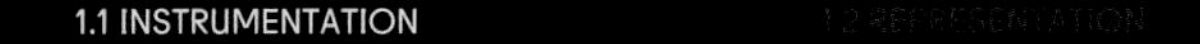

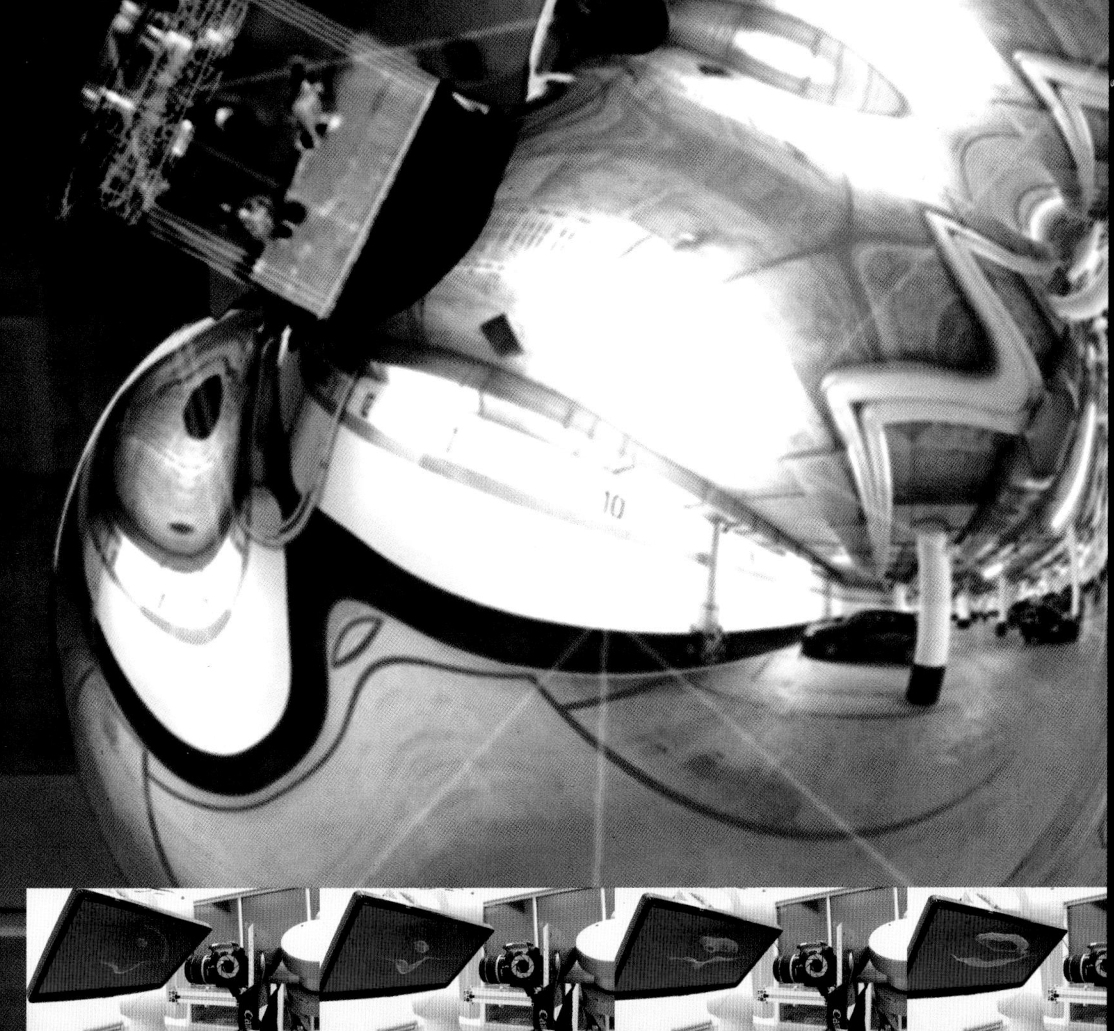

2.
03

2.
06

Effectors
End Effectors

TX90

2.
07

2.
07

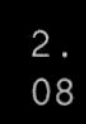
2.
08

2.
09

Effectors
End Effectors

2.
09

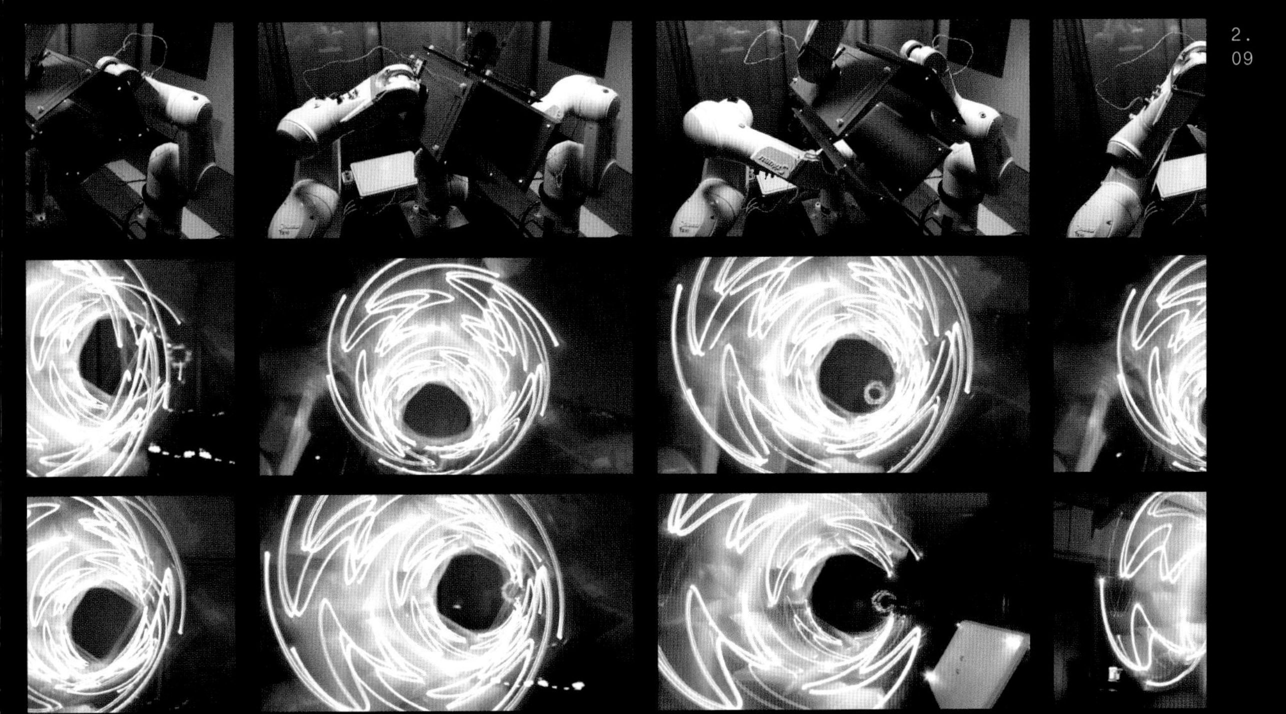

2. 09

2. 10

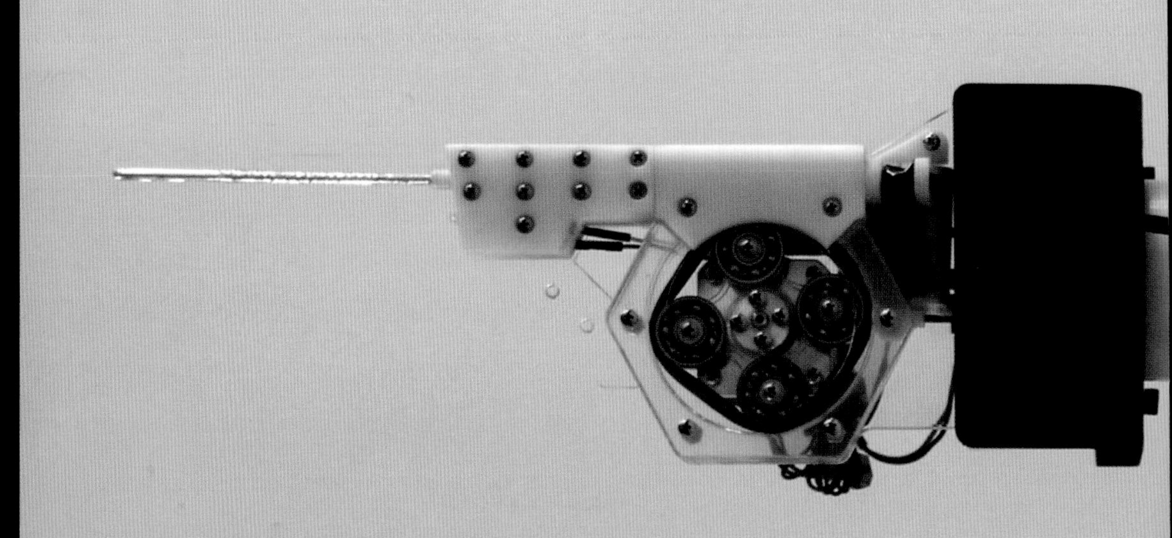

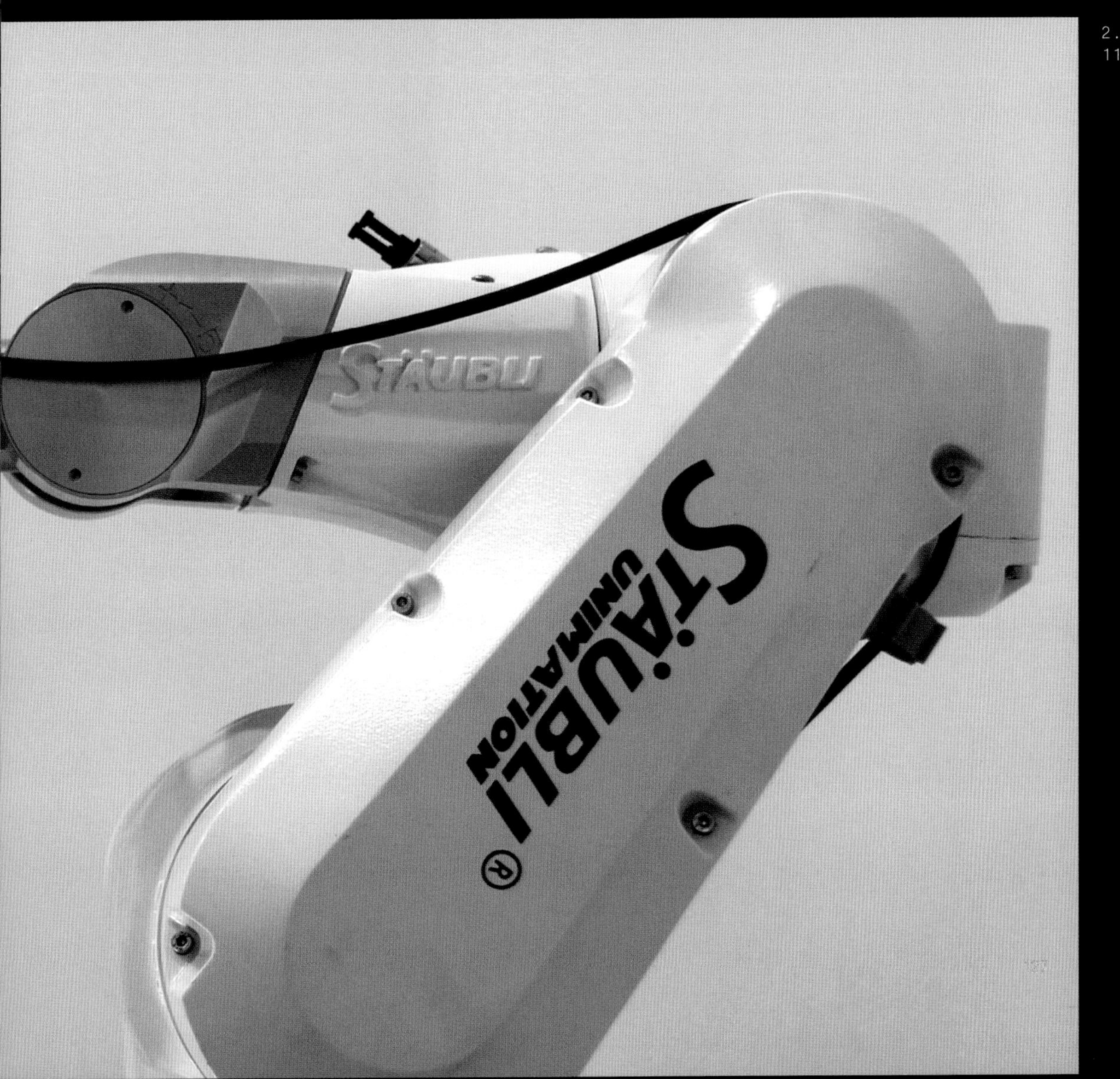
STÄUBLI
STÄUBLI
UNIMATION

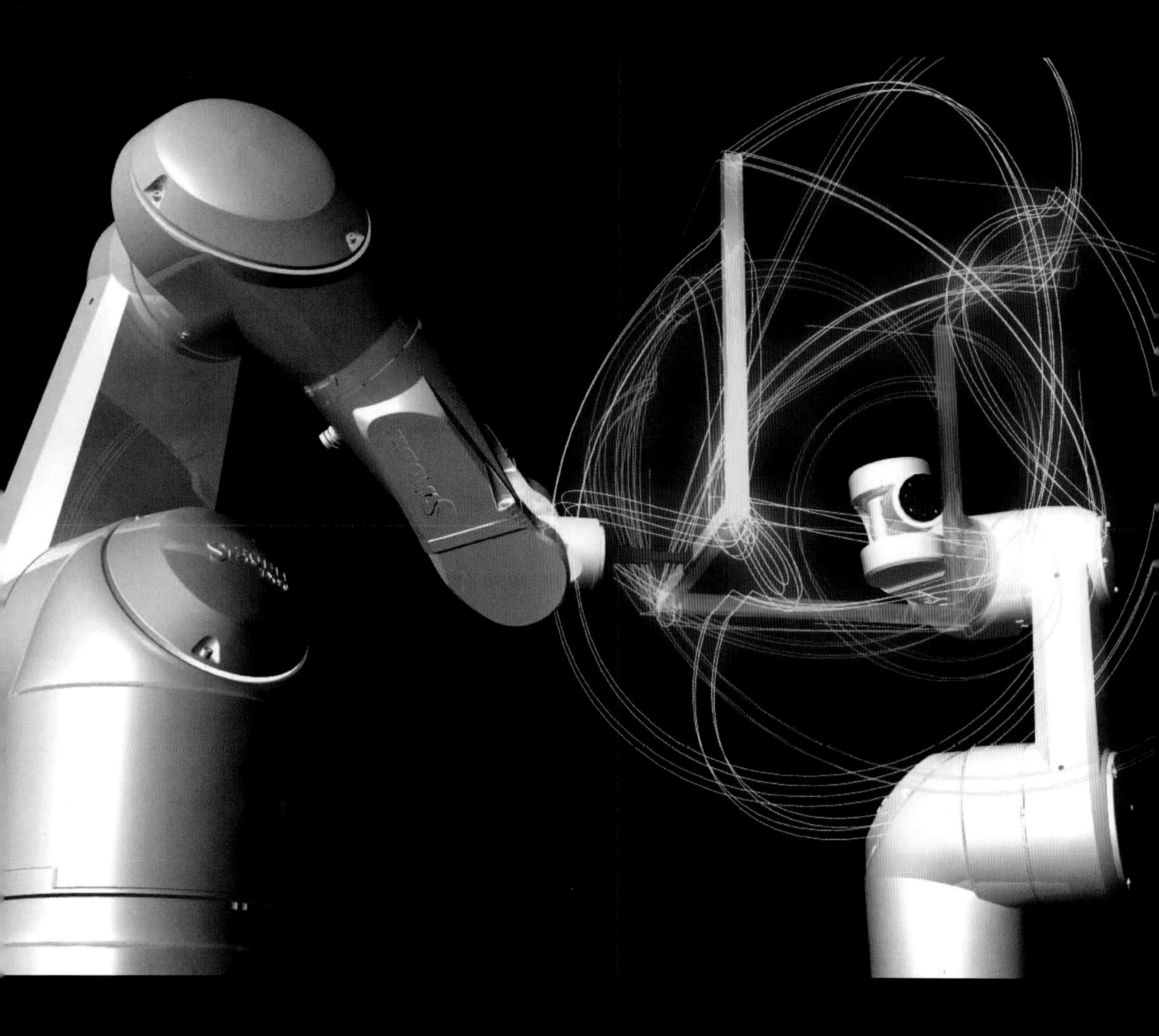

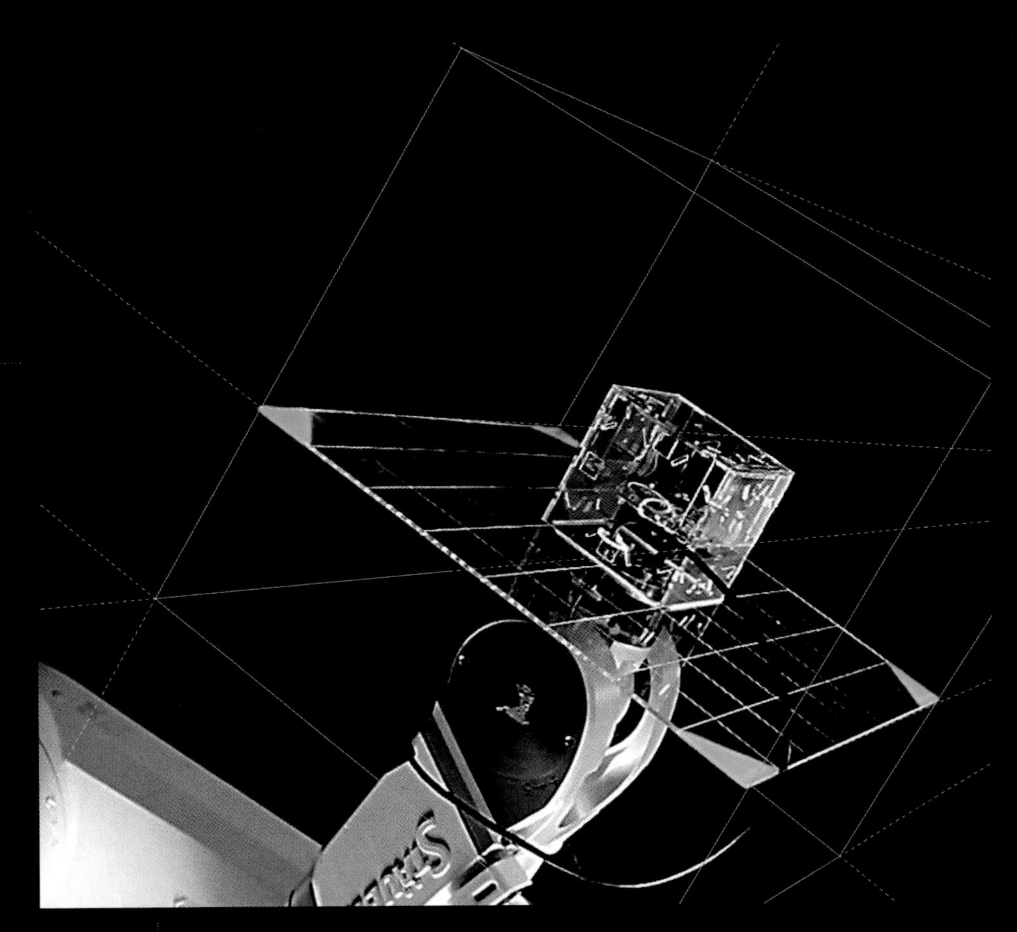

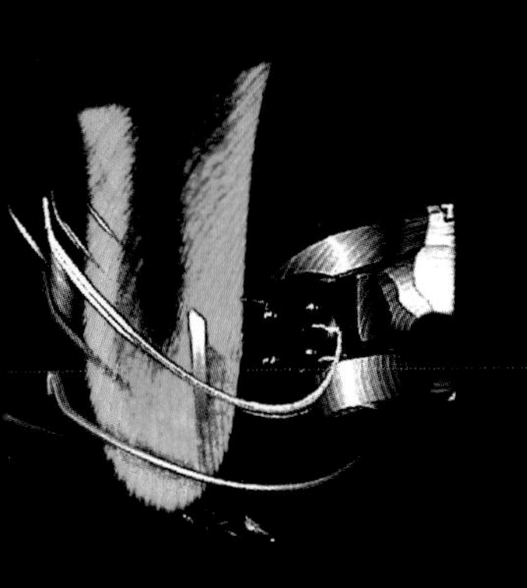

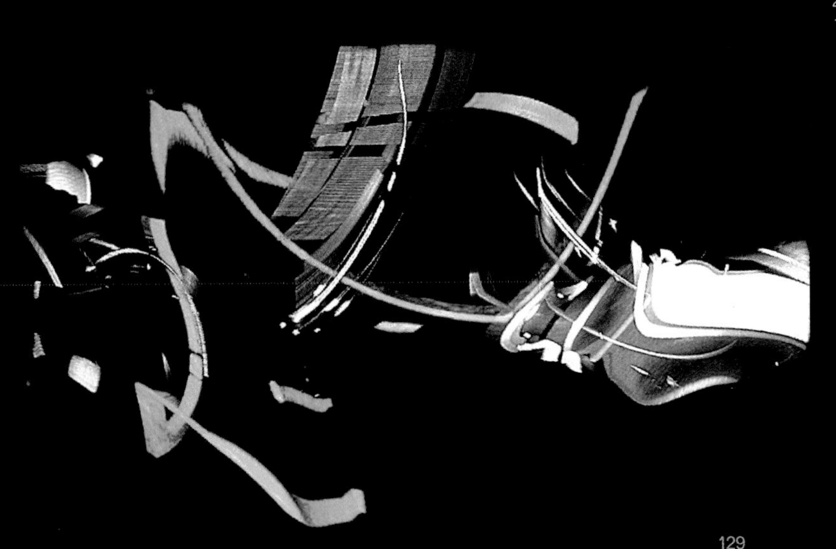

2.
15

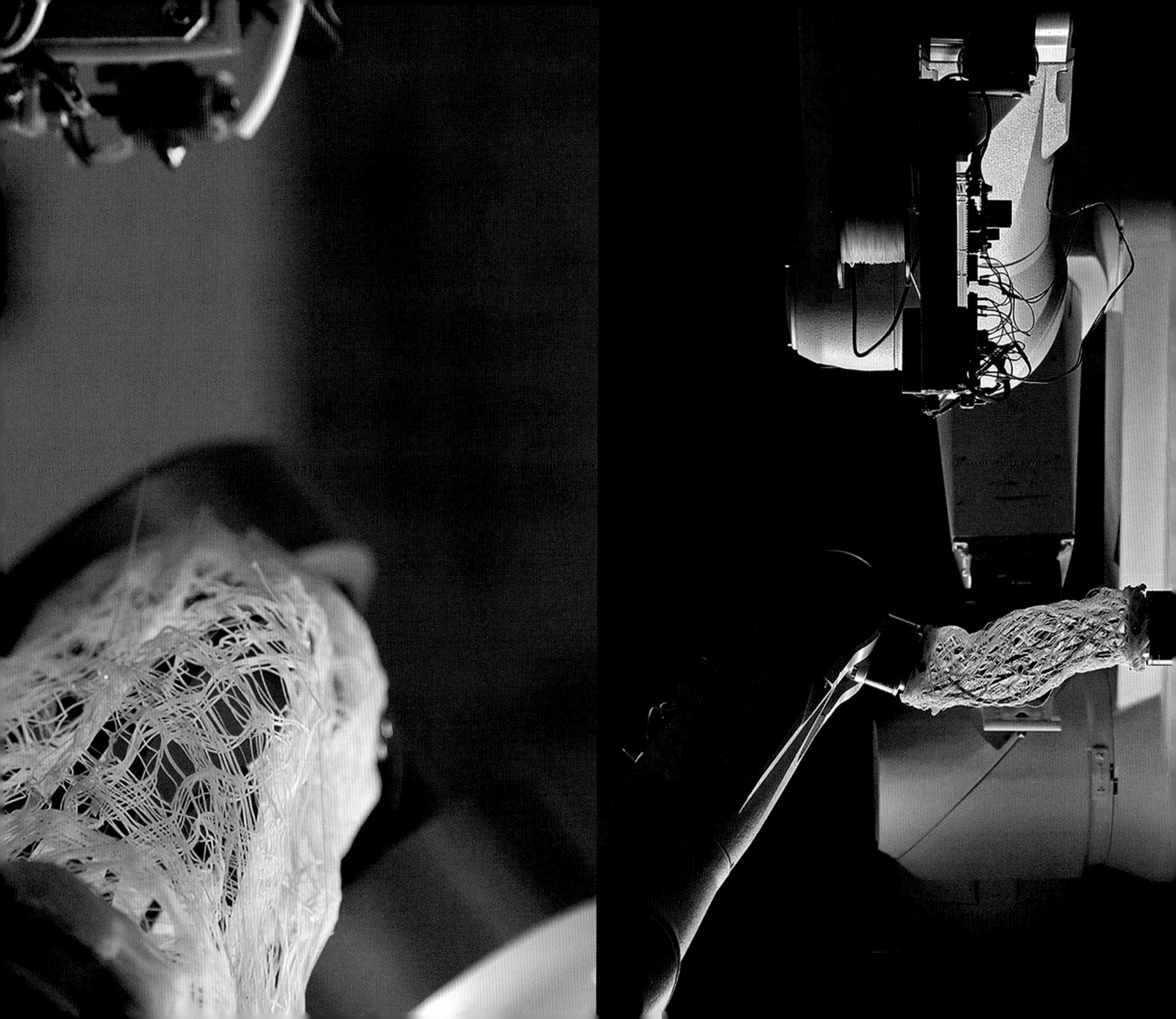

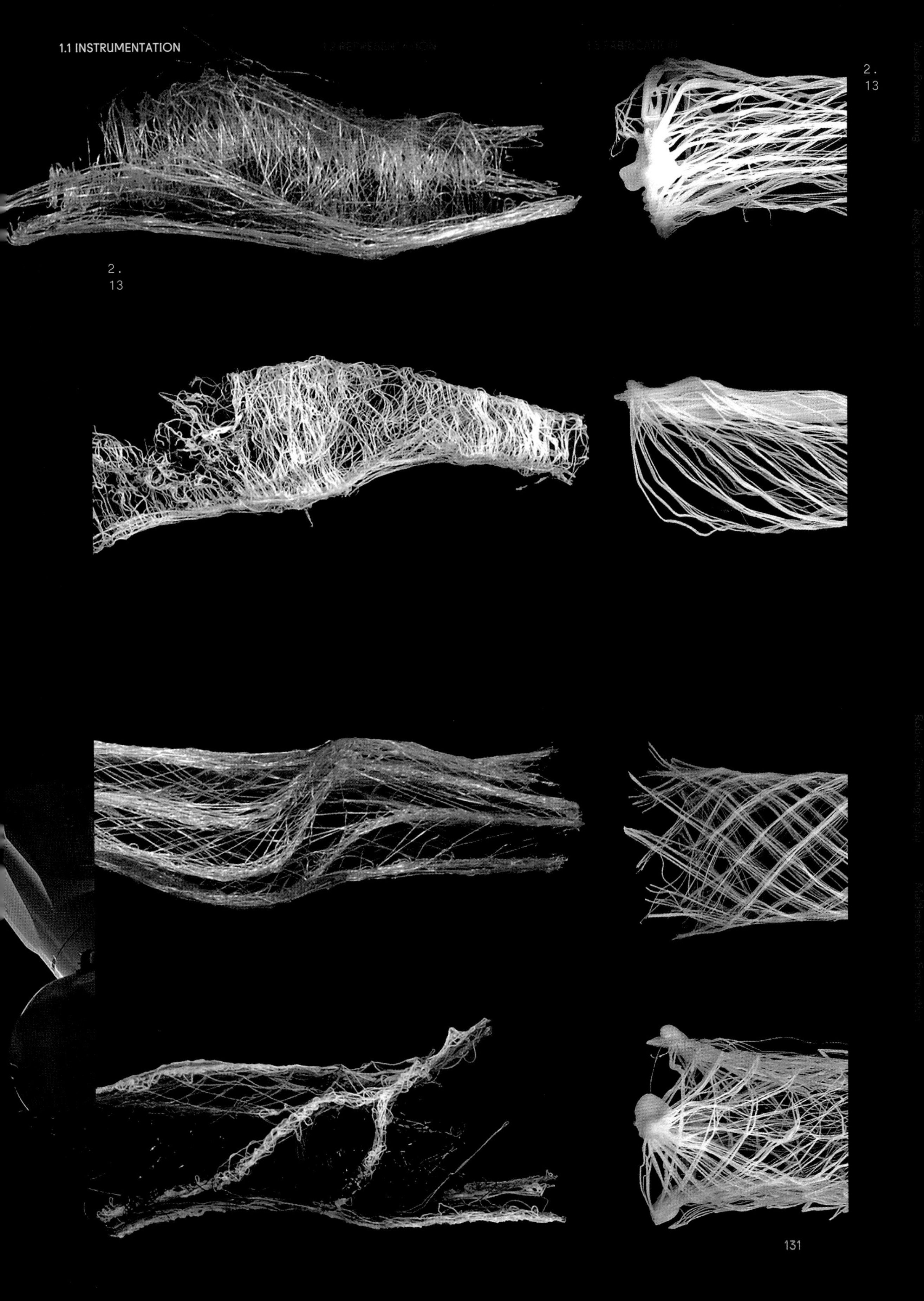

2.
13

2.
13

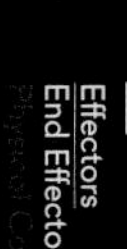

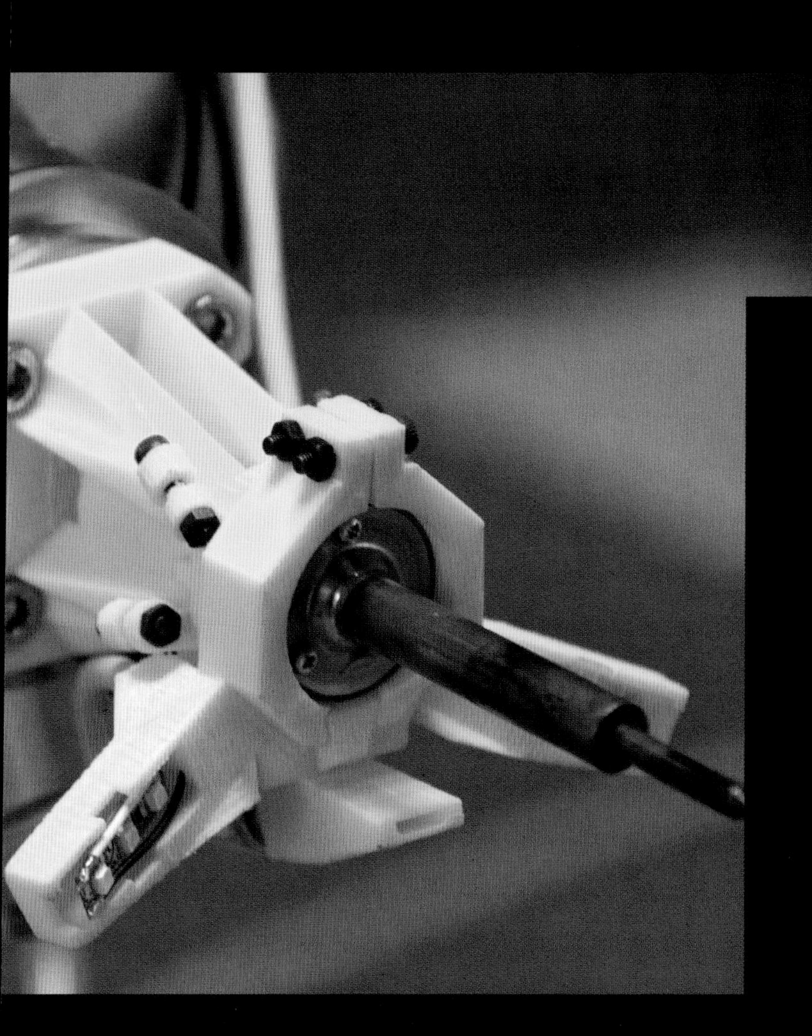

2.
16

2.
13

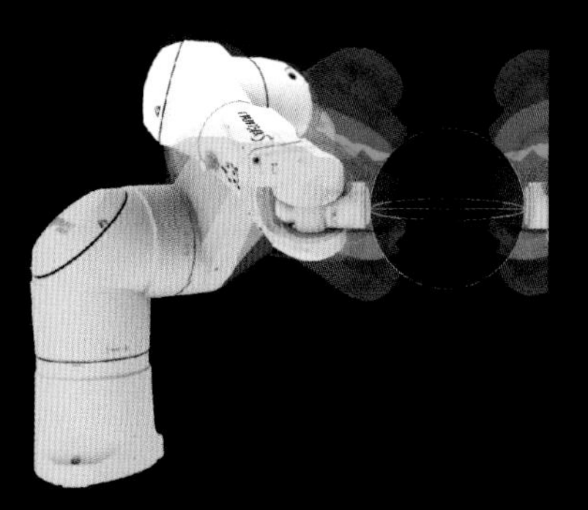

2.
13

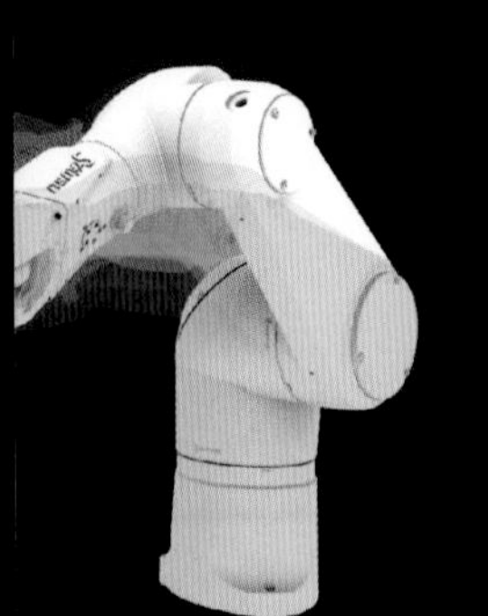

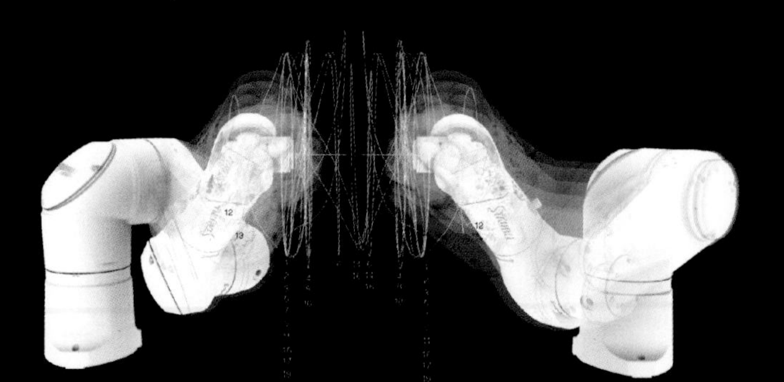

Physical Computing

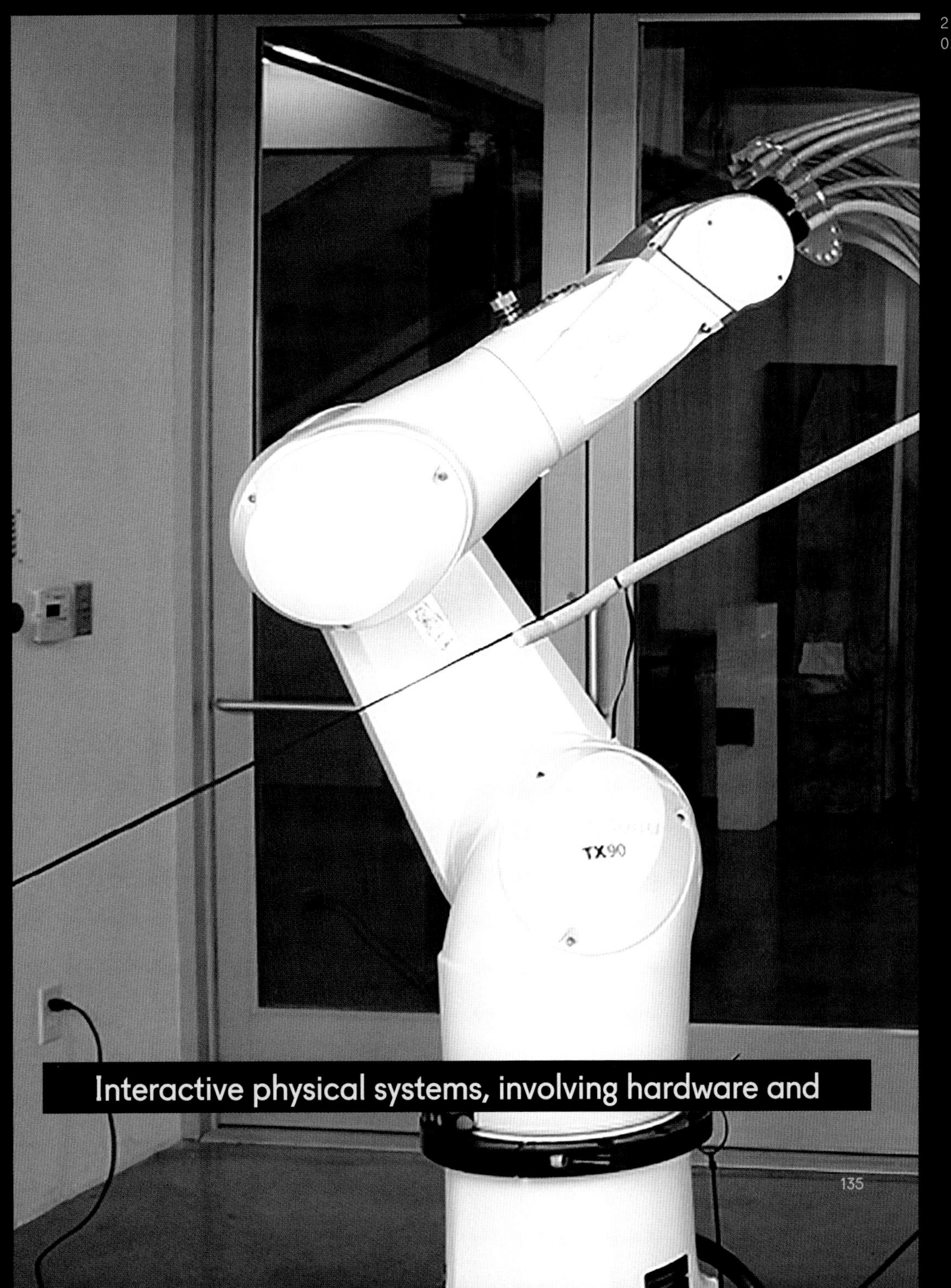

Interactive physical systems, involving hardware and

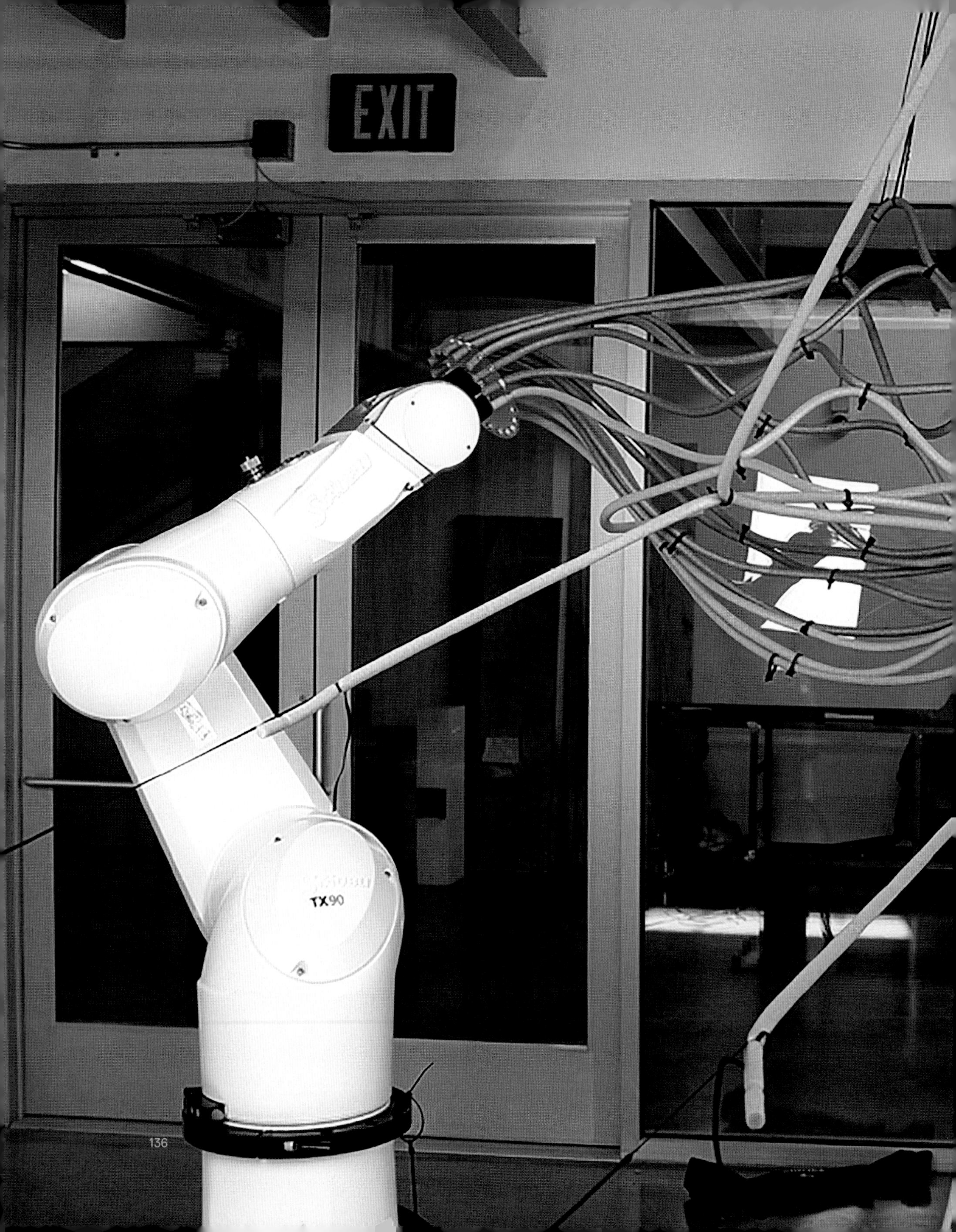
EXIT
TX90

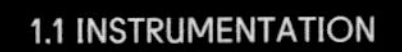

software, from Arduino microcontrollers to Raspberry Pi

single-board computers and actuators, can sense and

respond to the physical world.

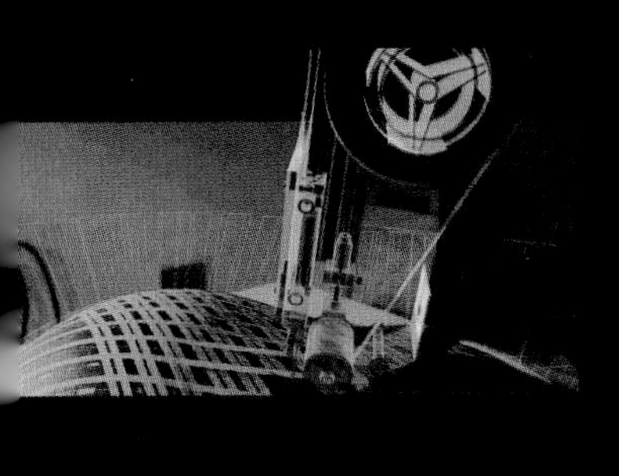

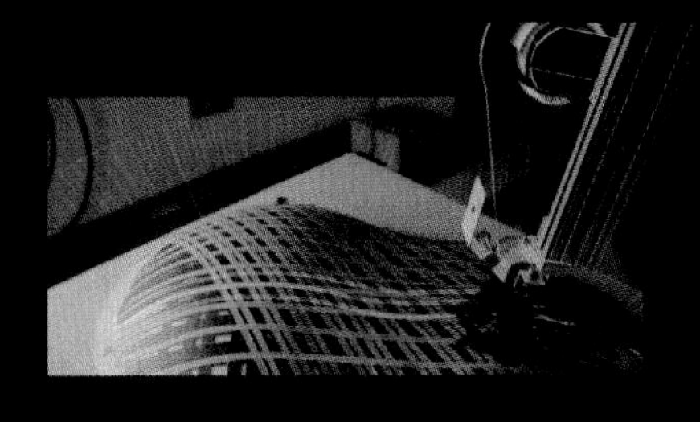

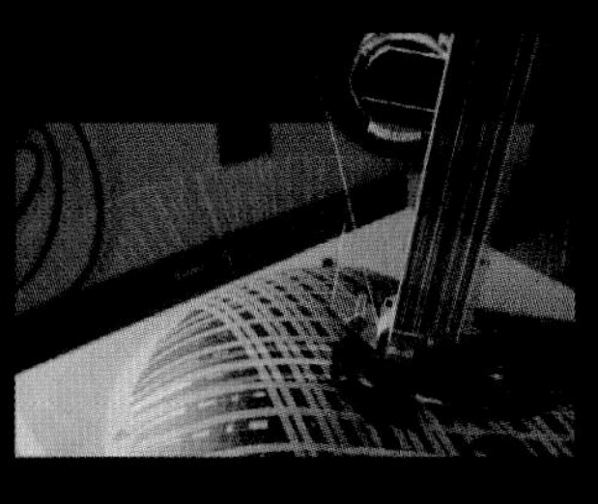

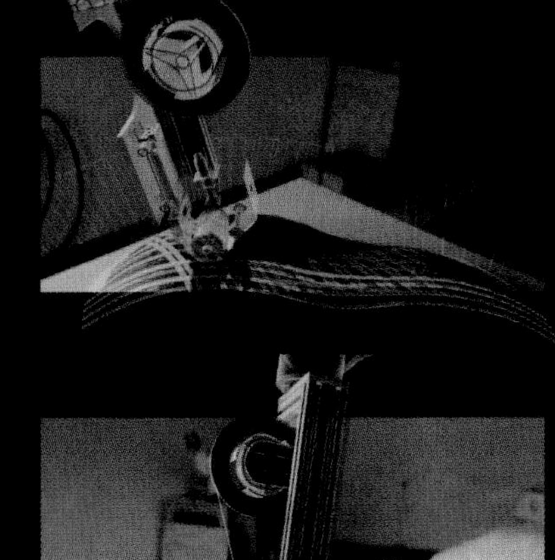

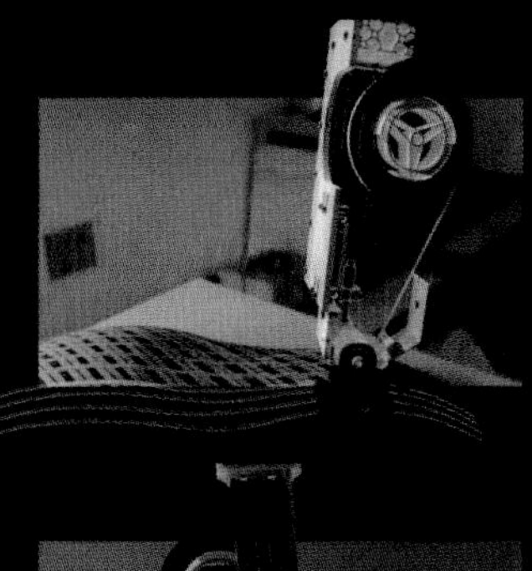

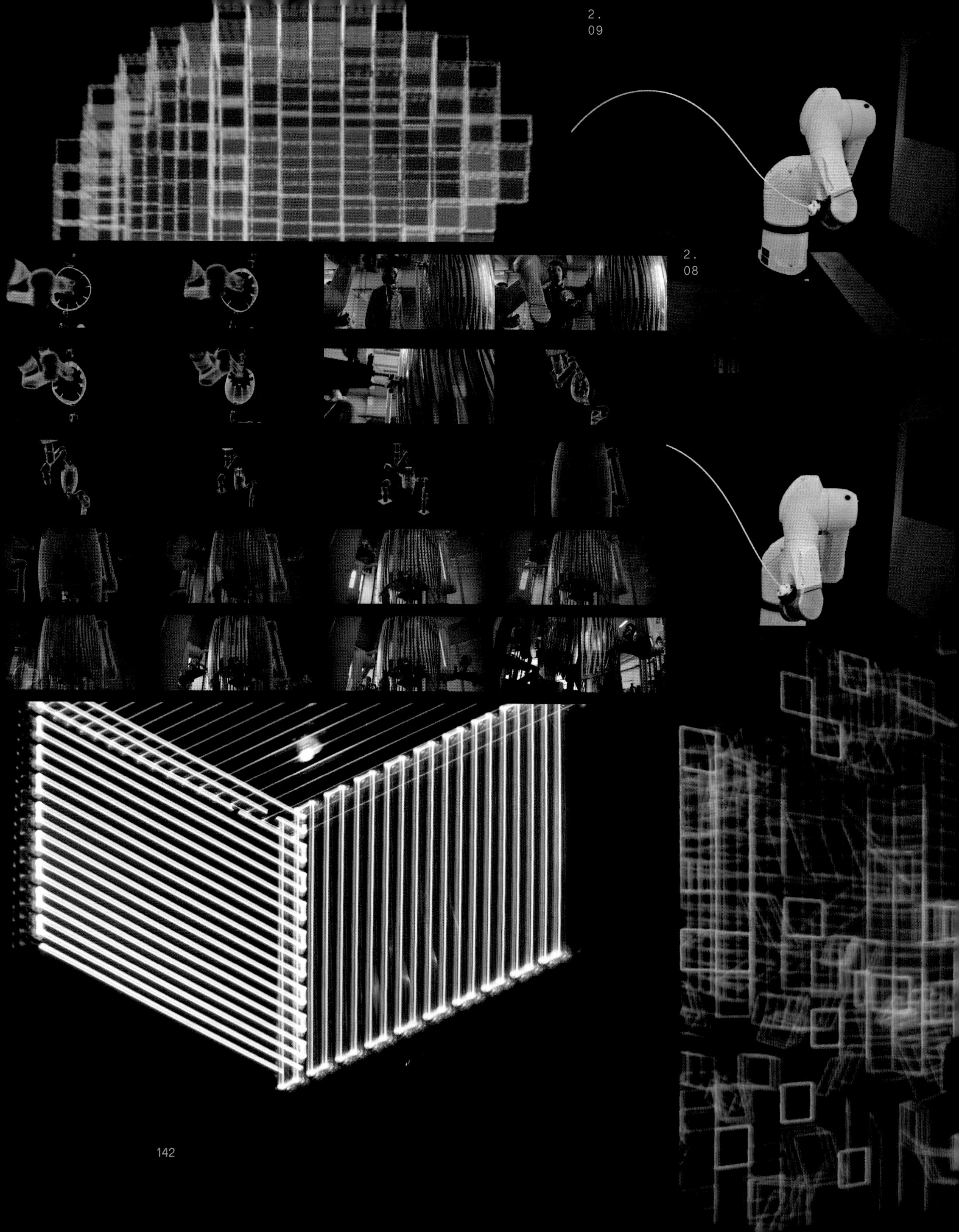
2.
09
2.
08

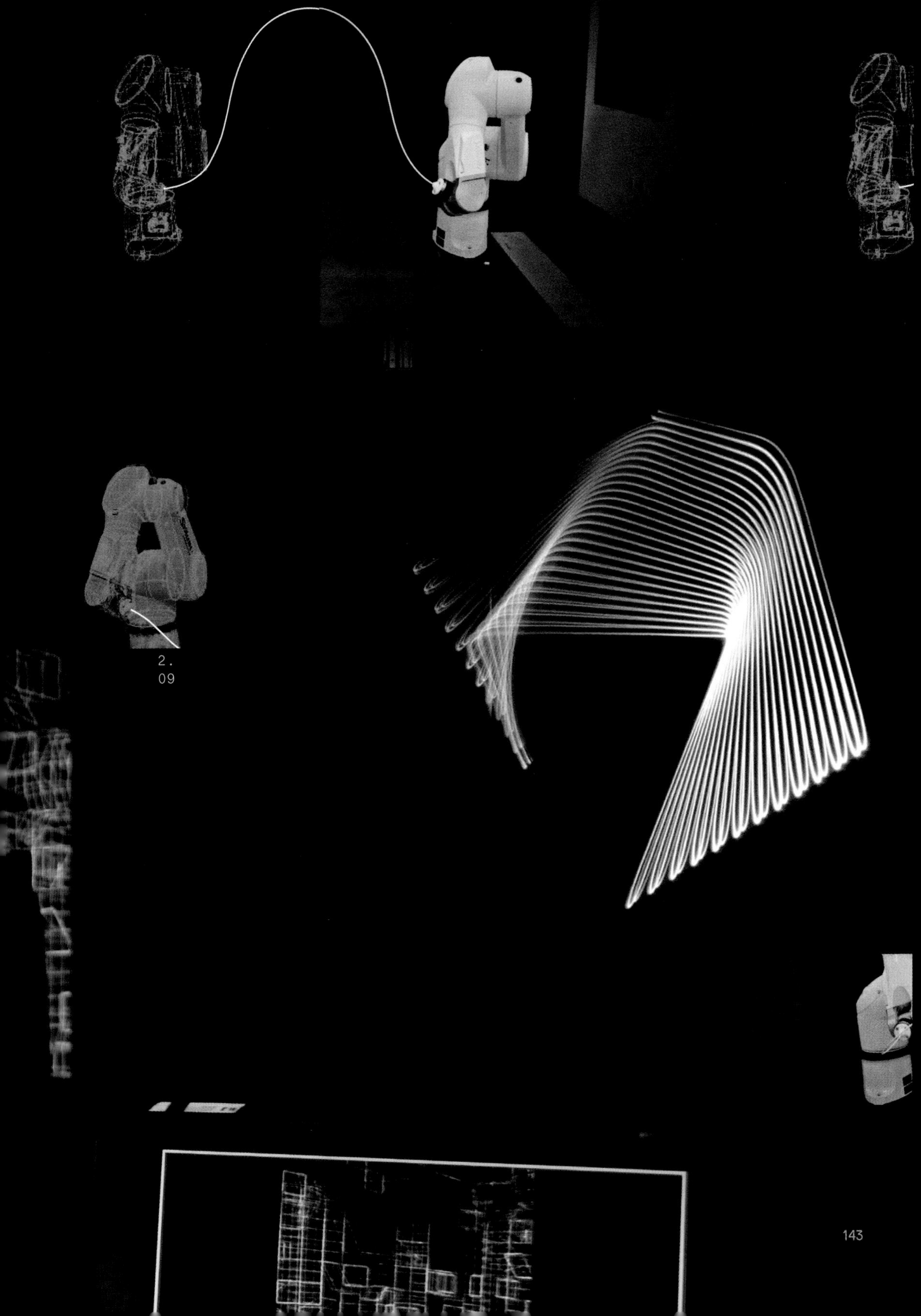

2.
10

2.
09

2.
09

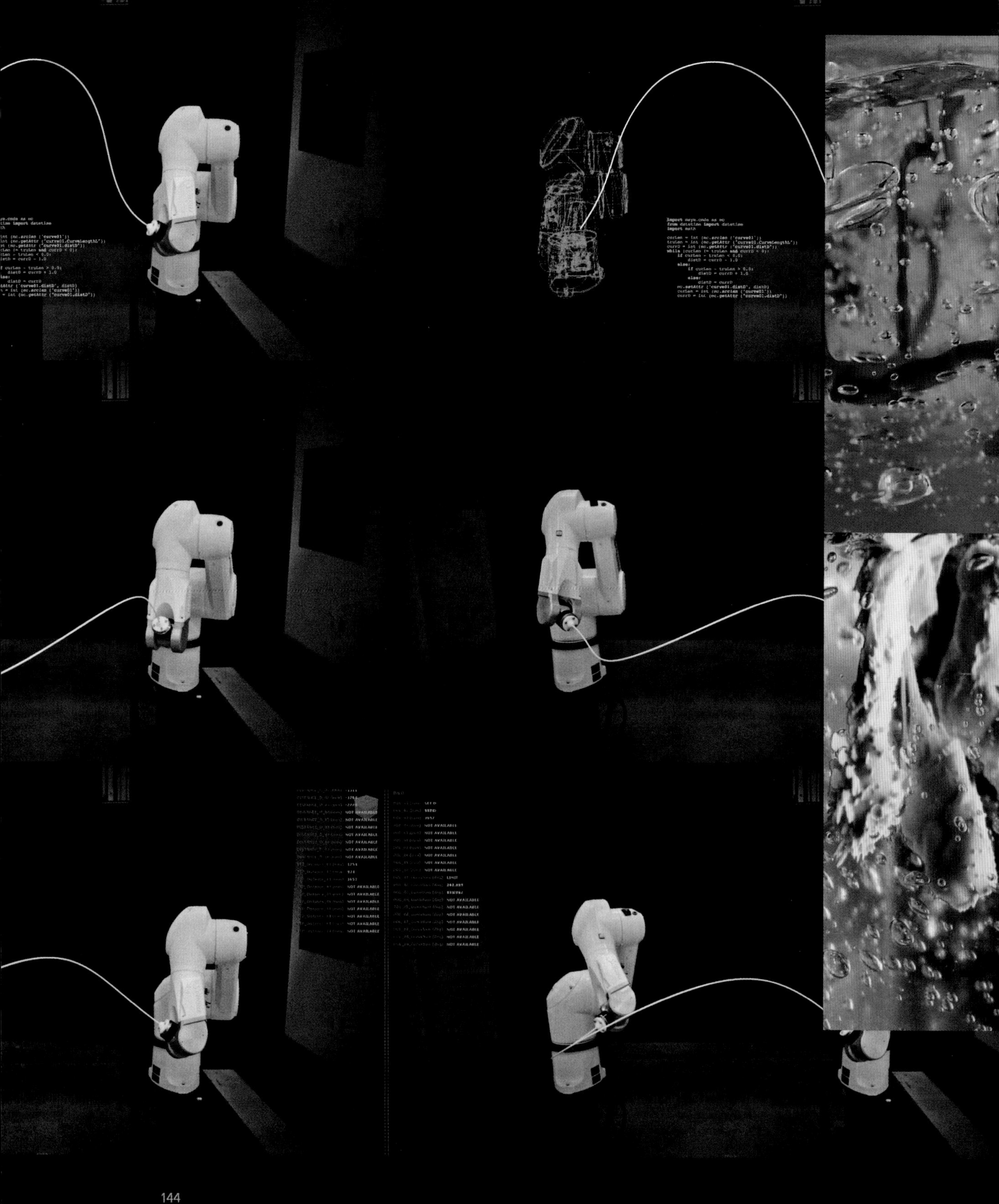

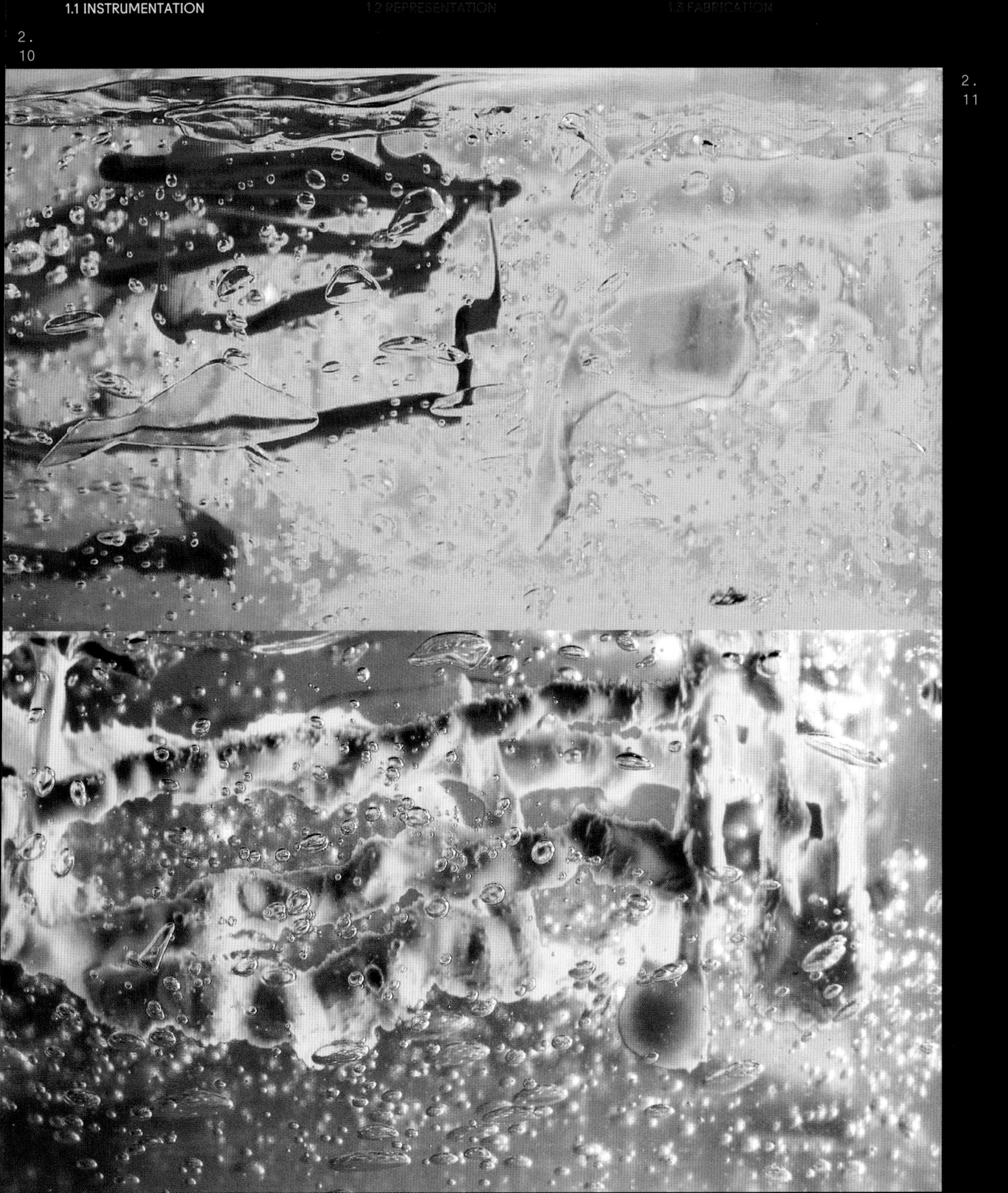

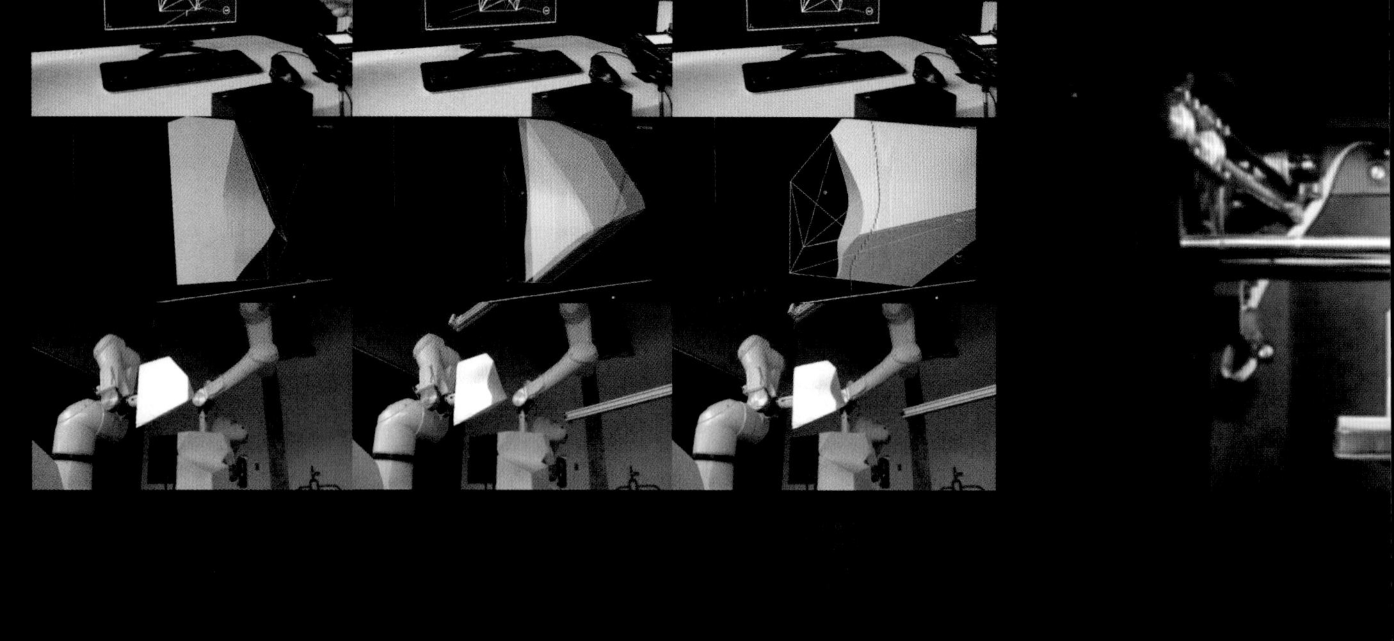

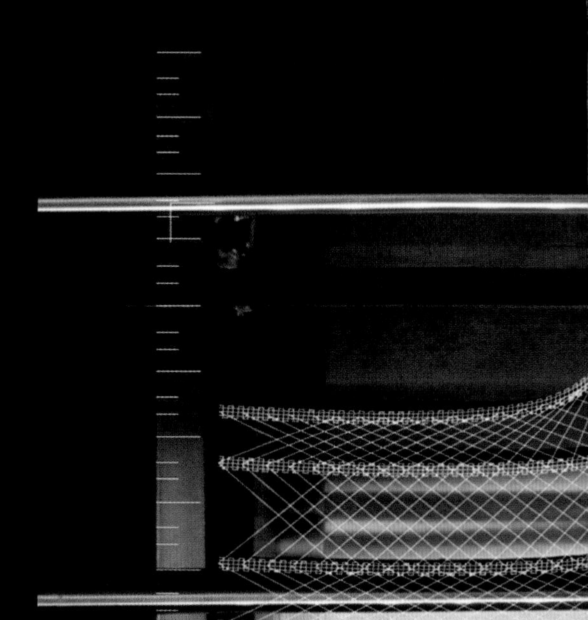

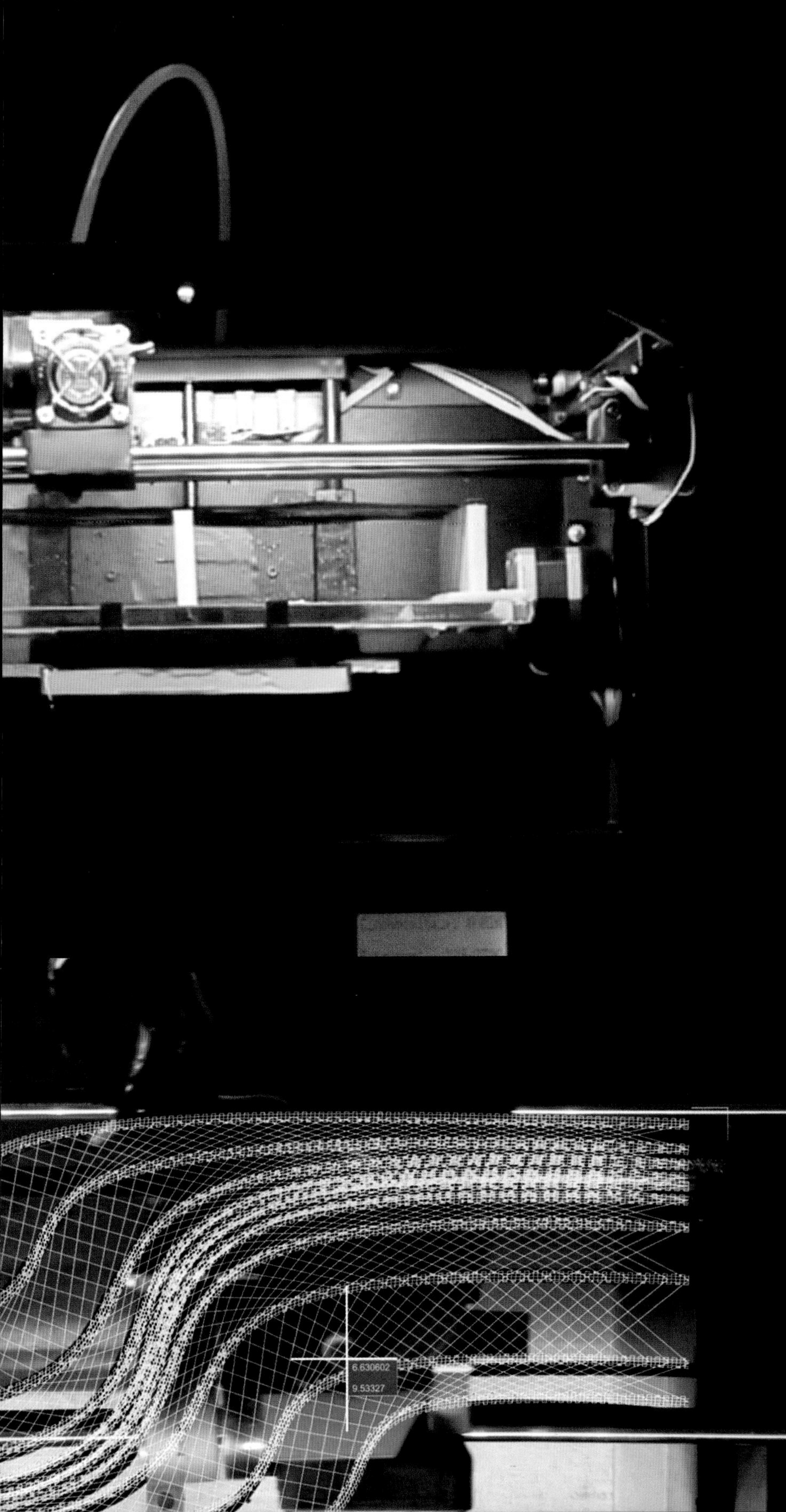
6.630602
9.53327

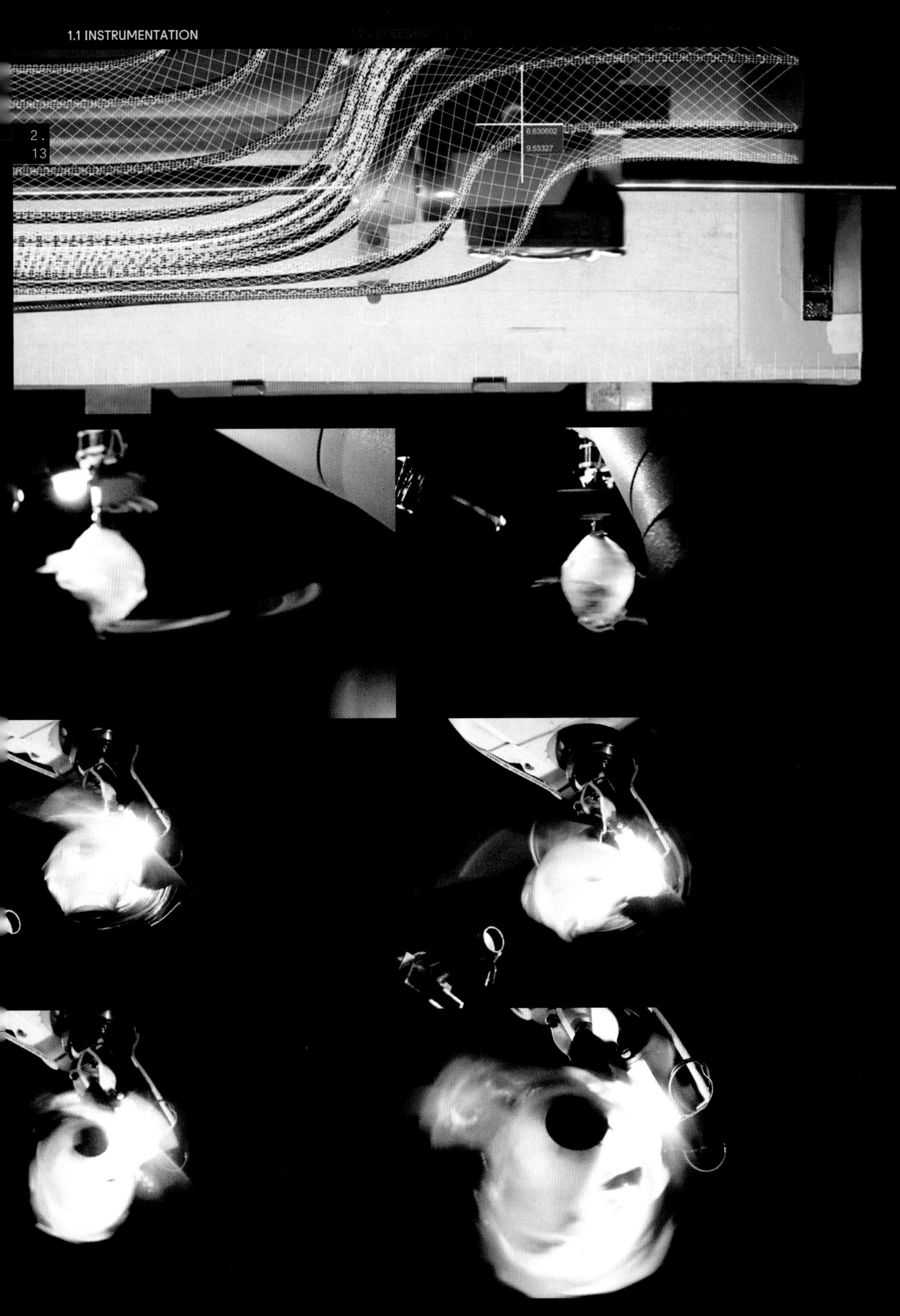

2.
13

2.
14

STÄUBLI
UNIMATION

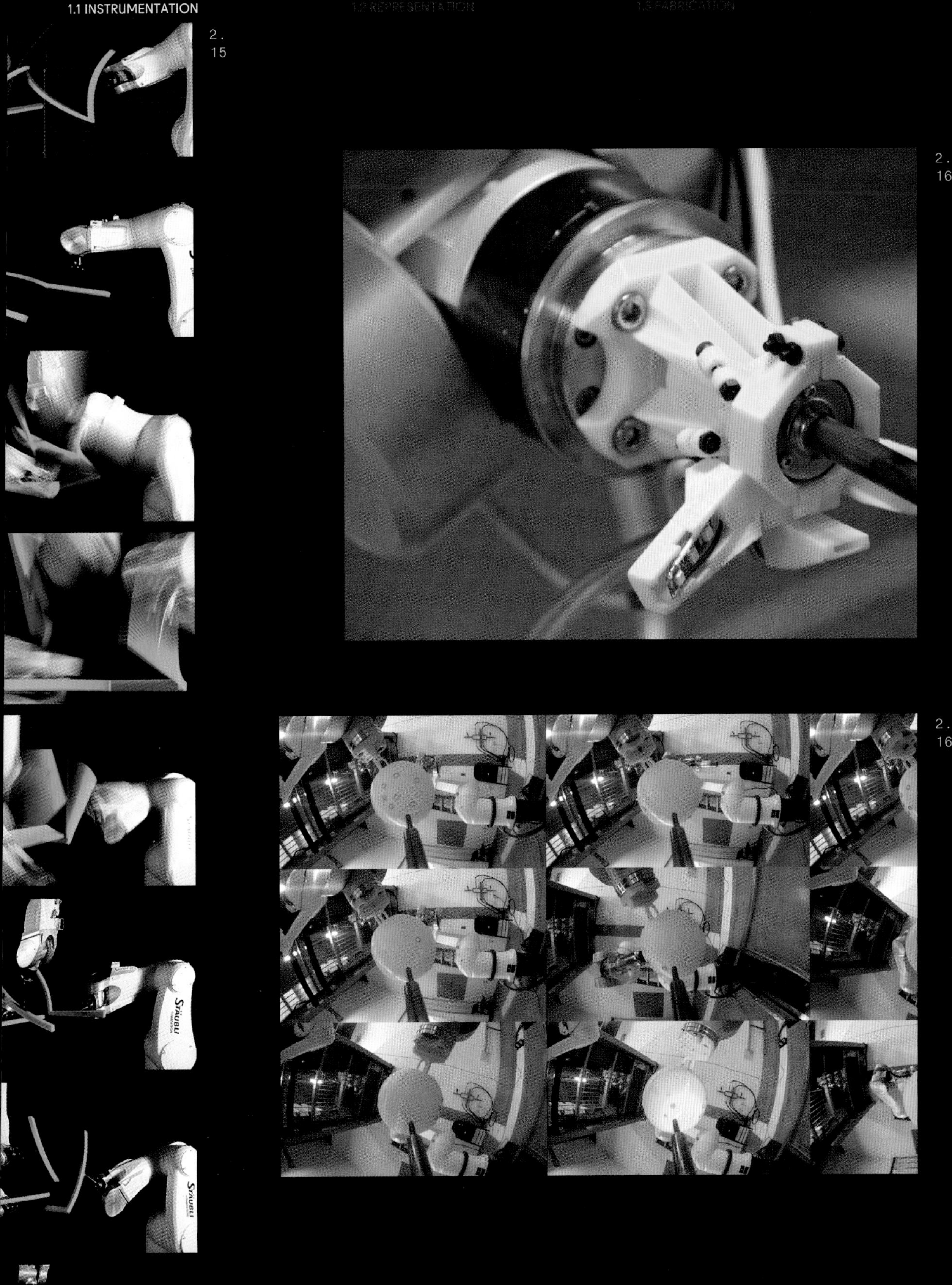

2.15

2.16

2.16

Imaging
Image Processing
Machine Vision

Fictioning
Object Animation
Physical Rendering
Robotic Cinematography

Digital/Physical Interfaces
Animated Motion Control
Object-Oriented Programming
Visual Programming

Synchronous Robotics
Multi-Robot Choreography
Real-Time
Rigging and Kinematics

Effectors
End Effectors
Physical Computing

Imaging
Image Processing
Machine Vision

Fictioning
Object Animation
Physical Rendering
Robotic Cinematography

Augmented Fabrication
Free-Form Fabrication
Image-Based Fabrication
Multiresolution Fabrication

Computational Materials
Scaffolds and Templates
Transitive Materials

Imaging
Image Processing
Machine Vision

Robot House proposes a new kind of apparatus of theoretical vision motivated by an interest in visual construction and the craftsmanship of visualization. Drawing on evolving genres of imaging, combinations of design and vision are updated and modified within new conditions and to suit the purposes of design scenarios. In these processes of "technical imaging," the image is used to directly manipulate something—images become tools. This speculative design platform both defamiliarizes and destabilizes representation, authorship, and human-centered perception, and even the digital/analog distinction itself. Work extends to a thoroughgoing rethinking of the role of the image in the generation of form through techniques of image processing, machine vision, and motion capture.

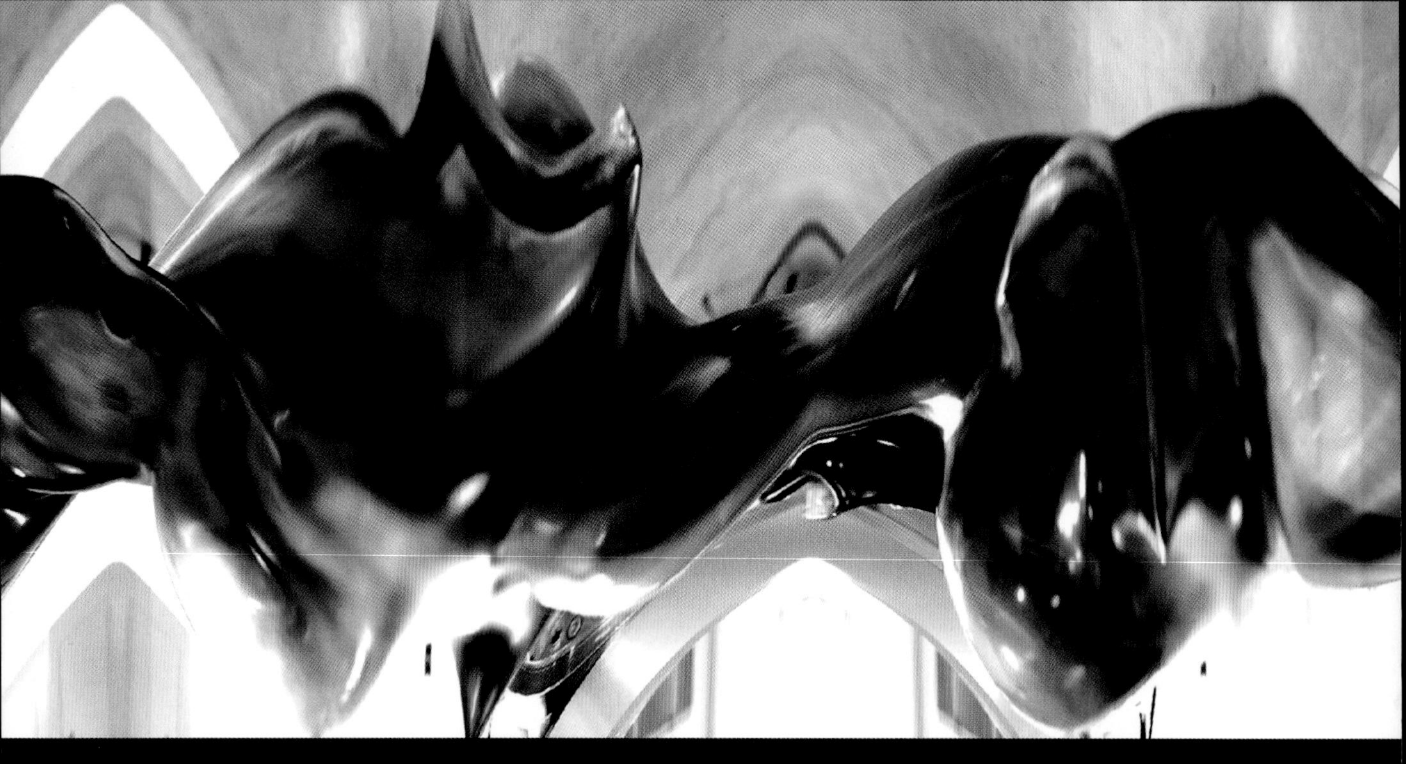

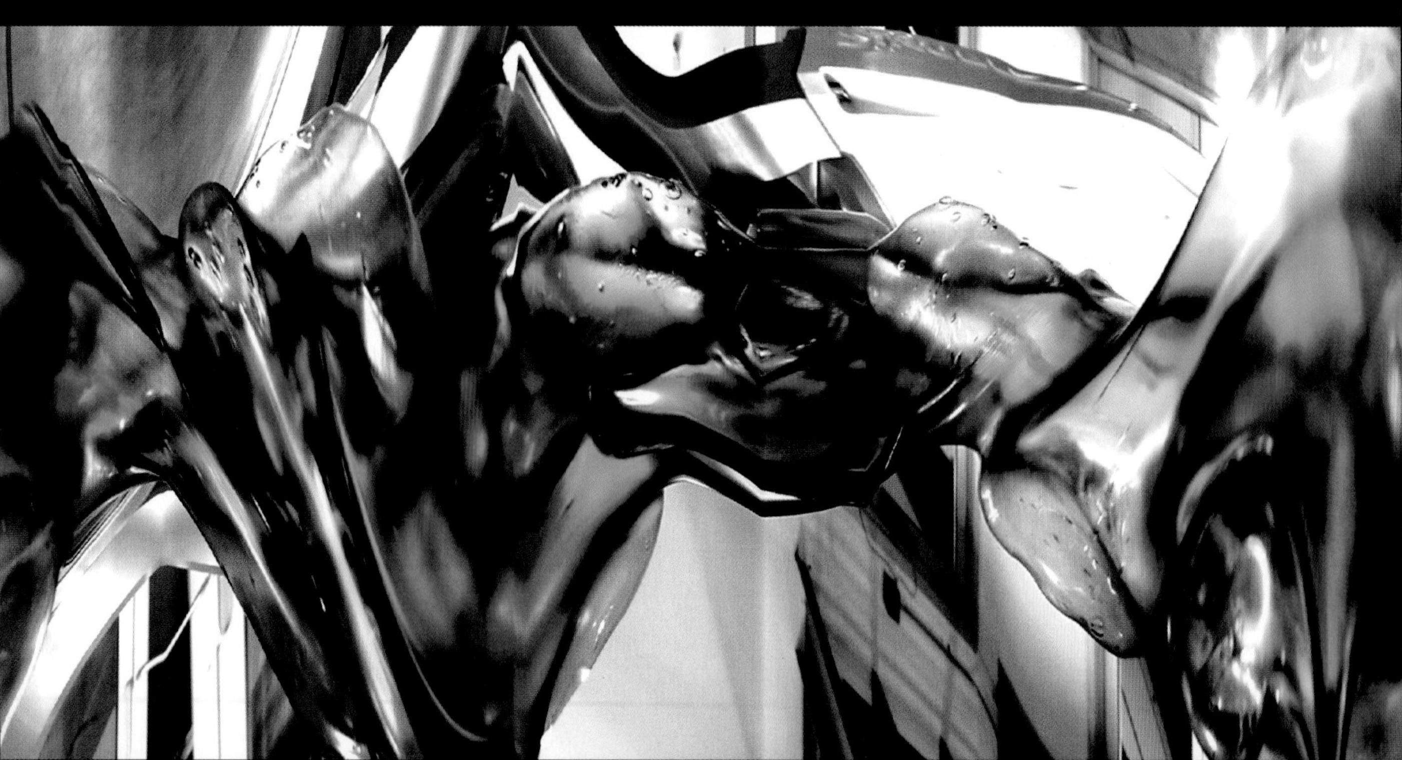

Image Processing

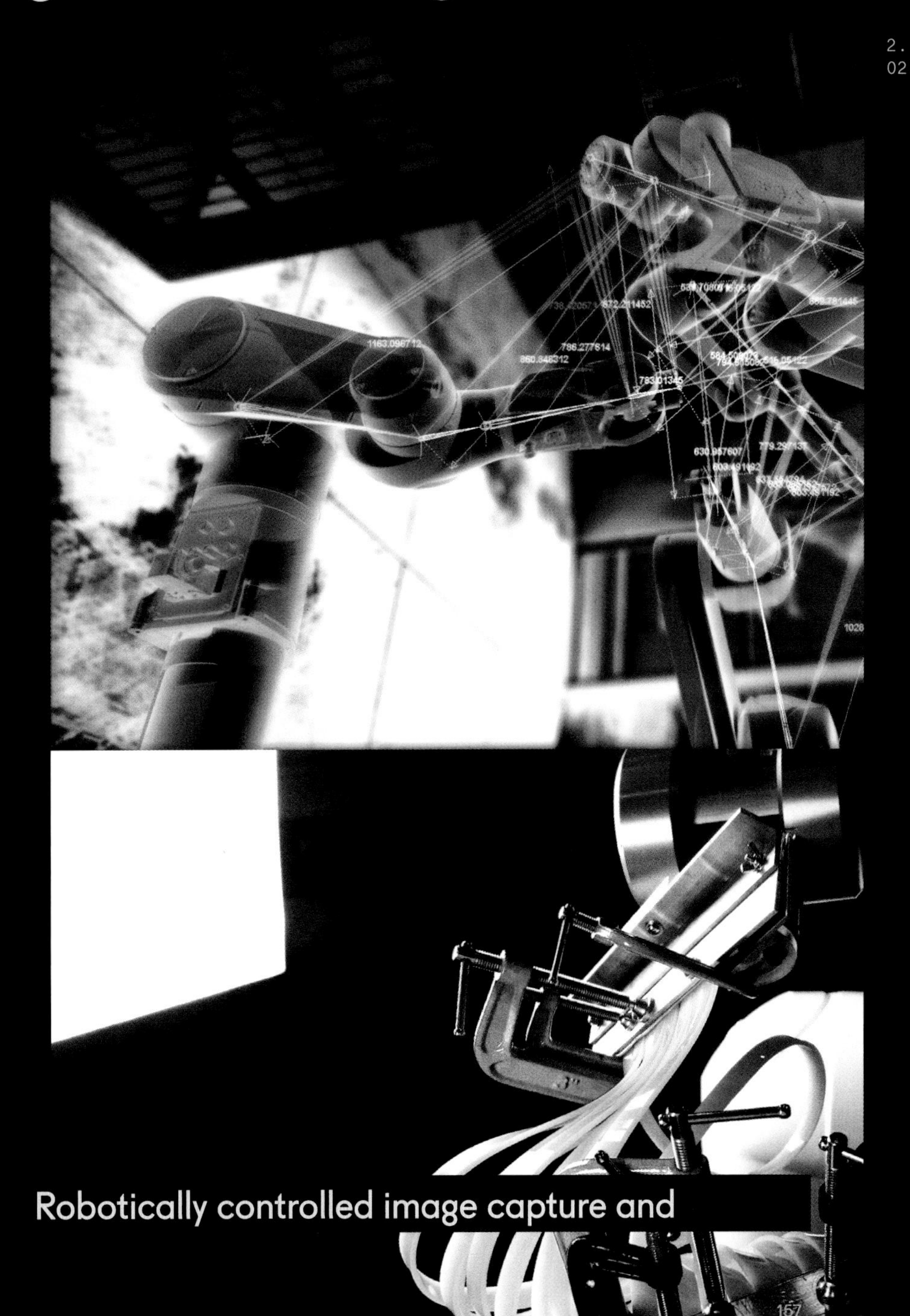

Robotically controlled image capture and

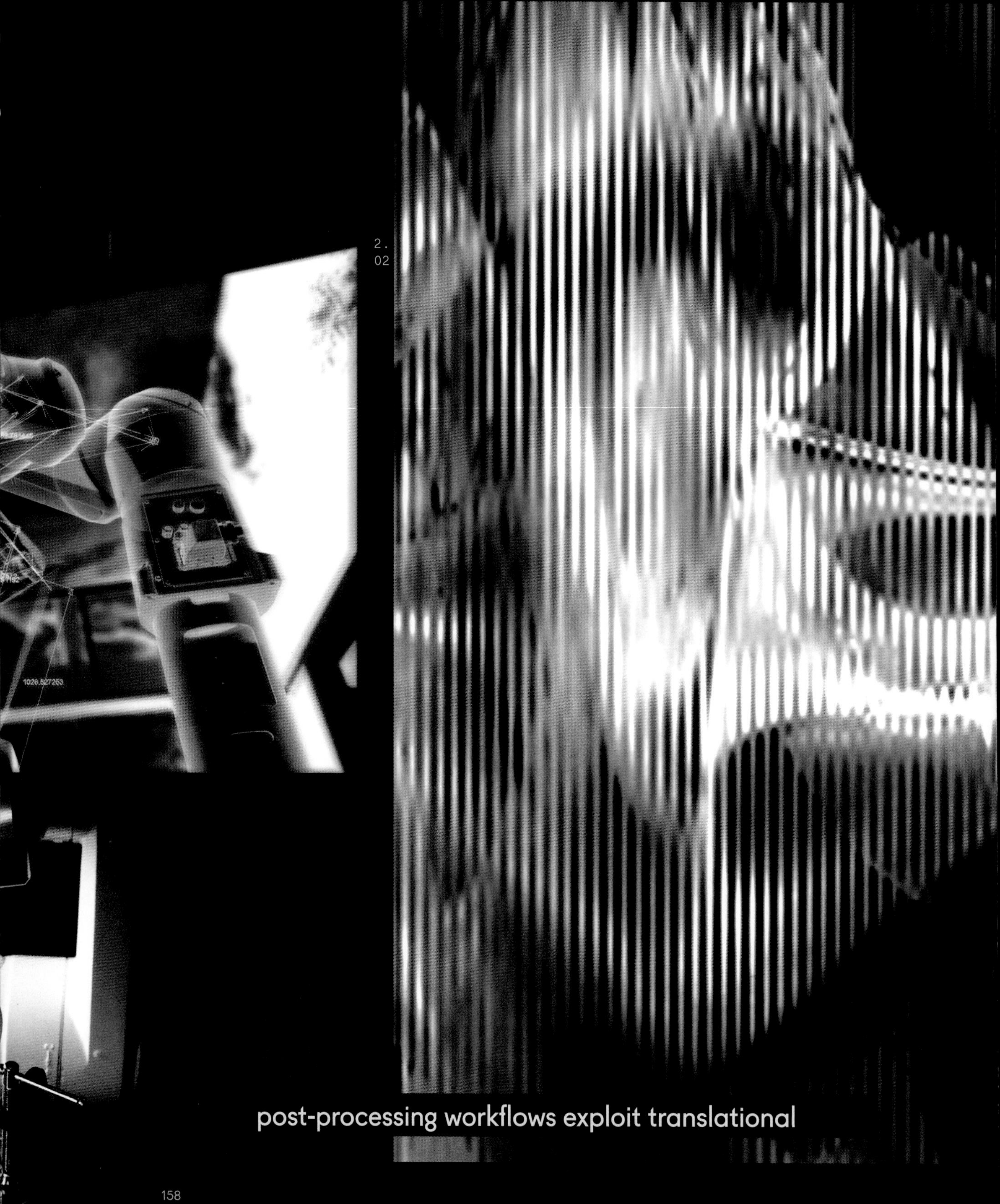

2.
02

post-processing workflows exploit translational

2.
03

2.
03

discrepancies and resolutions between digital and

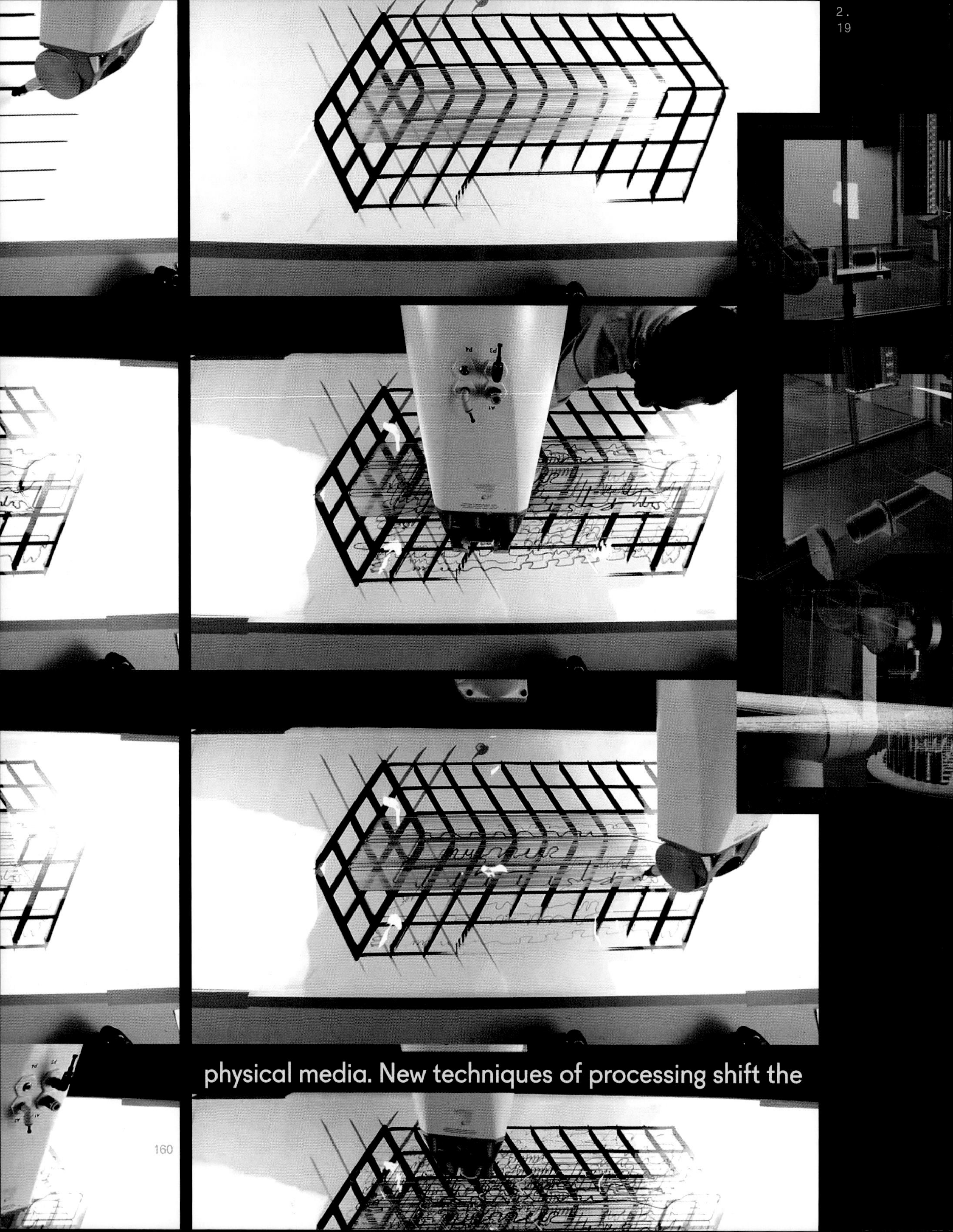

physical media. New techniques of processing shift the

2.
06

2.
08

hierarchies between image and geometry, image and

object in the definition of form.

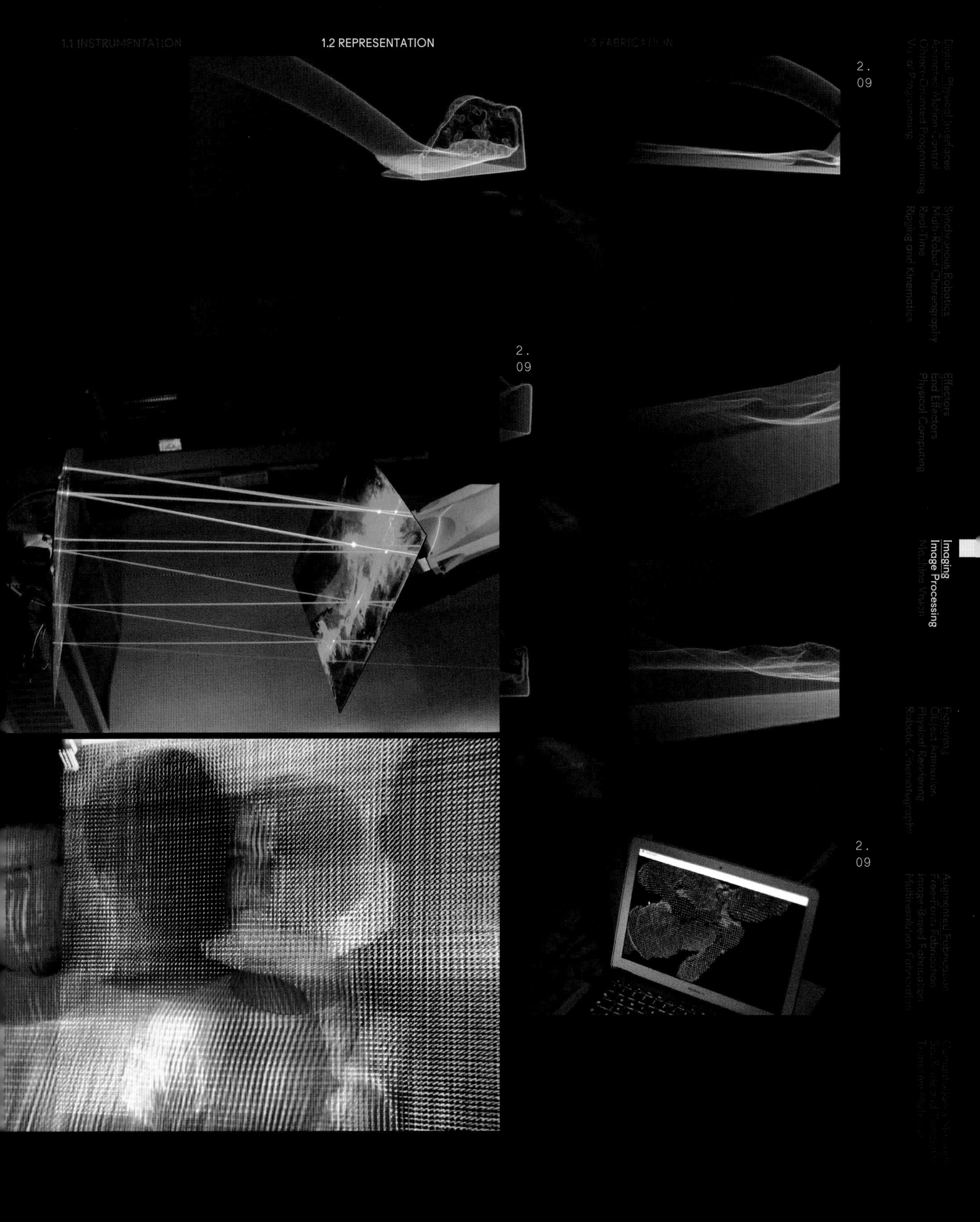

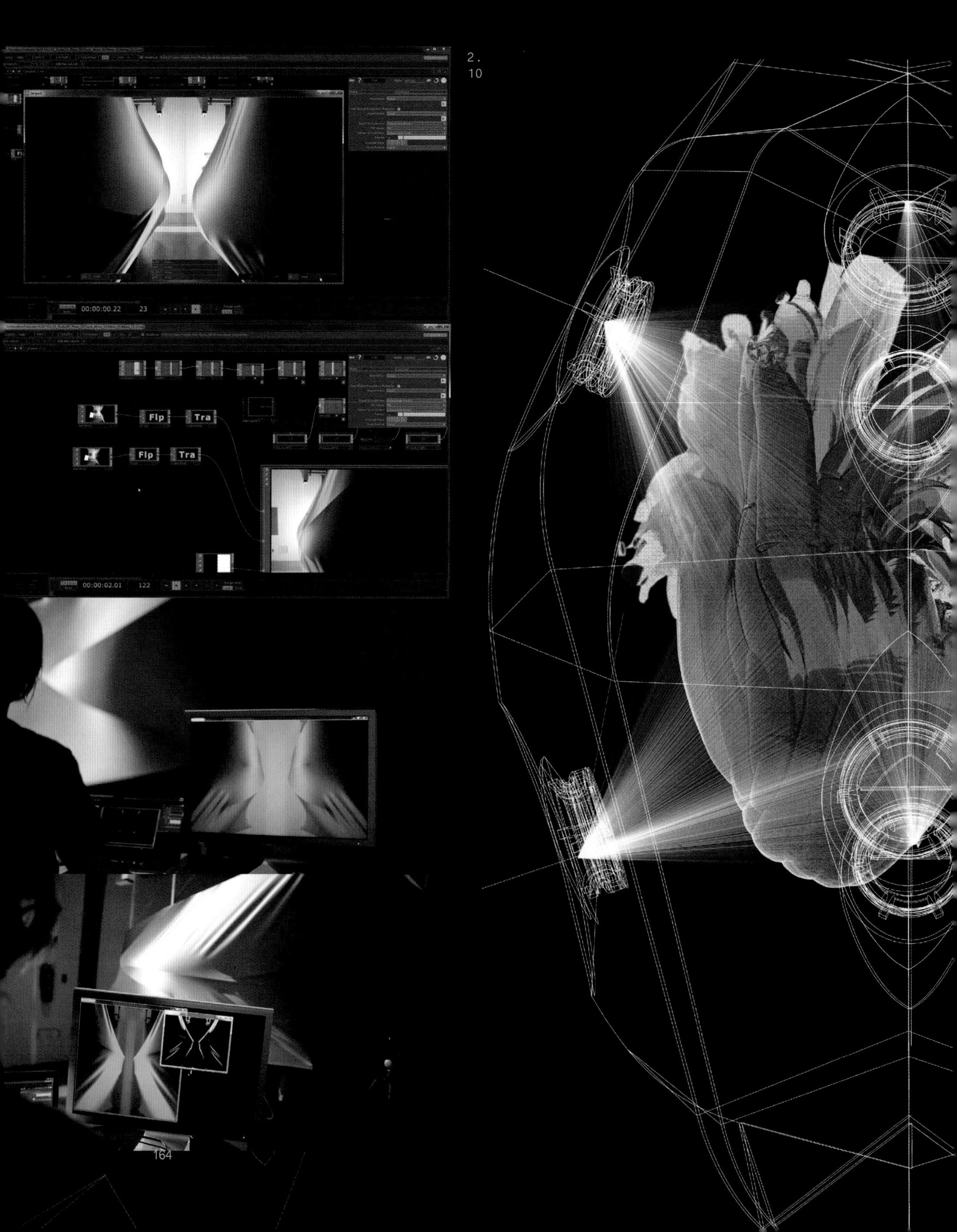
00:00:00.22
23
Flp
Tra
Flp
Tra
00:00:02.01
122

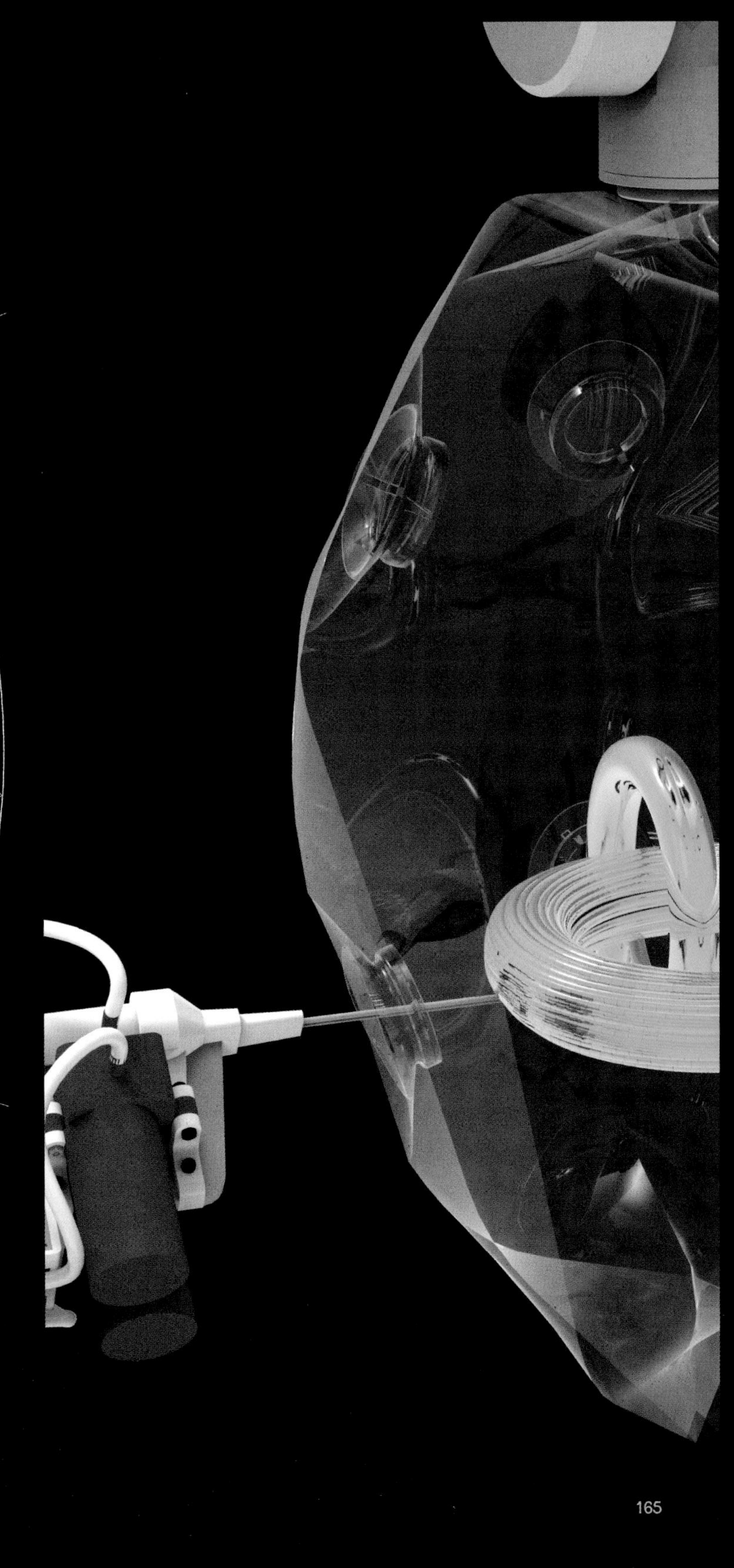

2.
11

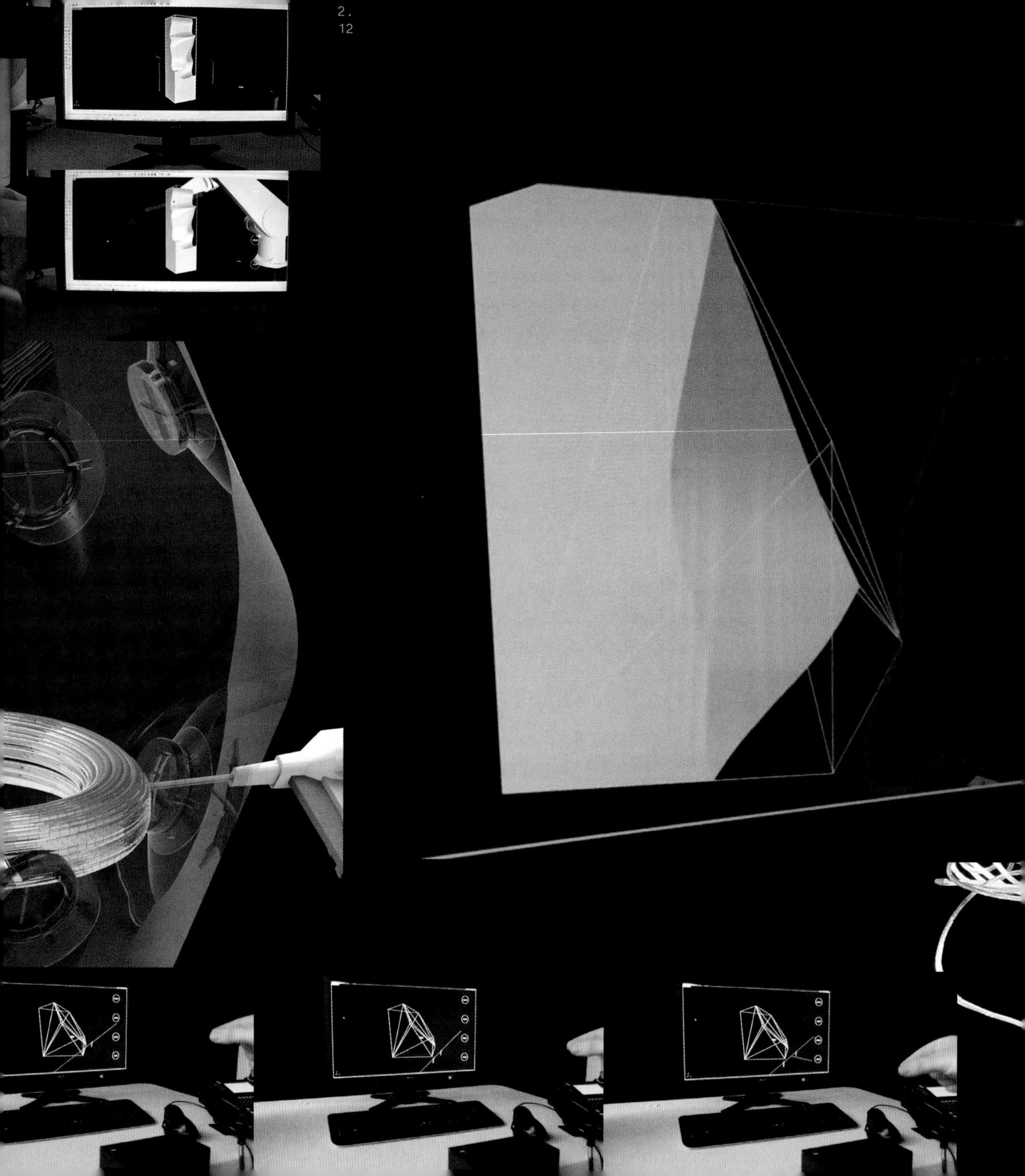

2.
12

2.
13

4,
20

scaffold transformations

scaffold rotations

extrusion pattern animated simulation

extrusion pattern generation / motion graph editor

Imaging
Image Processing

2. 19

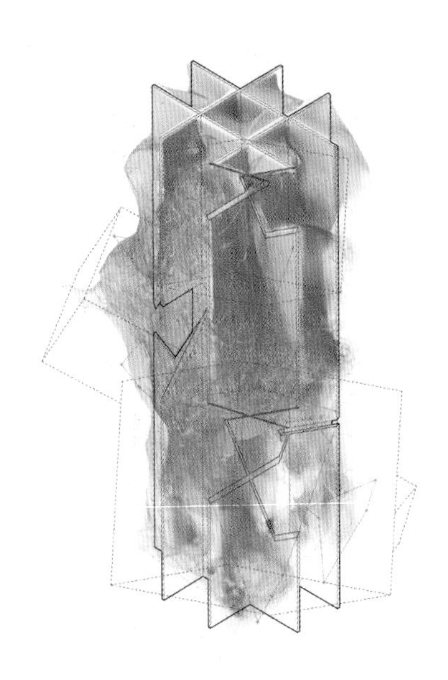

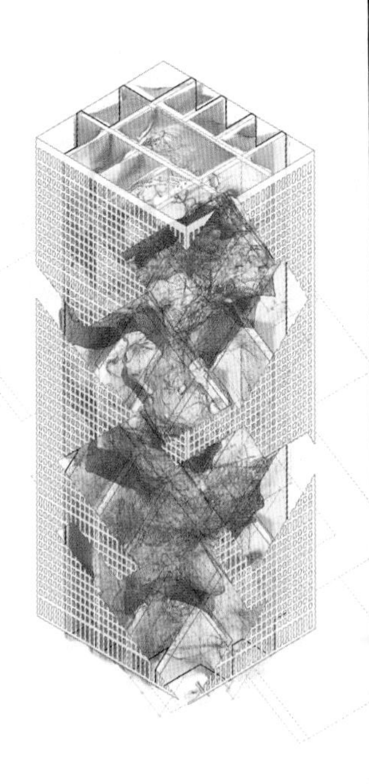

2. 17

2.19

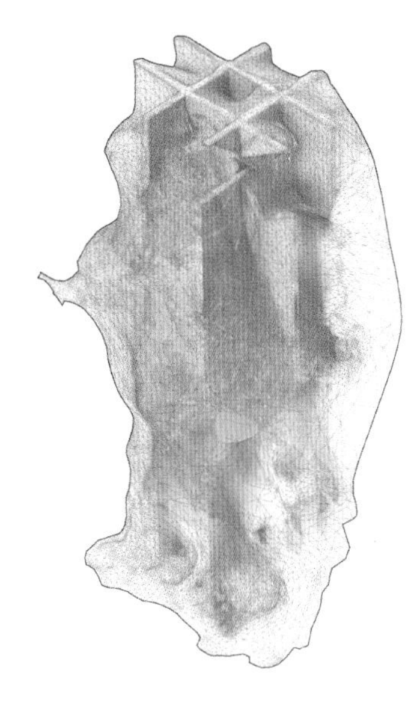

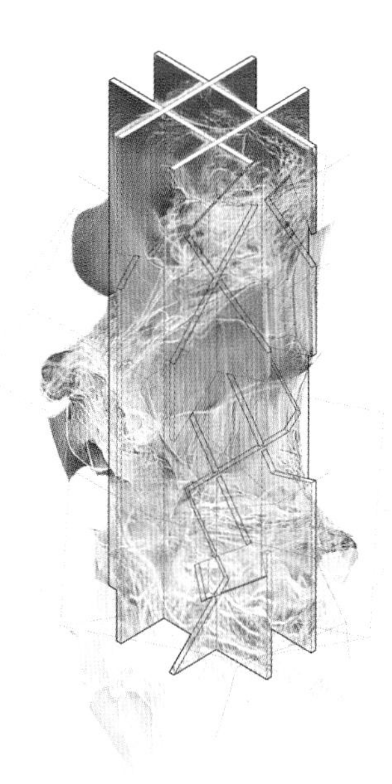

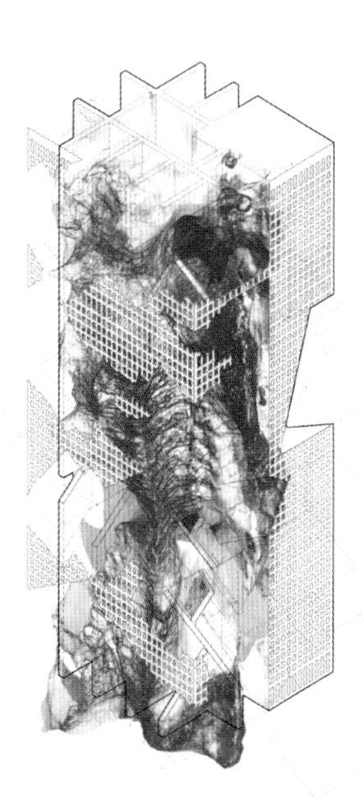

Machine Vision

Image- and light-based sourcing and parsing of

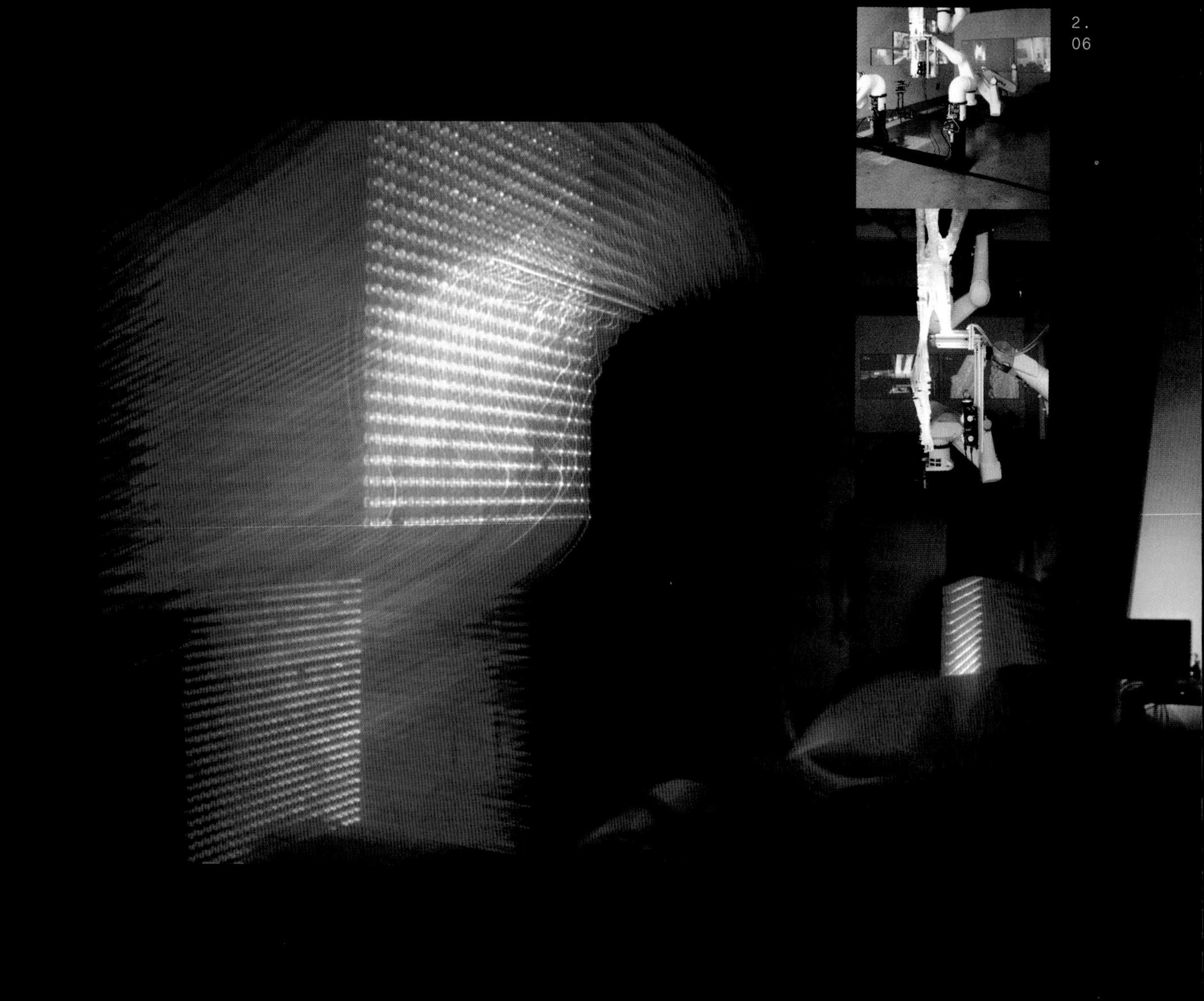

2.
06

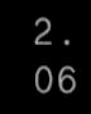

2.
06

information enables real-time motion control within

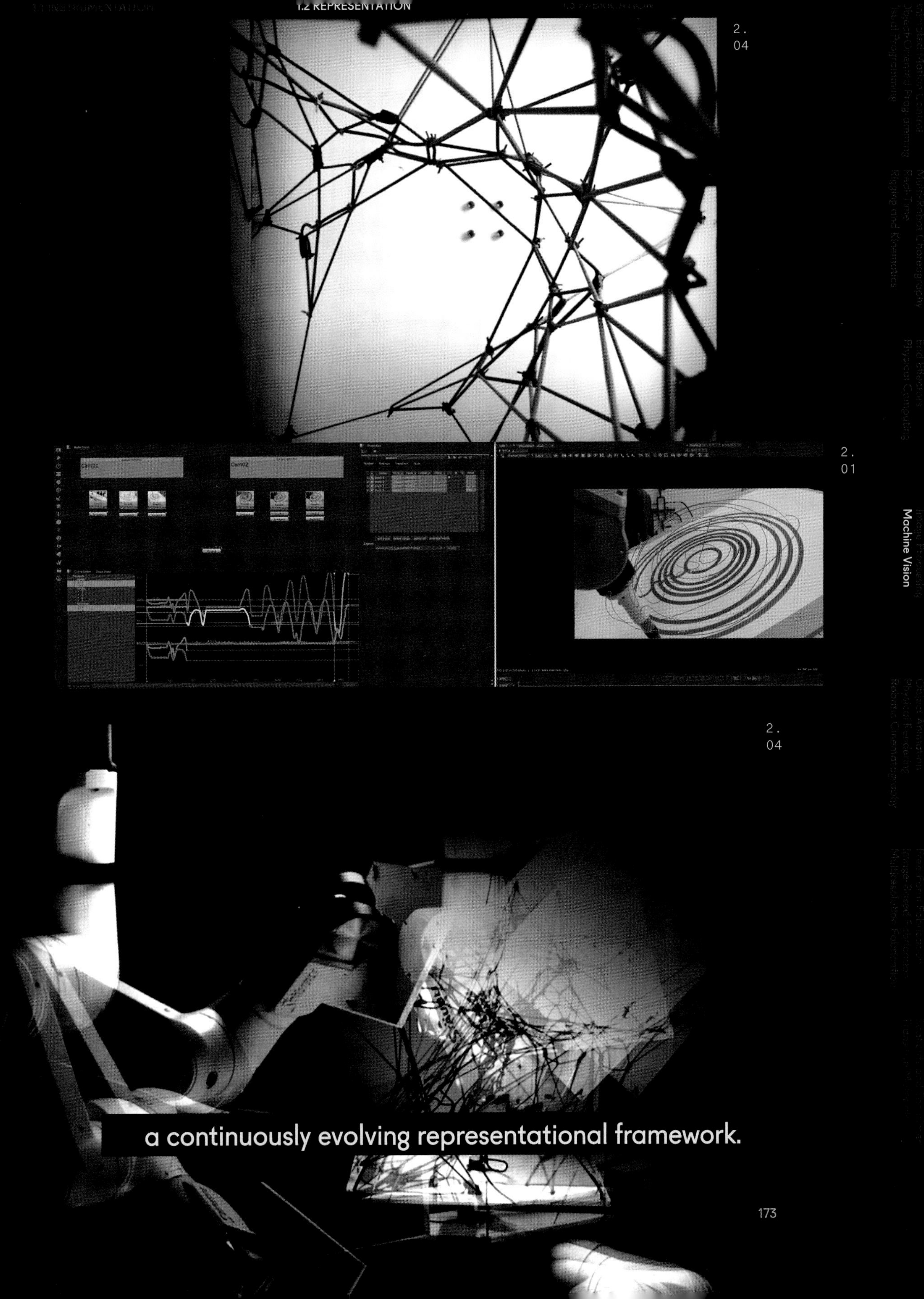

2.
04

2.
01

2.
04

a continuously evolving representational framework.

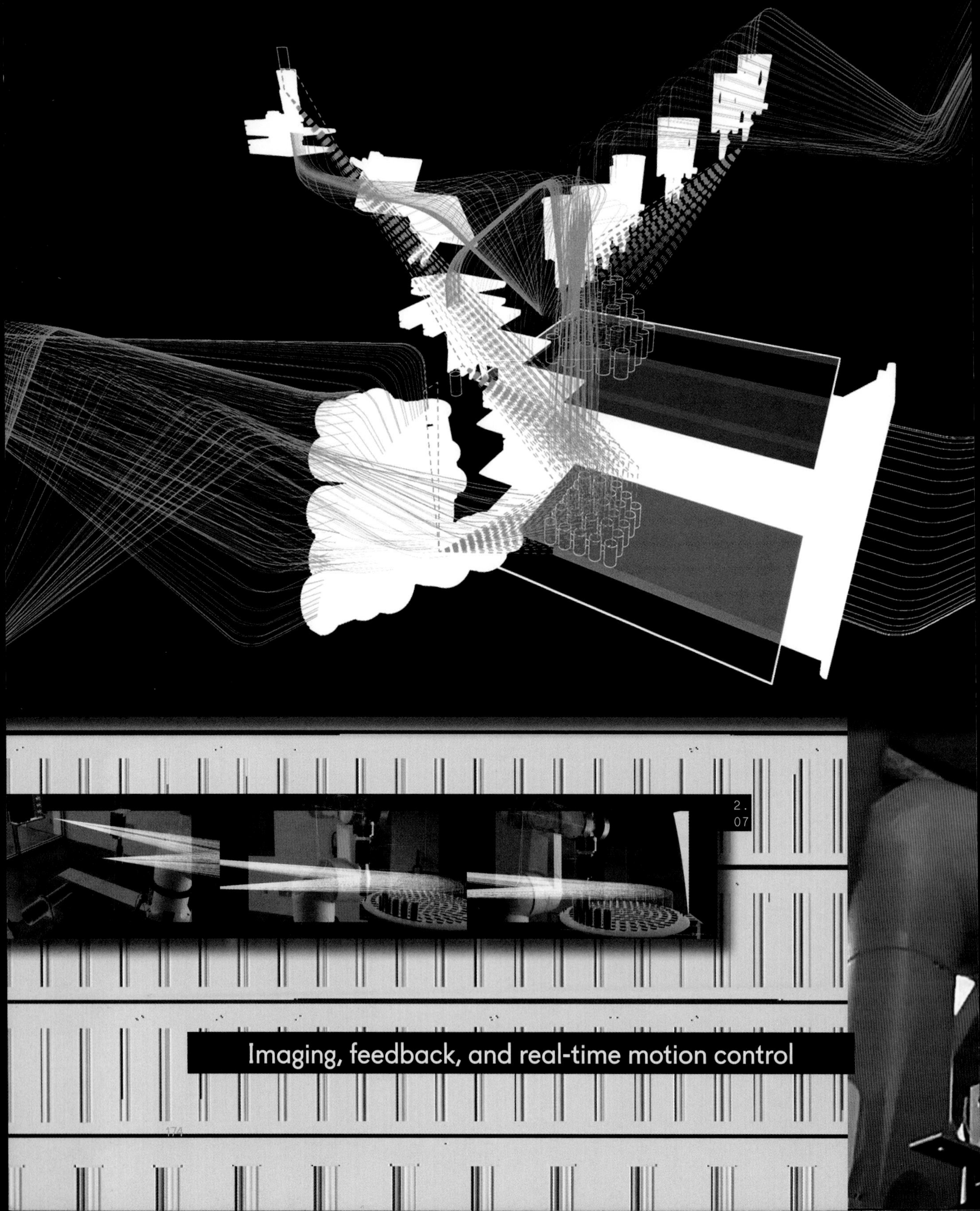

2.
07

Imaging, feedback, and real-time motion control

are instantiated via Maya, Grasshopper, and Firefly

workflows coupled with 3D scanning, digital video, time

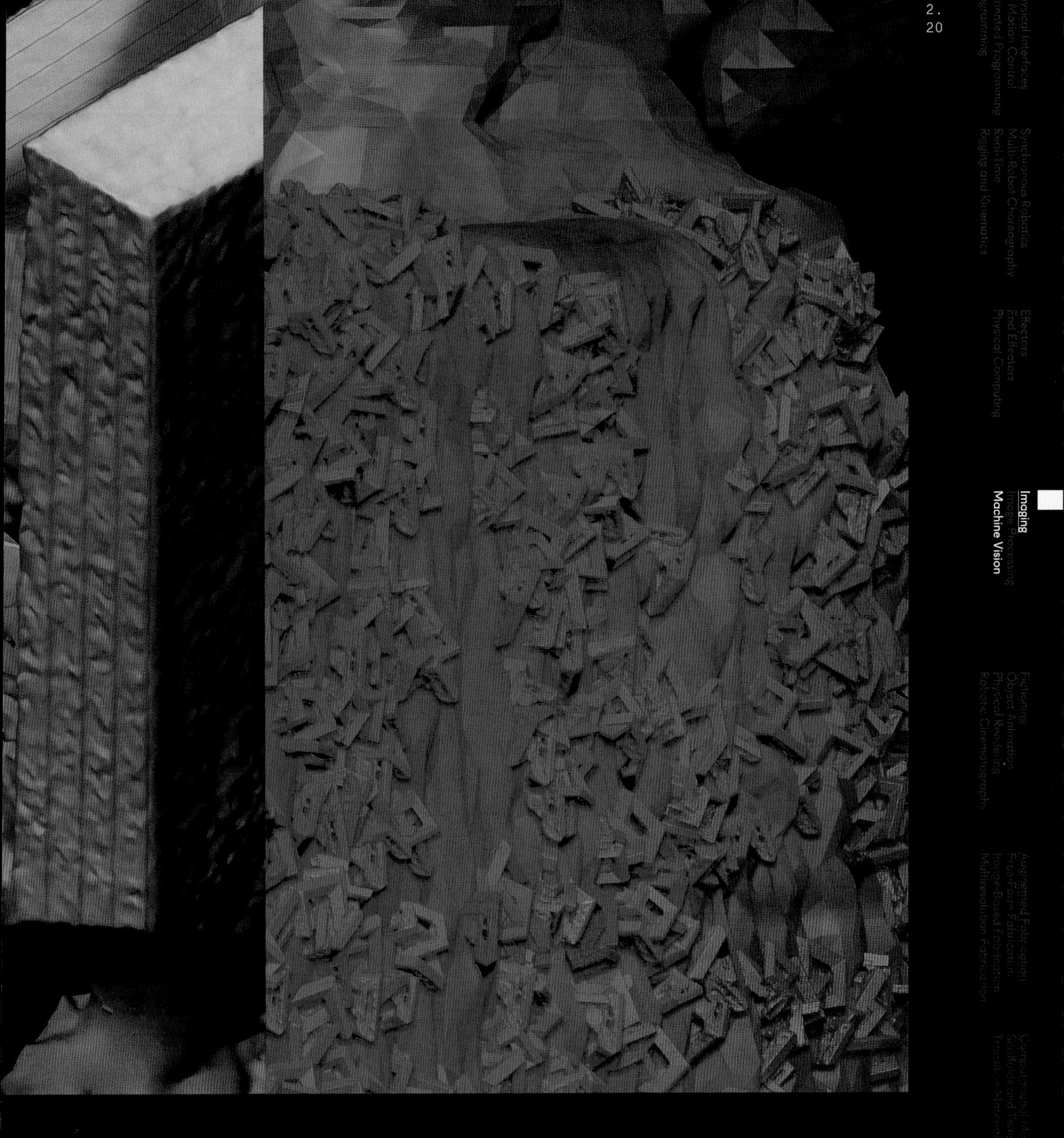

of flight, and high-speed video.

2.
06

2.
04

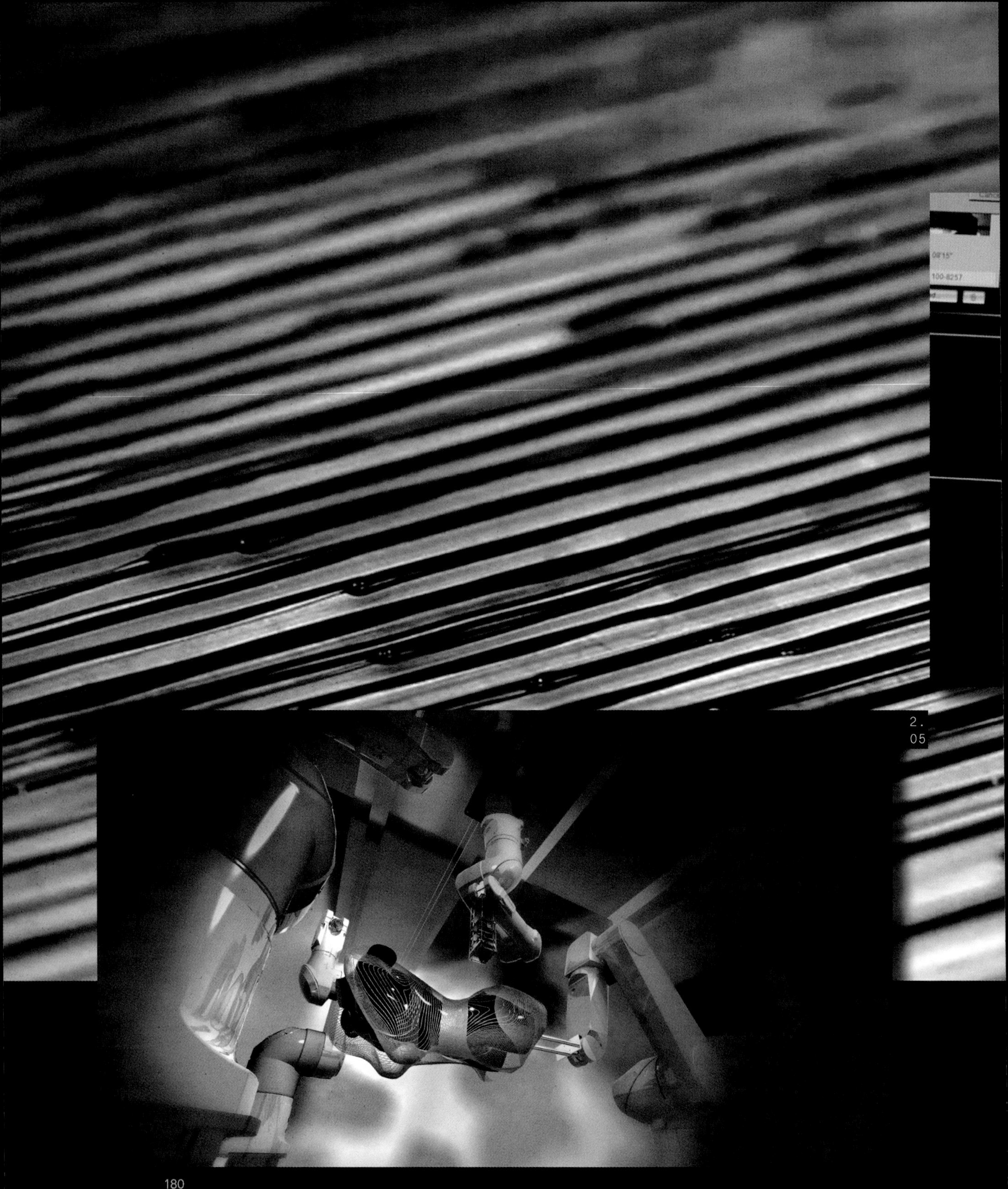

2.
05

2.
07
Channels Edit Object Show
r4path
SHAPES
r4pathShape
Display Render Anim
Layers Options Help
2.
07
2.
07
2.
07

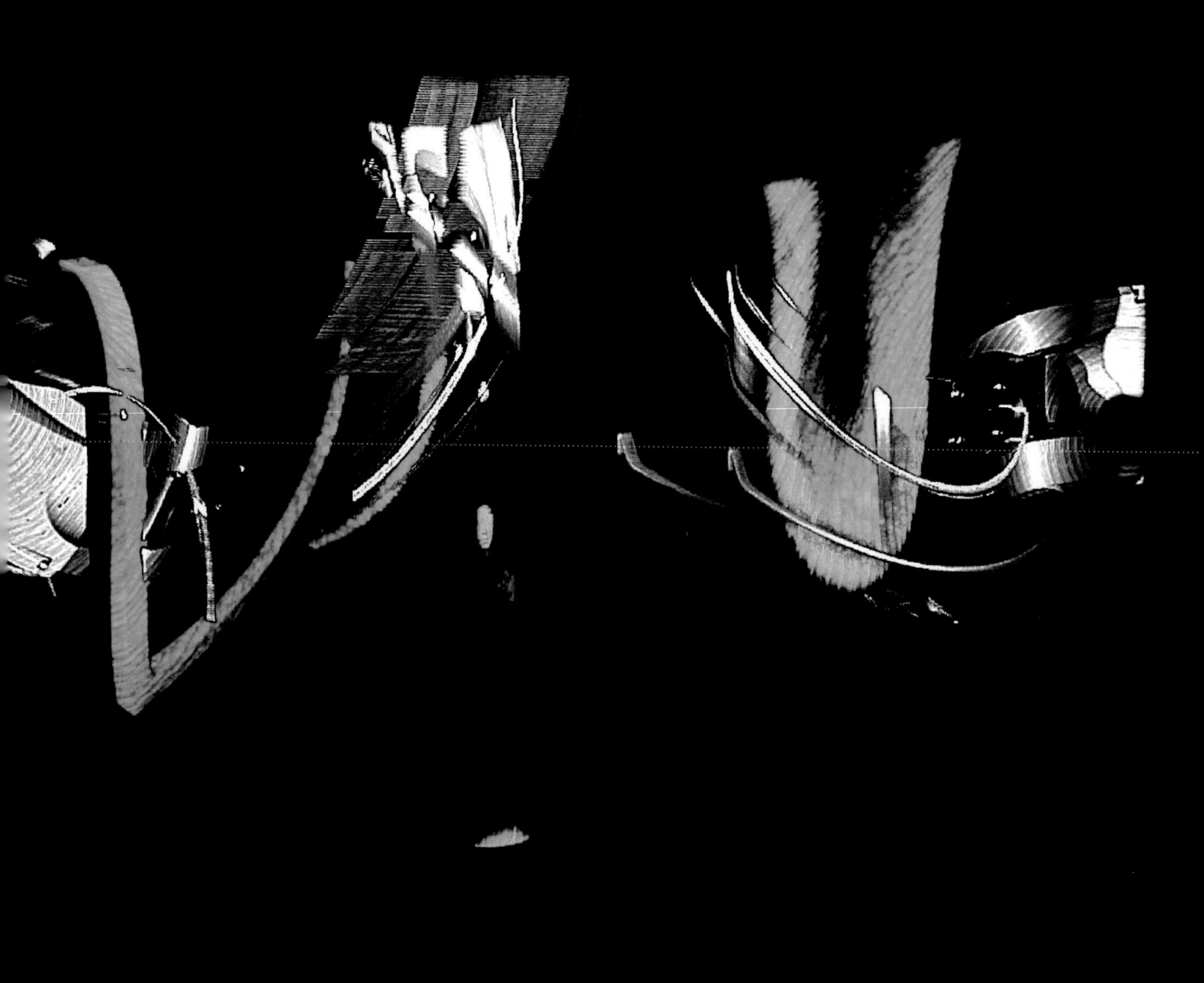

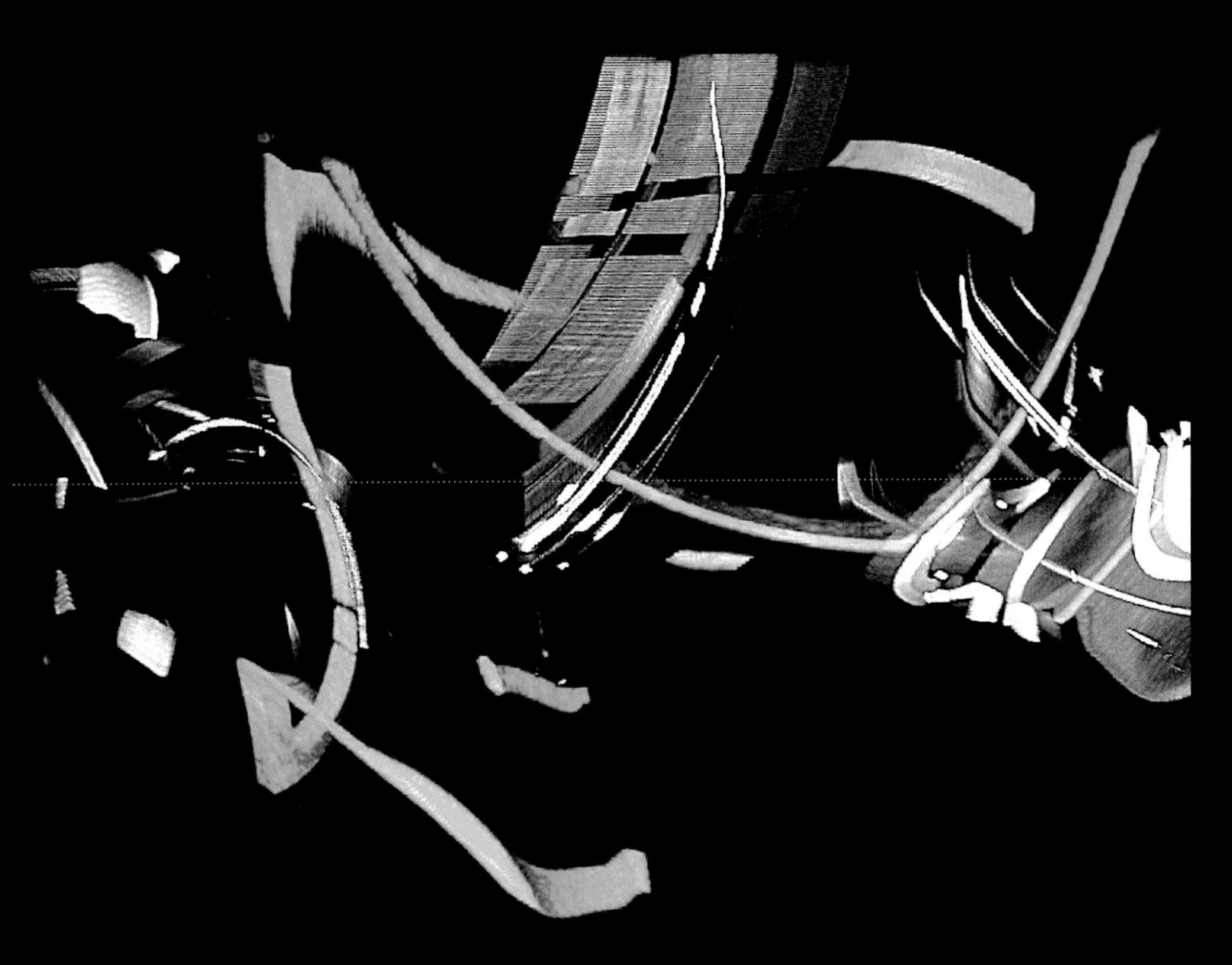

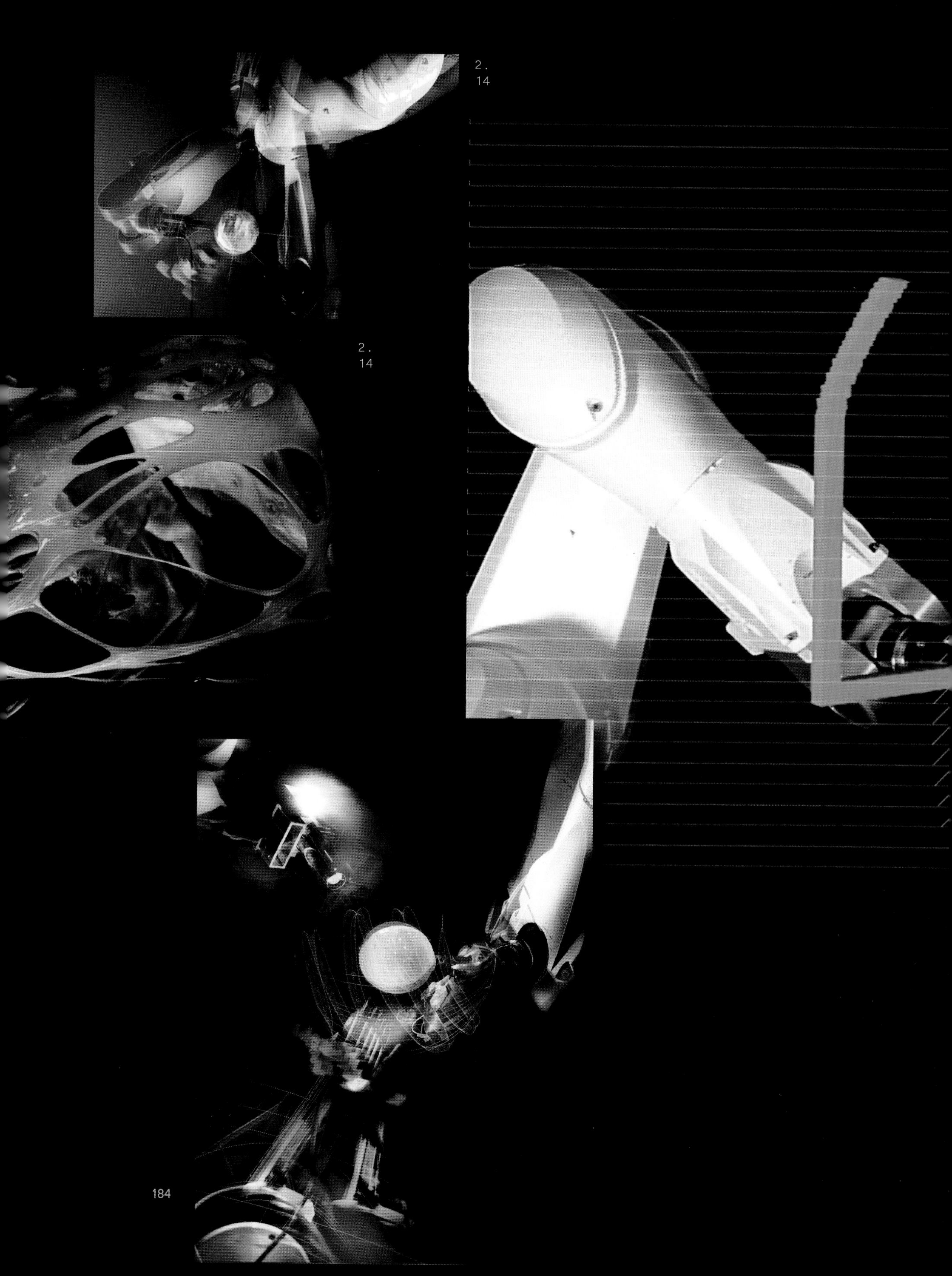
2.
14
2.
14

2.
15

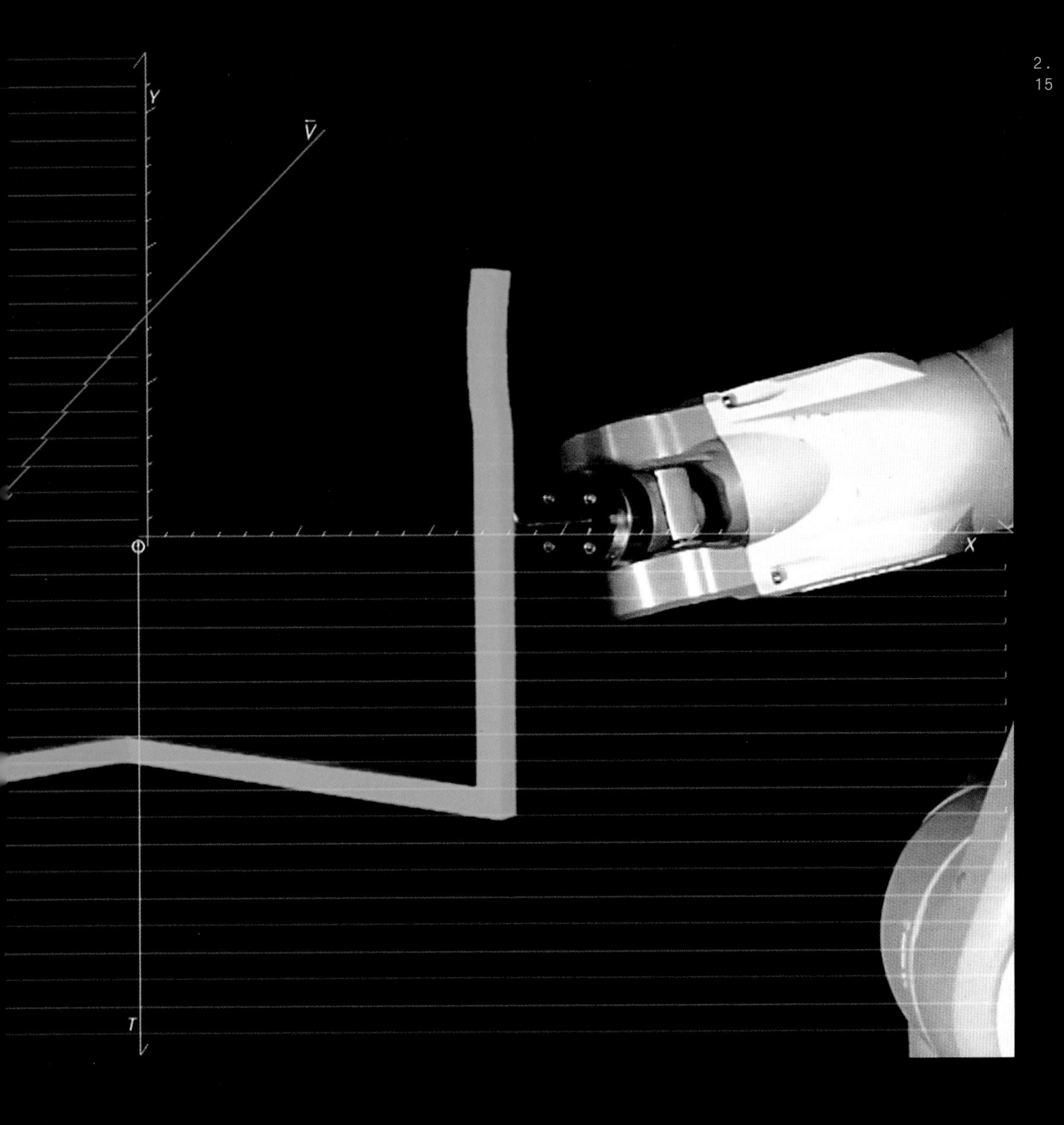

2.
16

2.
16

2.
16

2.
17

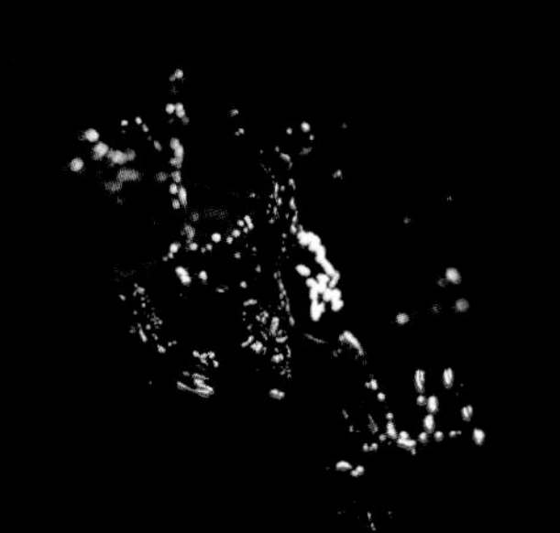

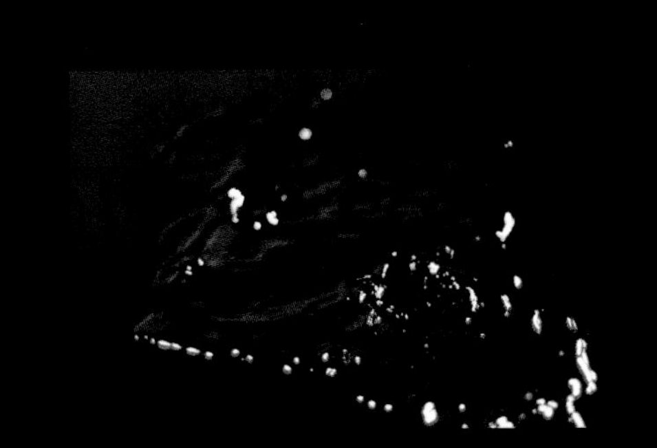

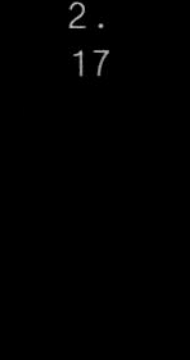

2.
17

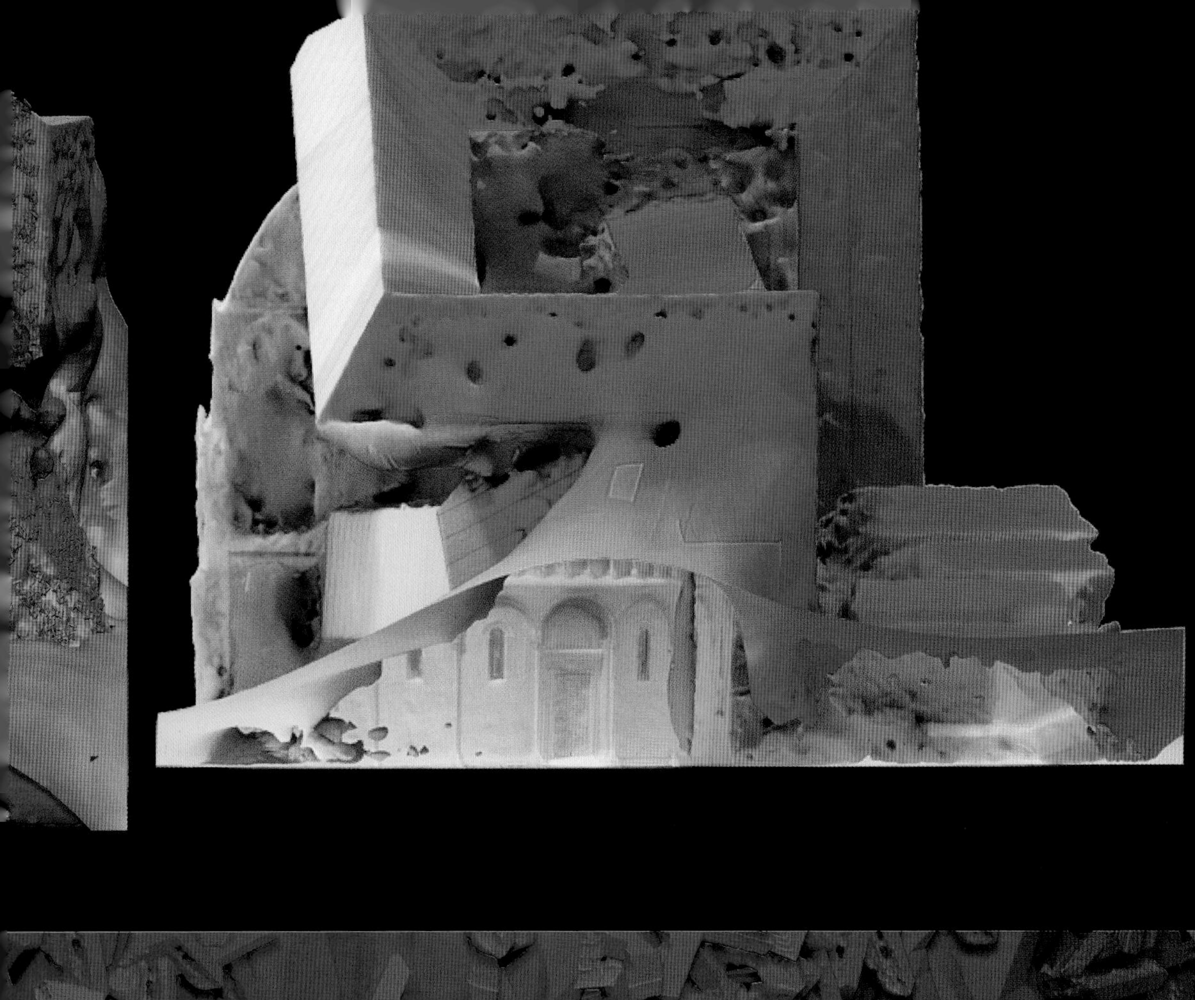

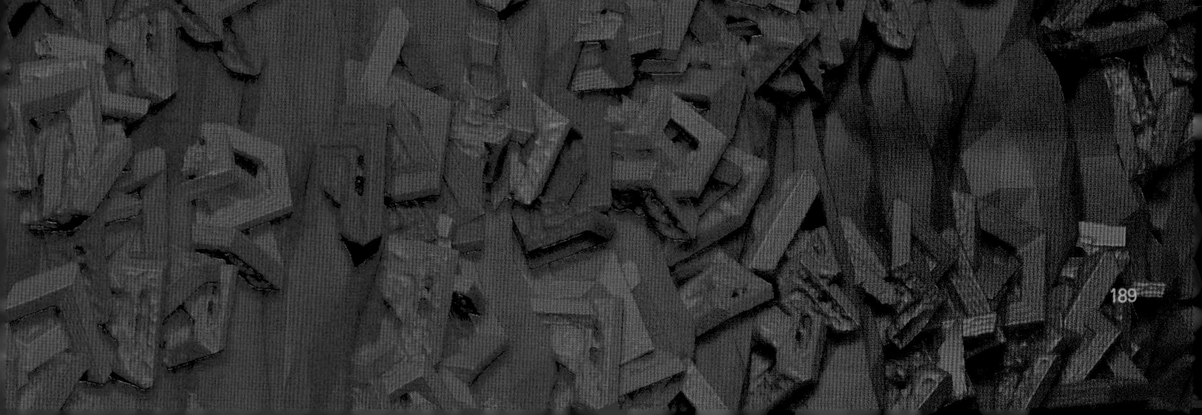

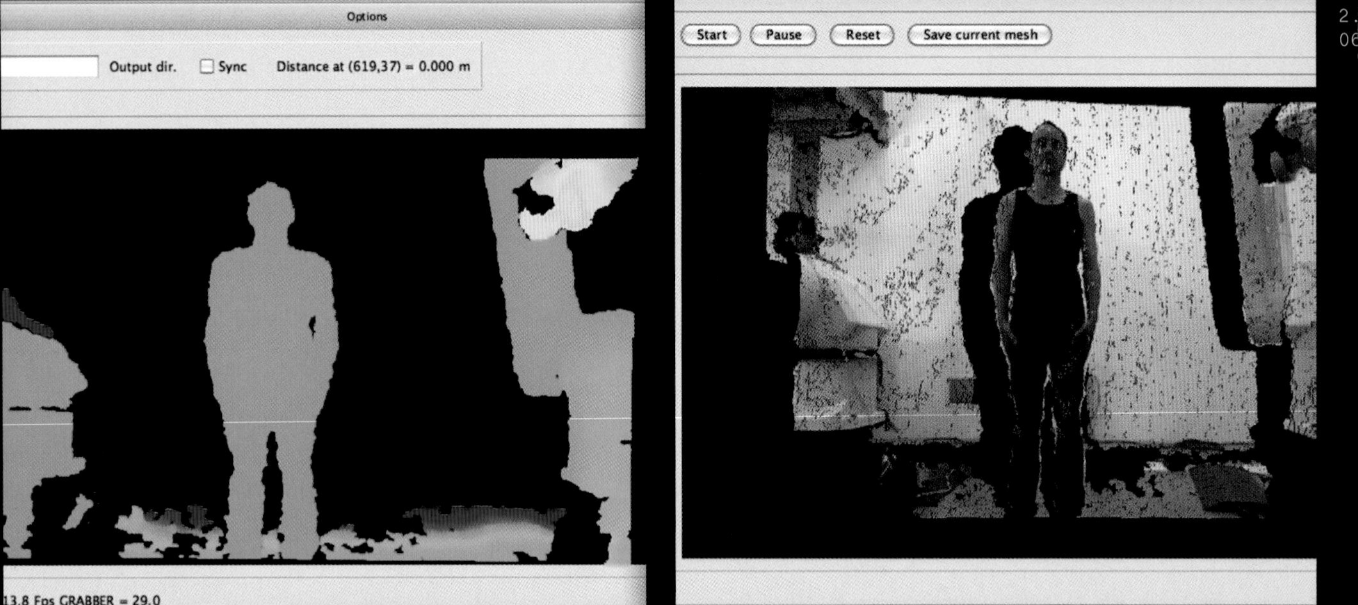

Options

Output dir. Sync Distance at (619,37) = 0.000 m

13.8 Fps GRABBER = 29.0

Start Pause Reset Save current mesh

Fictioning
Object Animation
Physical Rendering
Robotic Cinematography

A new medium is emerging that combines post-photographic cinematic techniques and real-time physical animation. Techniques add fiction to robots according to a precise logic and then elucidate this structure in real-time. The performative power of the robot is used to explore the contours of this new physical/cinematic convergence and its implications for architectural representation and form generation. A form of modeling is developed, involving simulation and emulation, that allows designers to construct novel methodologies (somewhere between theory and experiment) that emphasize the contingent dimensions of computation. Rather than positing a simple synthesis of digitality and analogicity, techniques maintain a relative autonomy of instances and objects to build theoretical or conceptual installations. Techniques of grafting, cloning, blurring, and looping bring together digital abstraction and material agency. A new meeting place is designed for fact and fiction, images and ideas, involving emerging media from object animation to physical rendering and robotic cinematography.

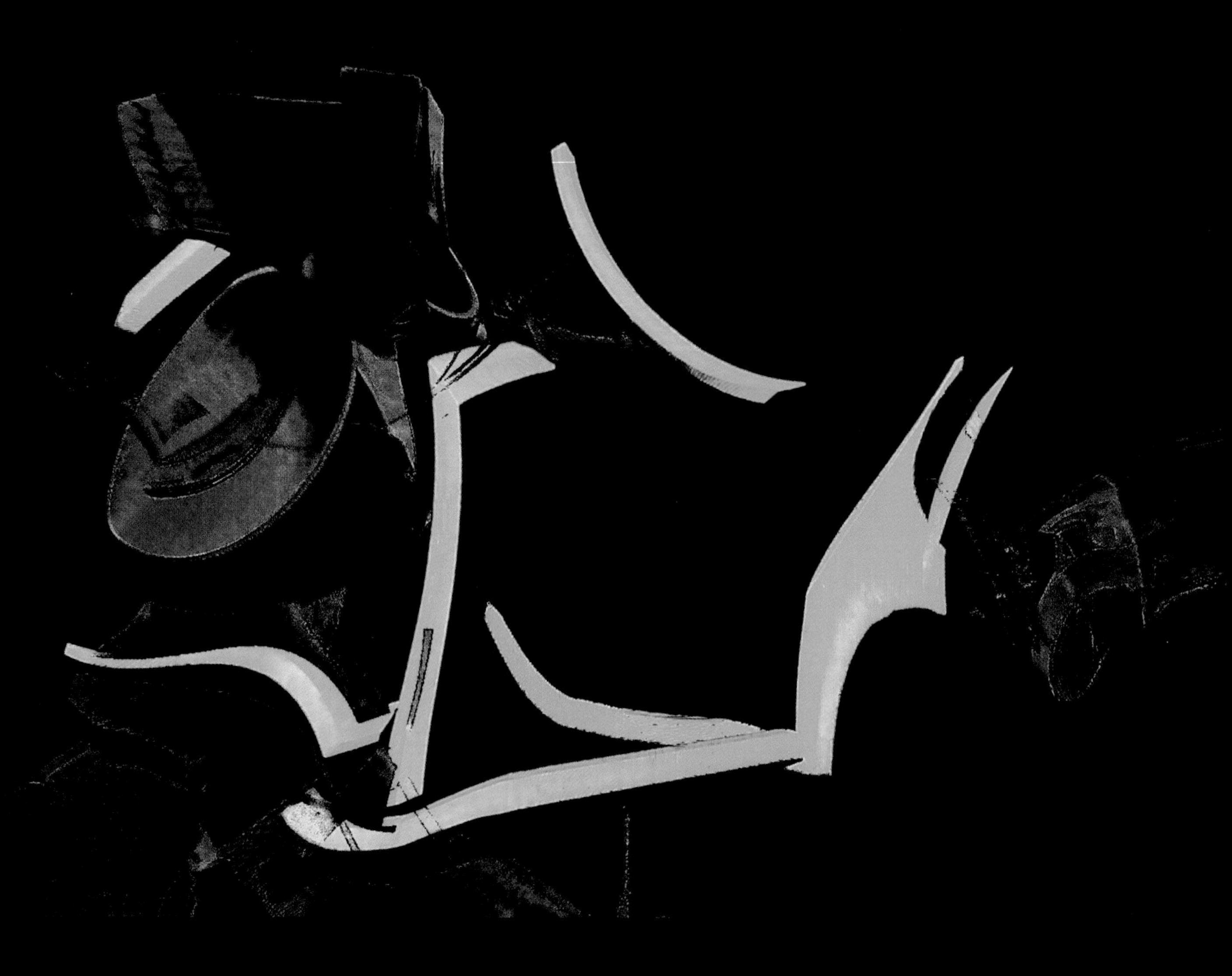

Object Animation

2.
15

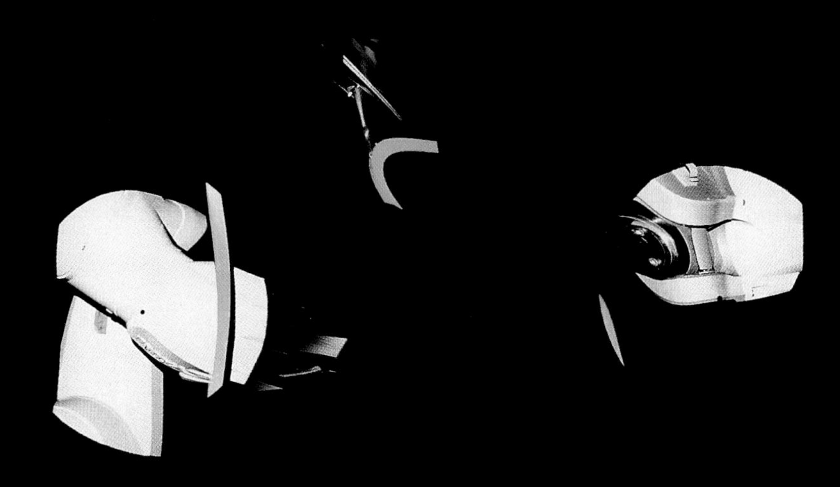

Object animation blends digital and physical

animation techniques on a robotic motion stage,

expanding established animation techniques such as

2.
18

2.
17

stop motion, model animation, live-action animation,

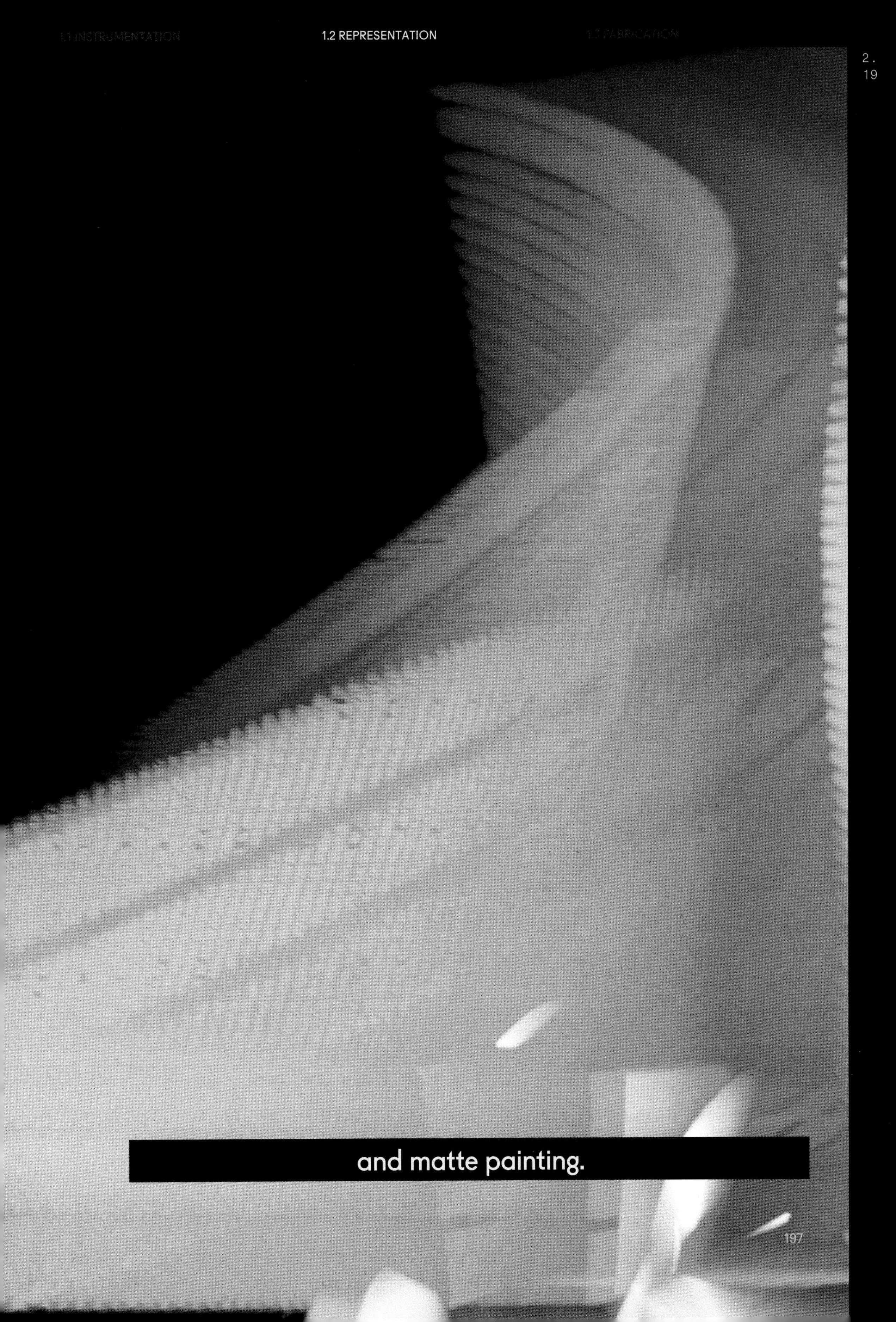
and matte painting.

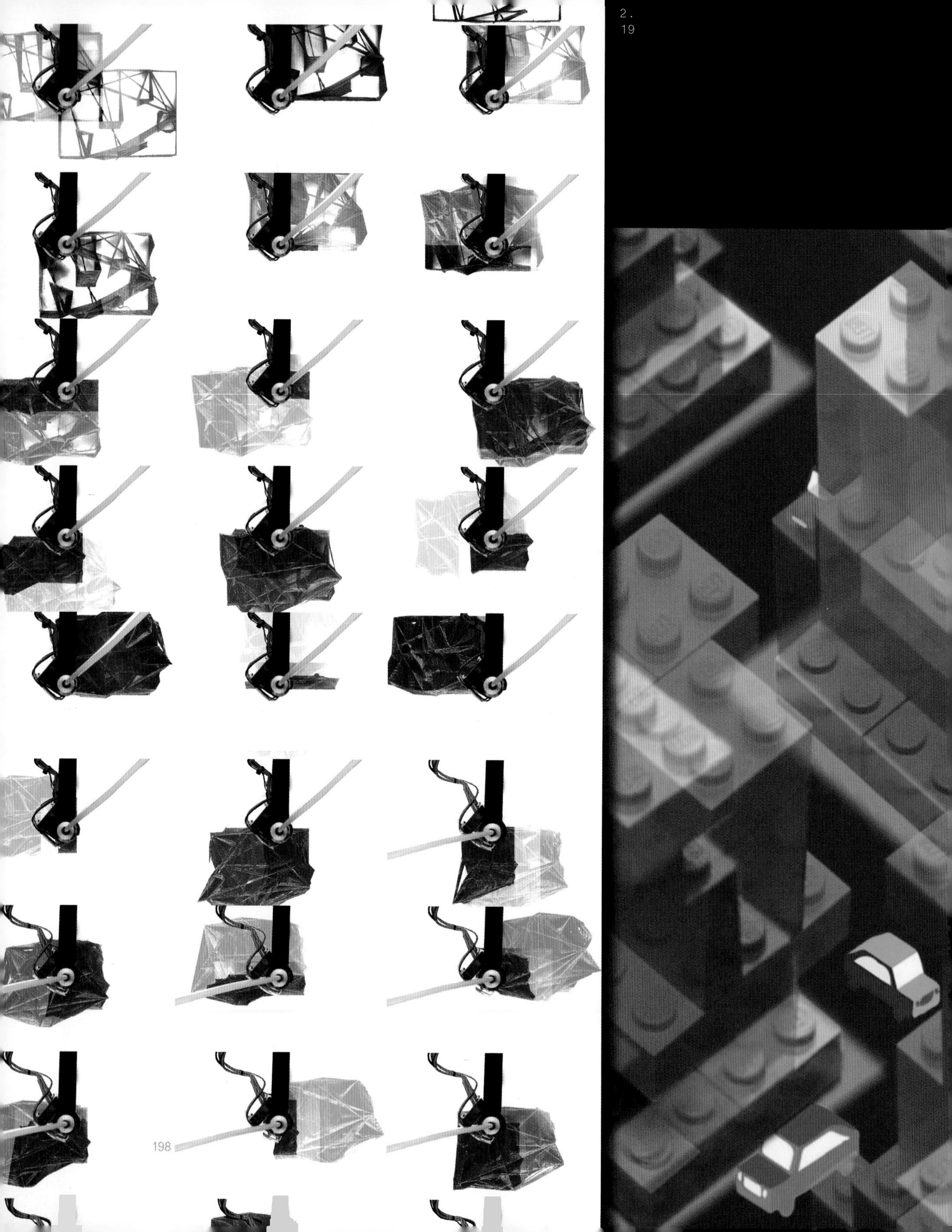
2.
19

2.
18

2.
21

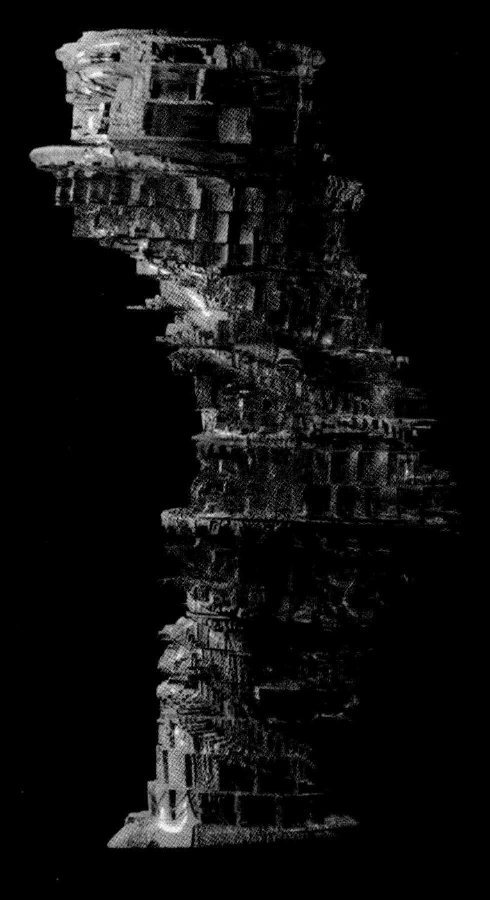

2.
22

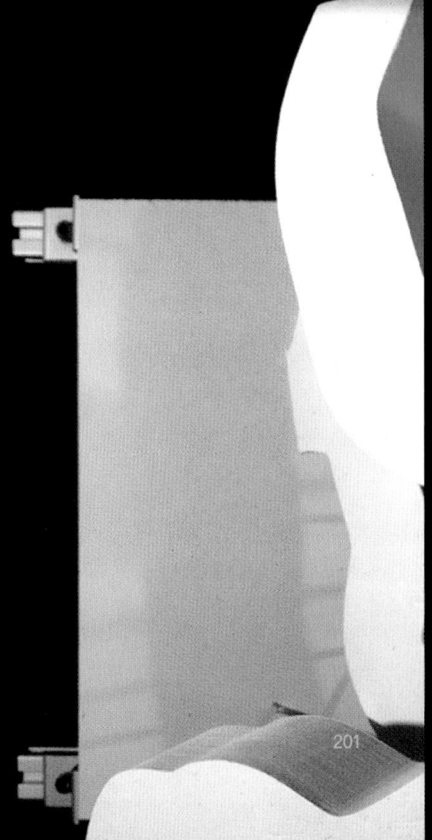

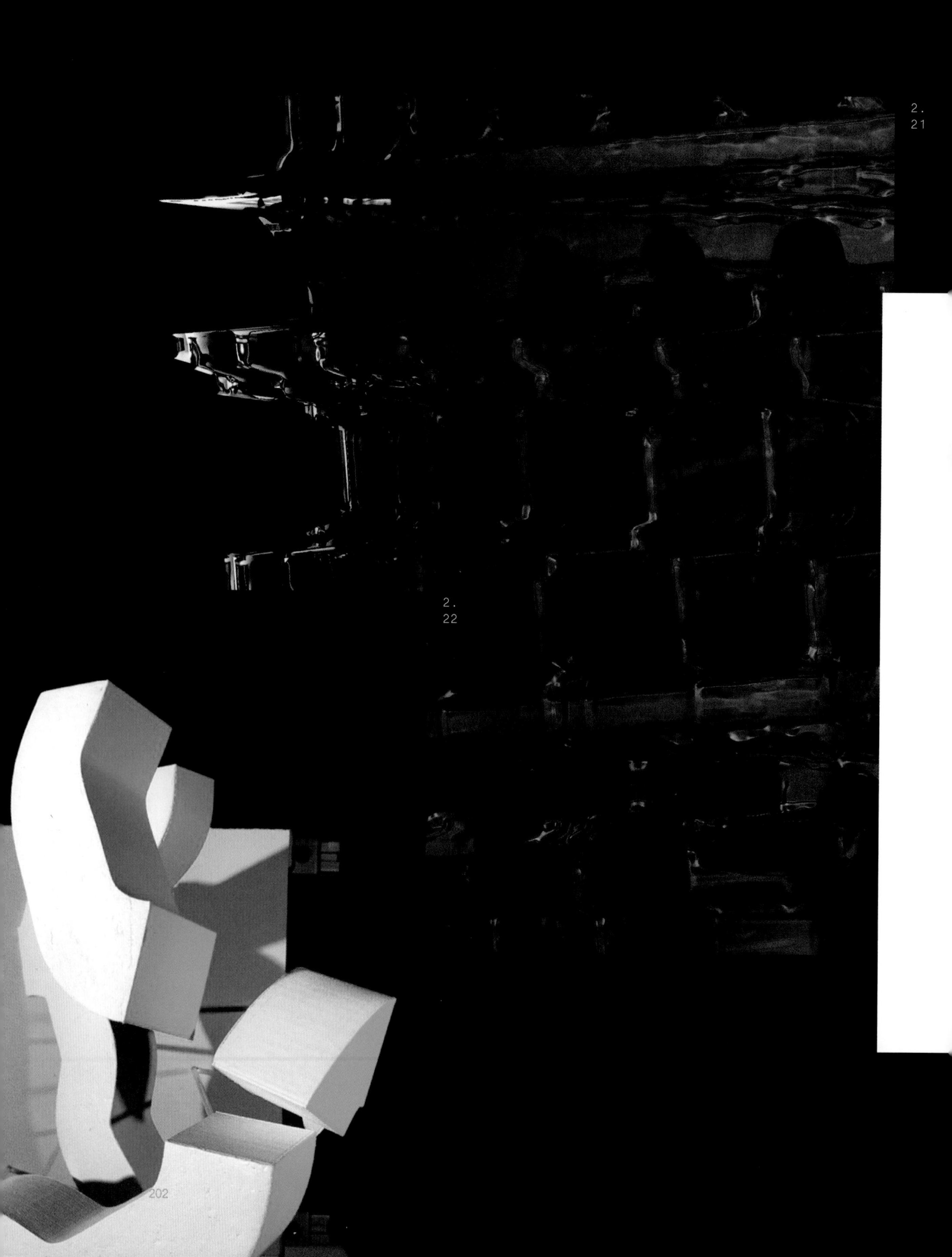

2.
21

2.
22

Physical Rendering

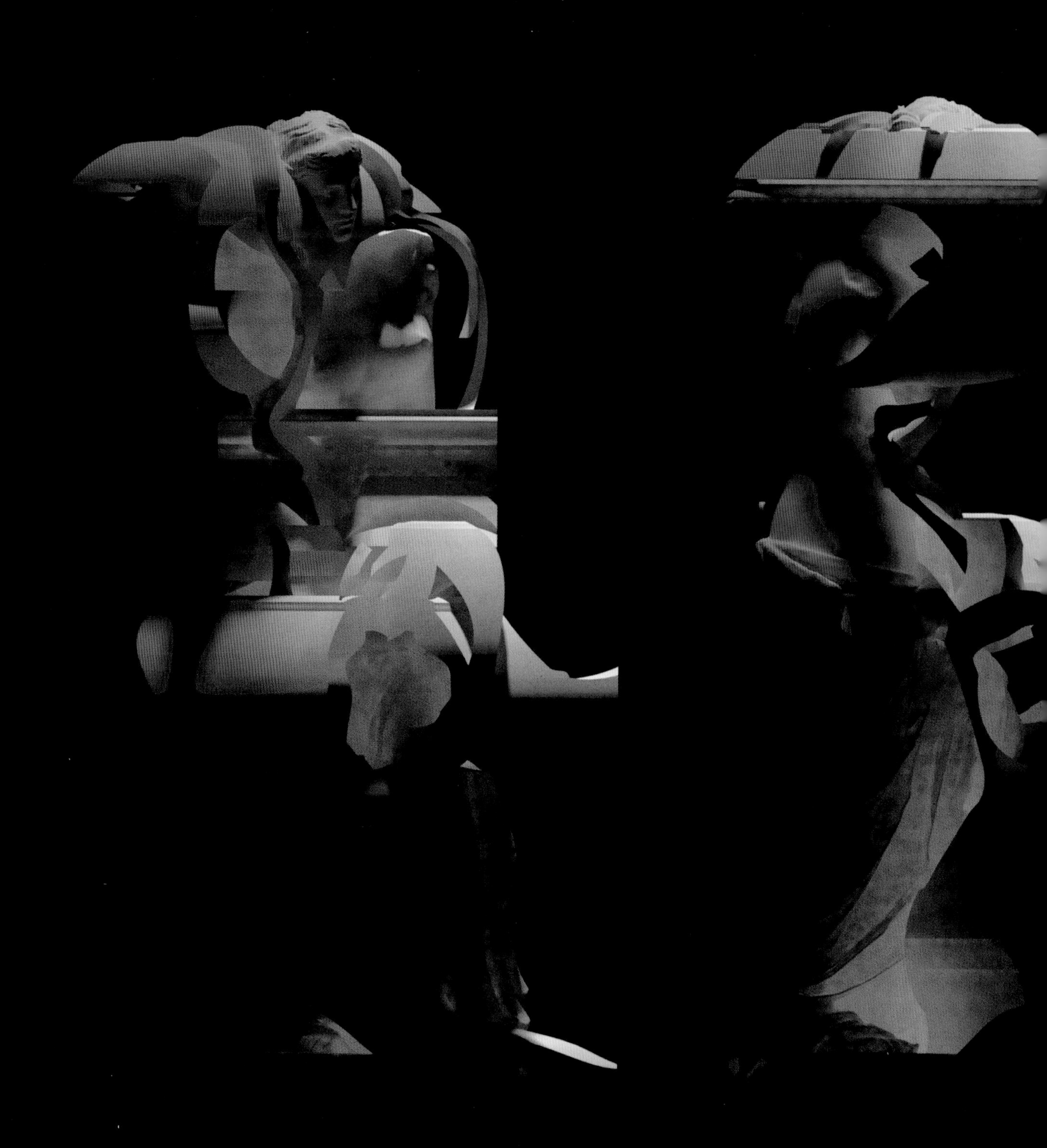

graphics techniques and physical objects. Calibrating

objects and camera positions, this representation uses

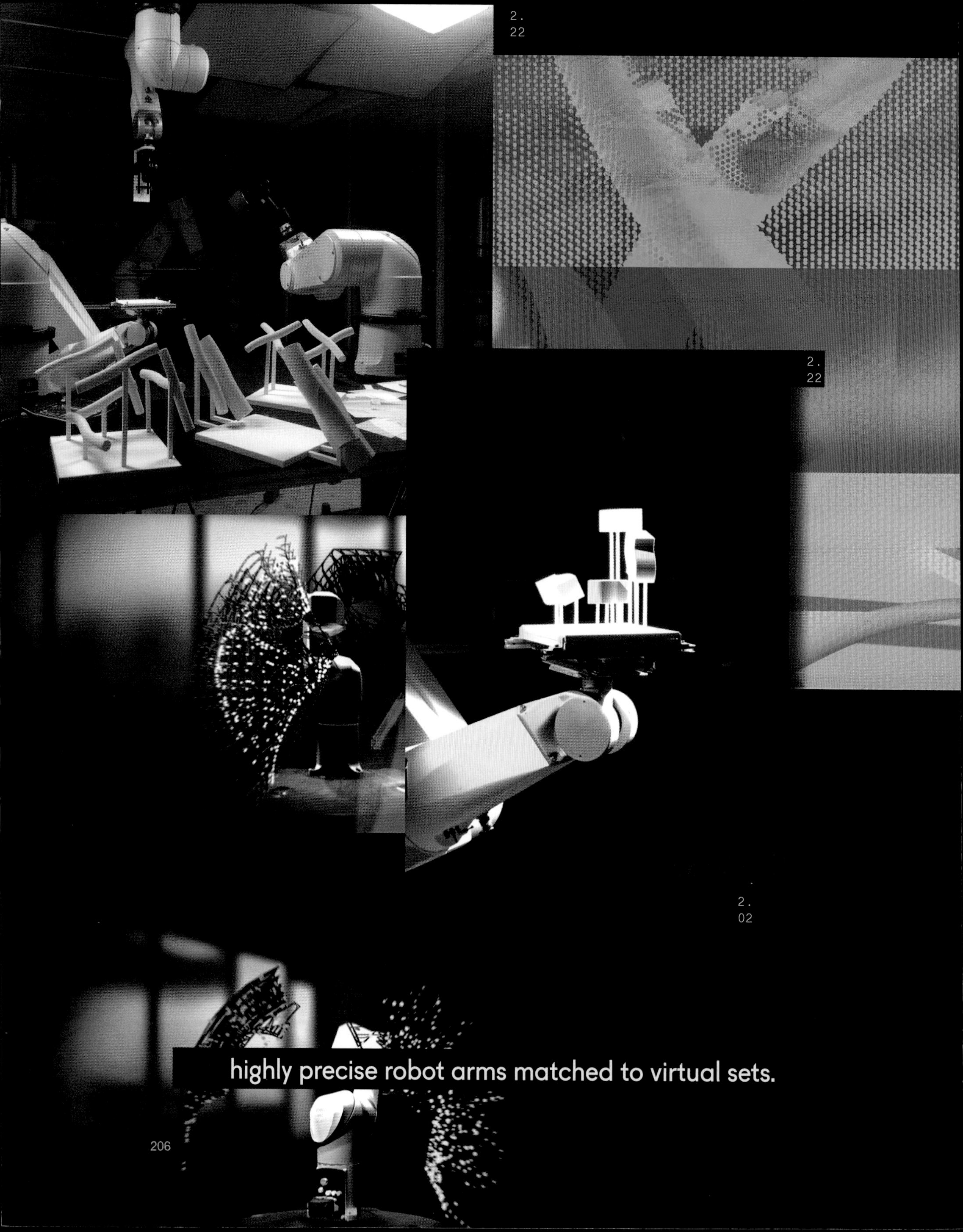

highly precise robot arms matched to virtual sets.

2.
22

Robotic Cinematography

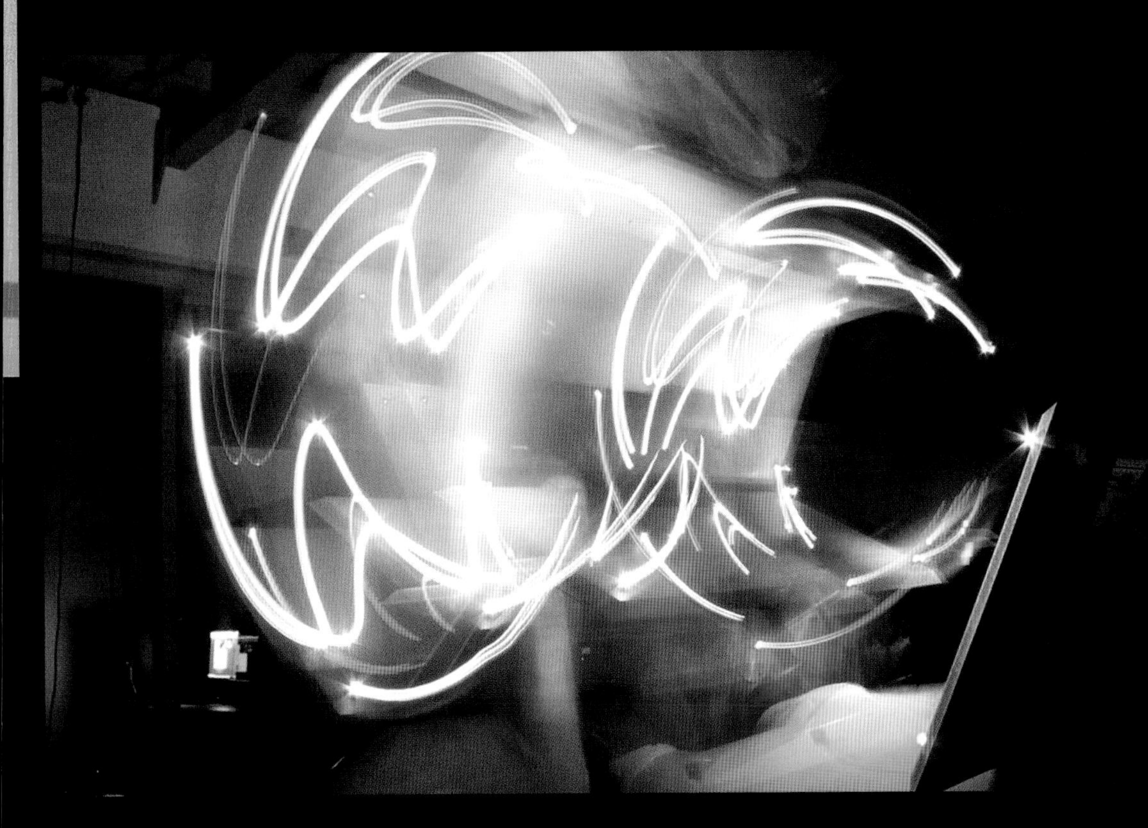

2.
09

Camera moves can be pre-visualized in advance

and converted into motion control data that drives

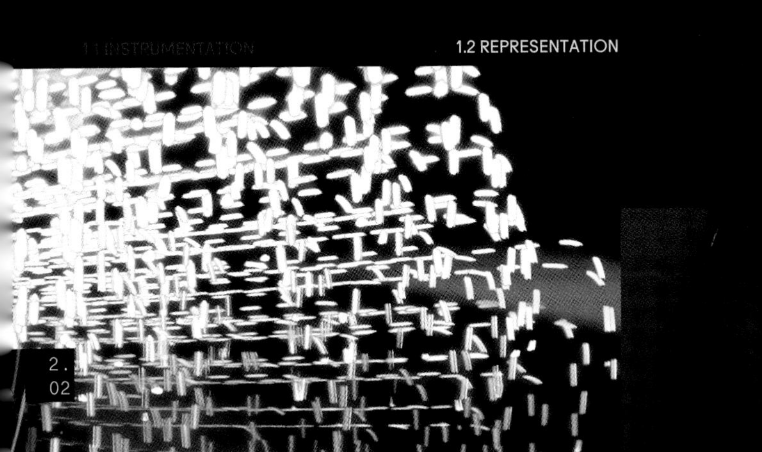

2.
09

2.
09

robot-mounted cameras and any number of end

effectors along the same path as the 3D camera. This

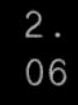

process can be reversed to generate live 3D cameras.

4, 20

Real-time motion capture systems can be mixed within

camera data streams, allowing virtual elements to be

inserted into live shots.

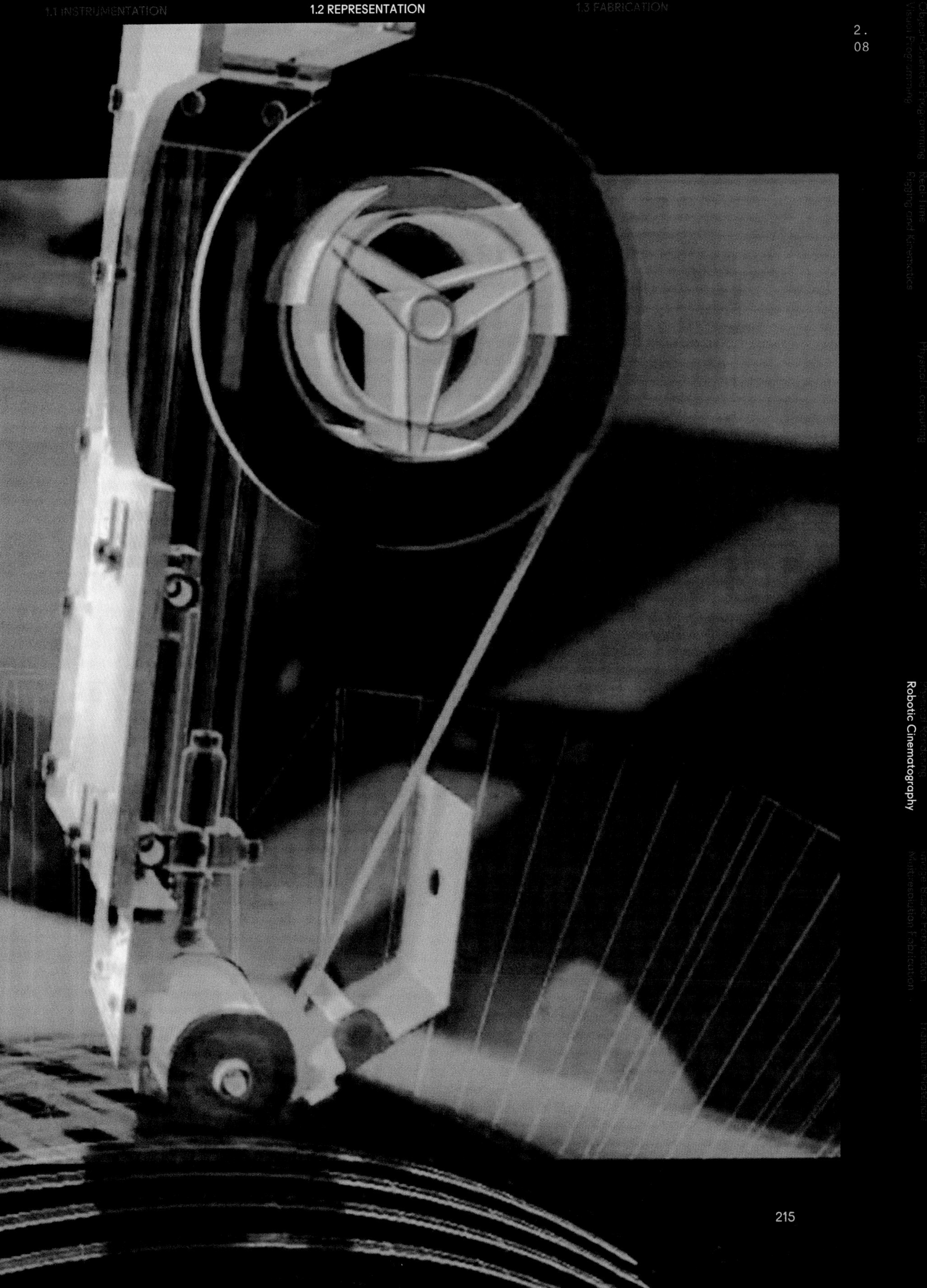

2.
09

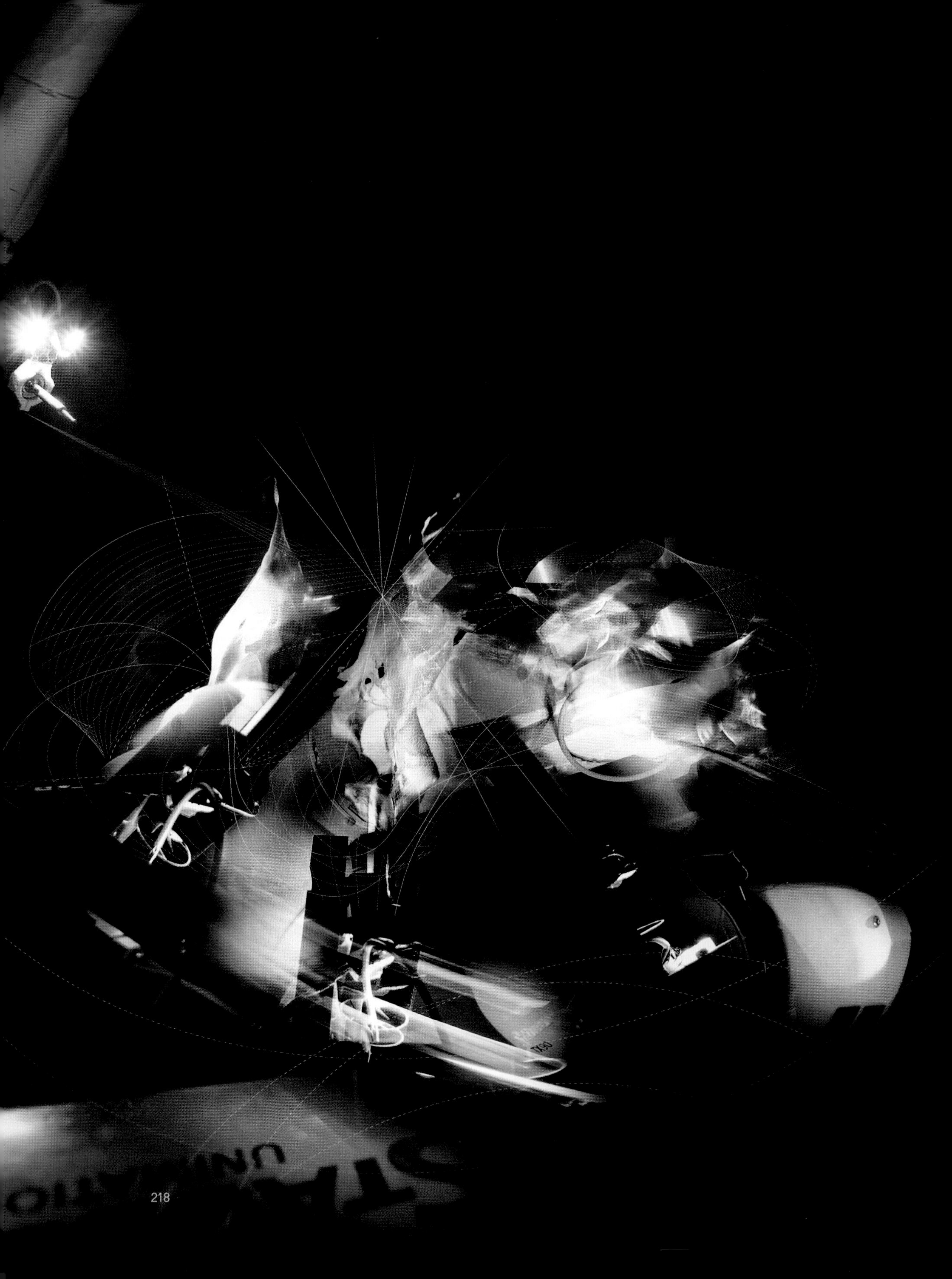

Augmented Fabrication
Free-Form Fabrication
Image-Based Fabrication
Multiresolution Fabrication

Computational Materials
Scaffolds and Templates
Transitive Materials

Augmented Fabrication
Free-Form Fabrication
Image-Based Fabrication
Multiresolution Fabrication

Projects are not simply fabricating objects with robots but creating a new type of fictional, or "representational," object. Breaking down the hierarchy of geometry, image, and object, these new design and production processes are image-driven and often do not require the intermediary of 3D digital models. Multiresolution imaging is directly allied to new forms of multimaterial and mixed-resolution fabrication. Work is a production or a performance involving various ideas of fabrication: free-form, image-based, and multiresolution.

Free-Form Fabrication

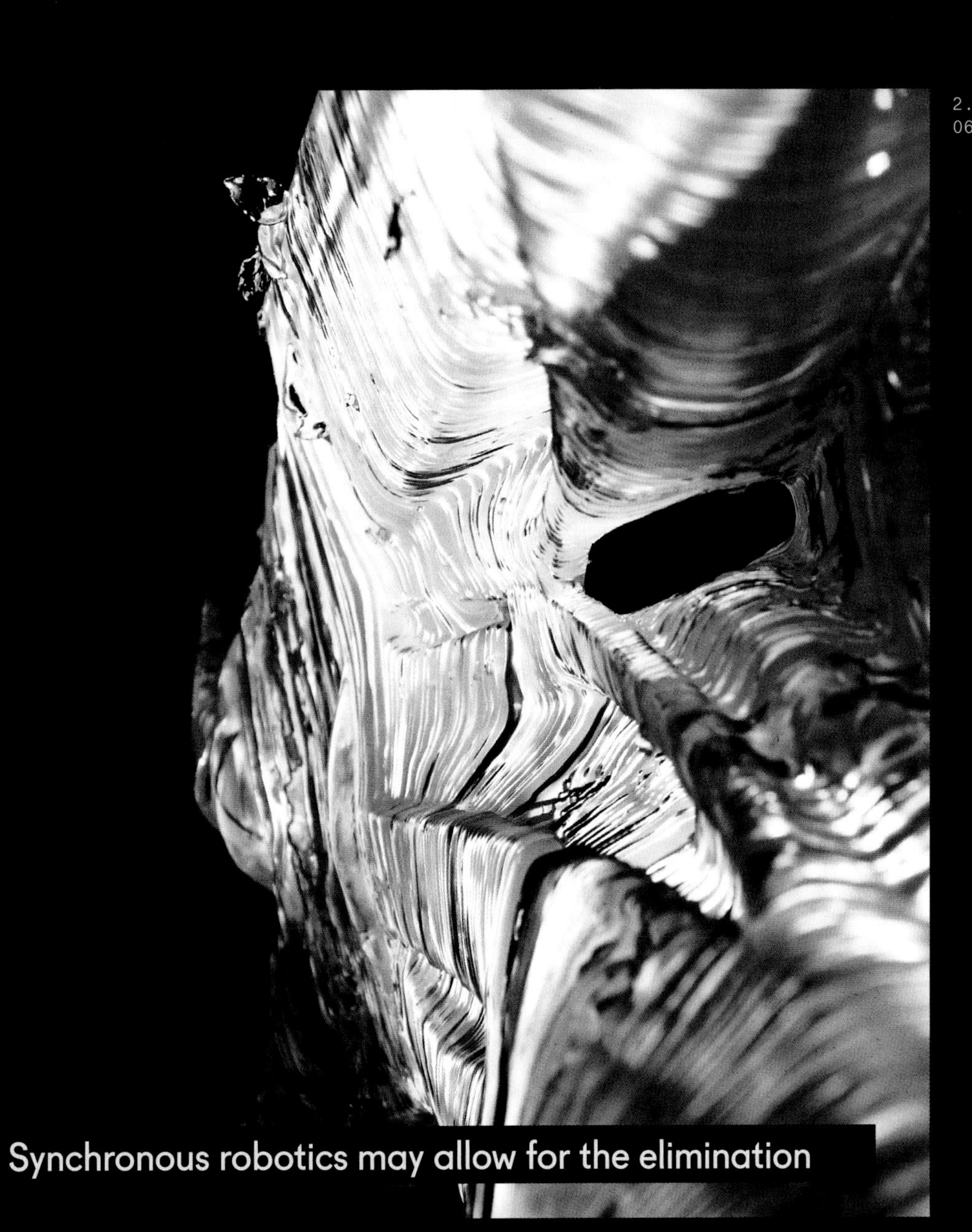

Synchronous robotics may allow for the elimination

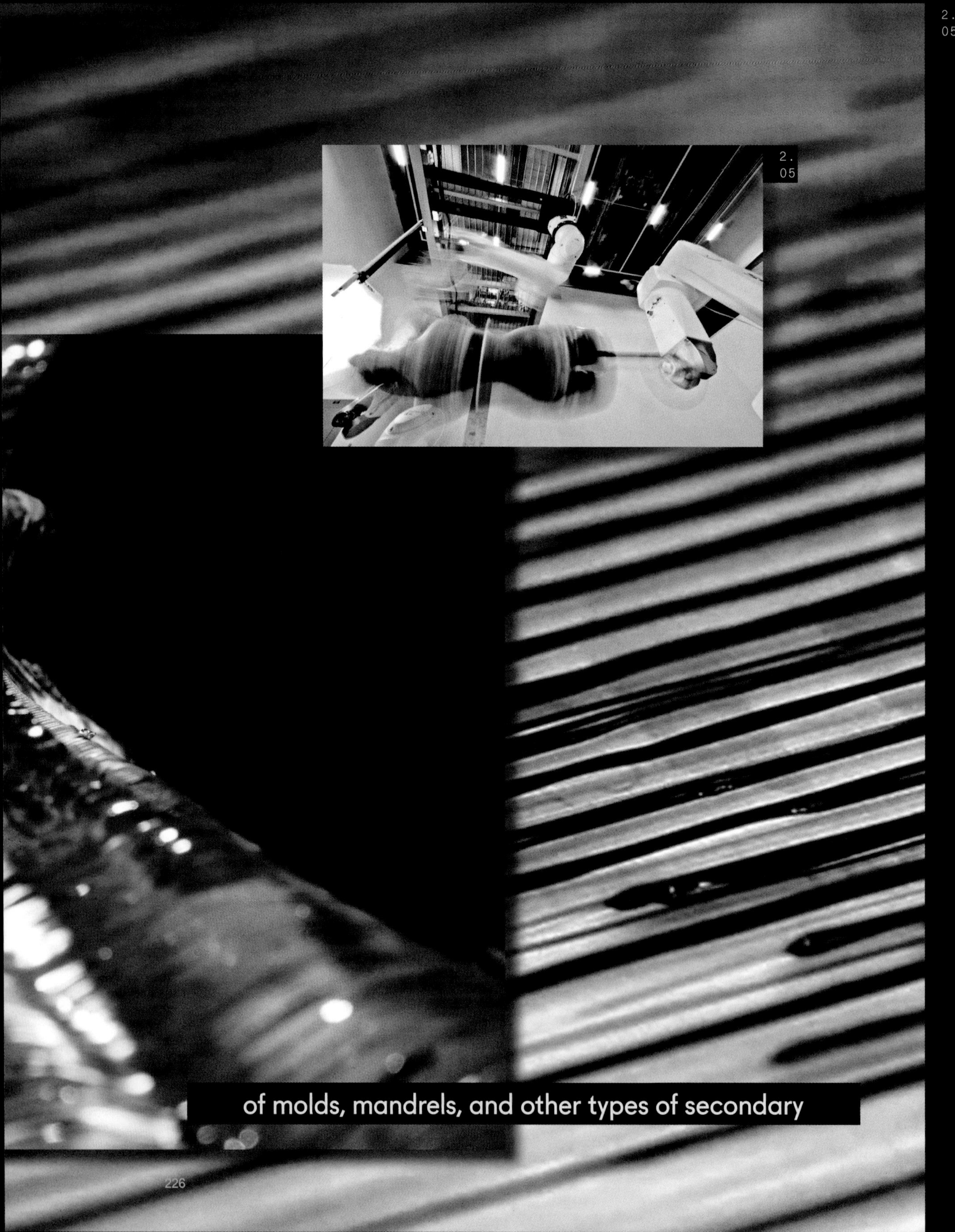

of molds, mandrels, and other types of secondary

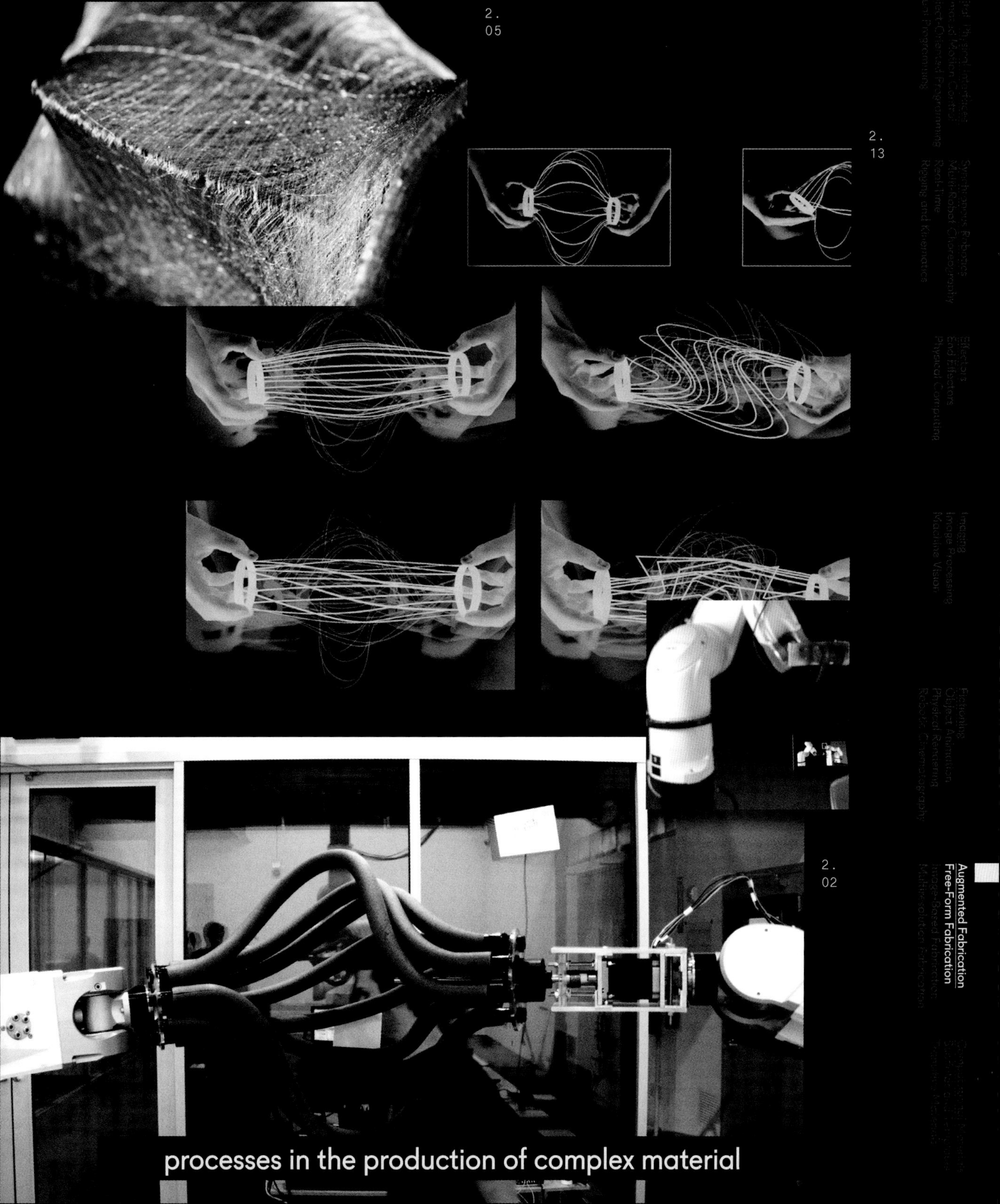

processes in the production of complex material

forms, including advanced composites. Techniques

include thermoforming, robotic 3D printing,

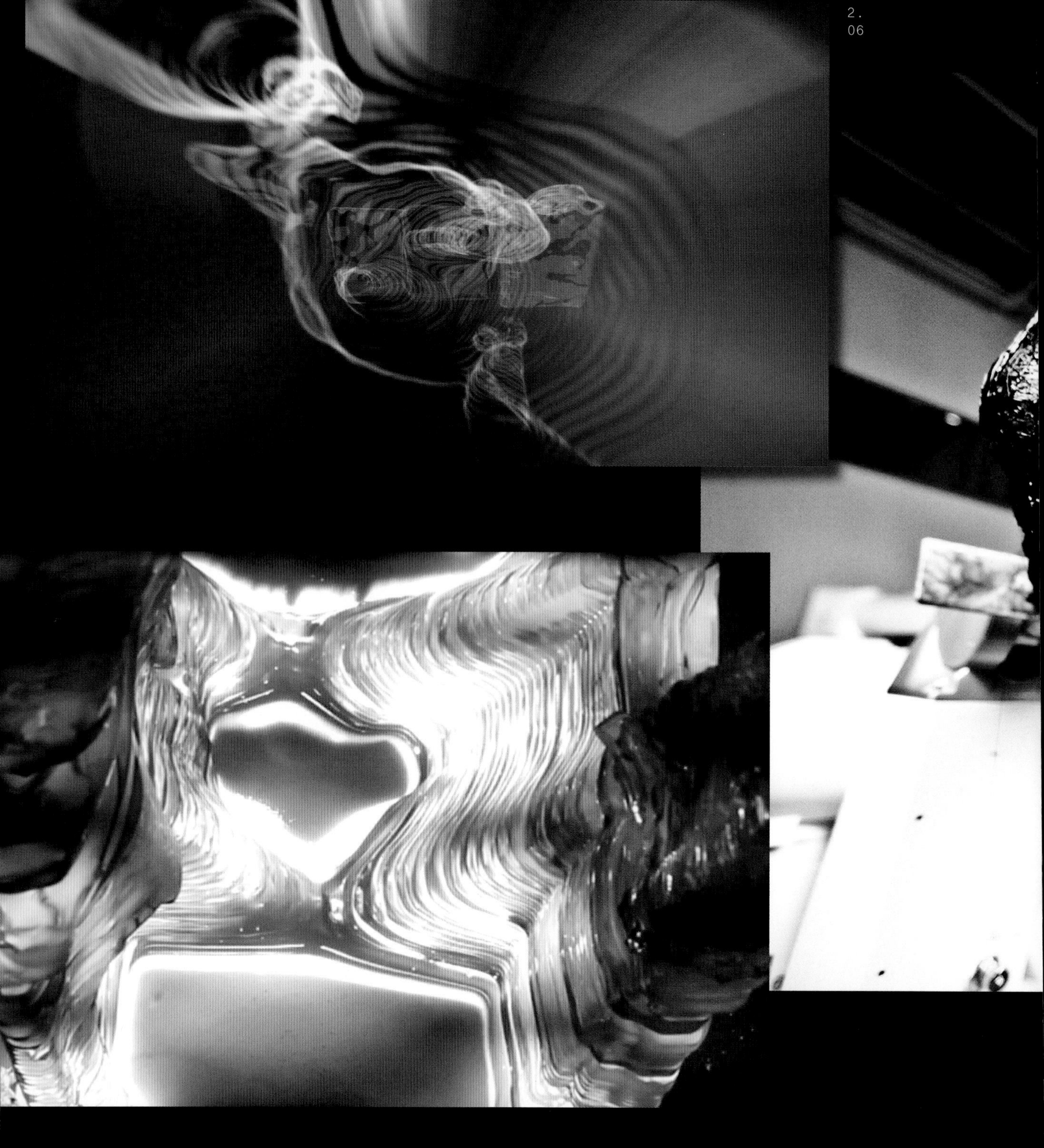

photo-polymerization, advanced fiber placement

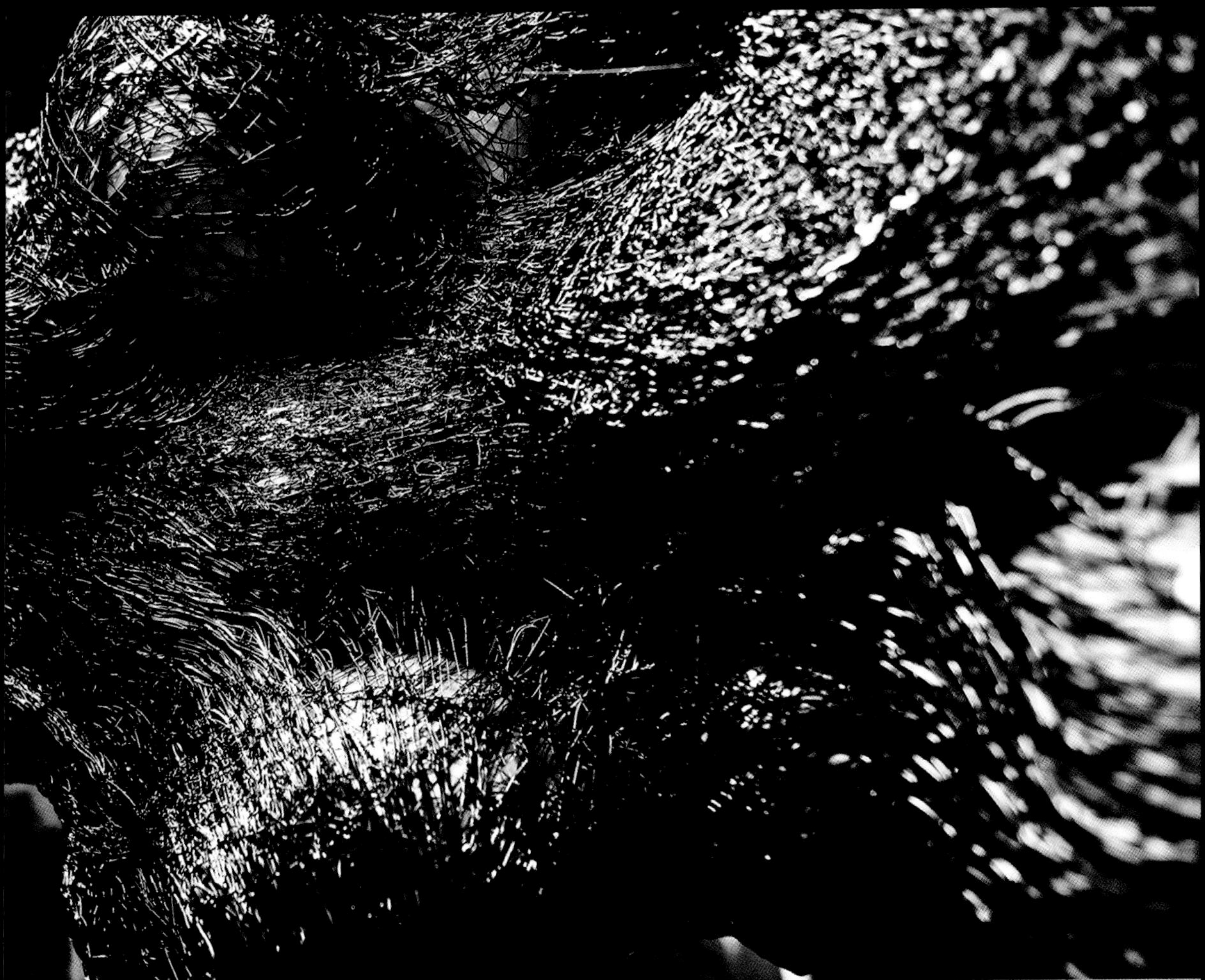

2.
05

2.
04

(AFP), automated tapelaying (ATL), and filament

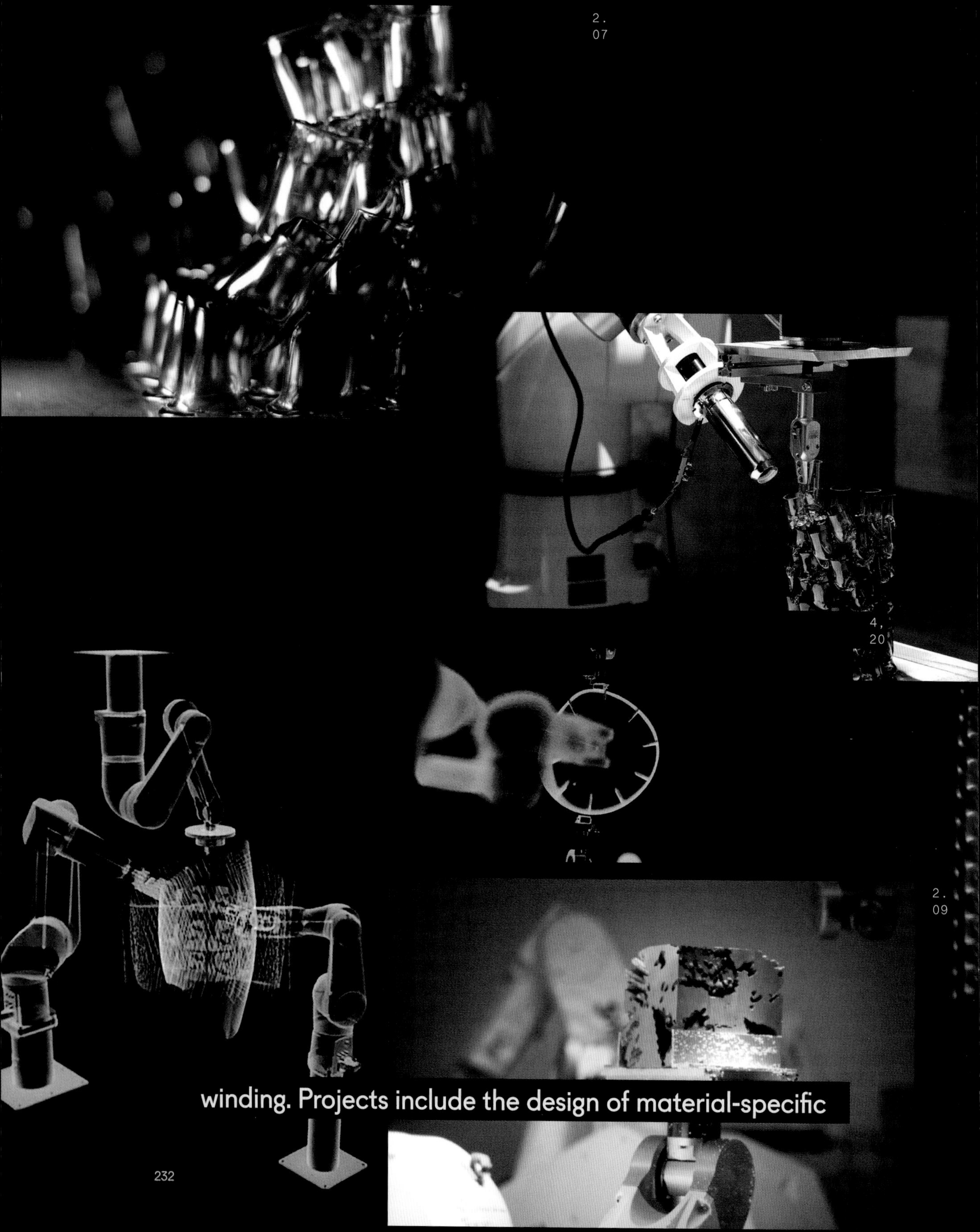

winding. Projects include the design of material-specific

workflows and end effectors. Reversible, additive,

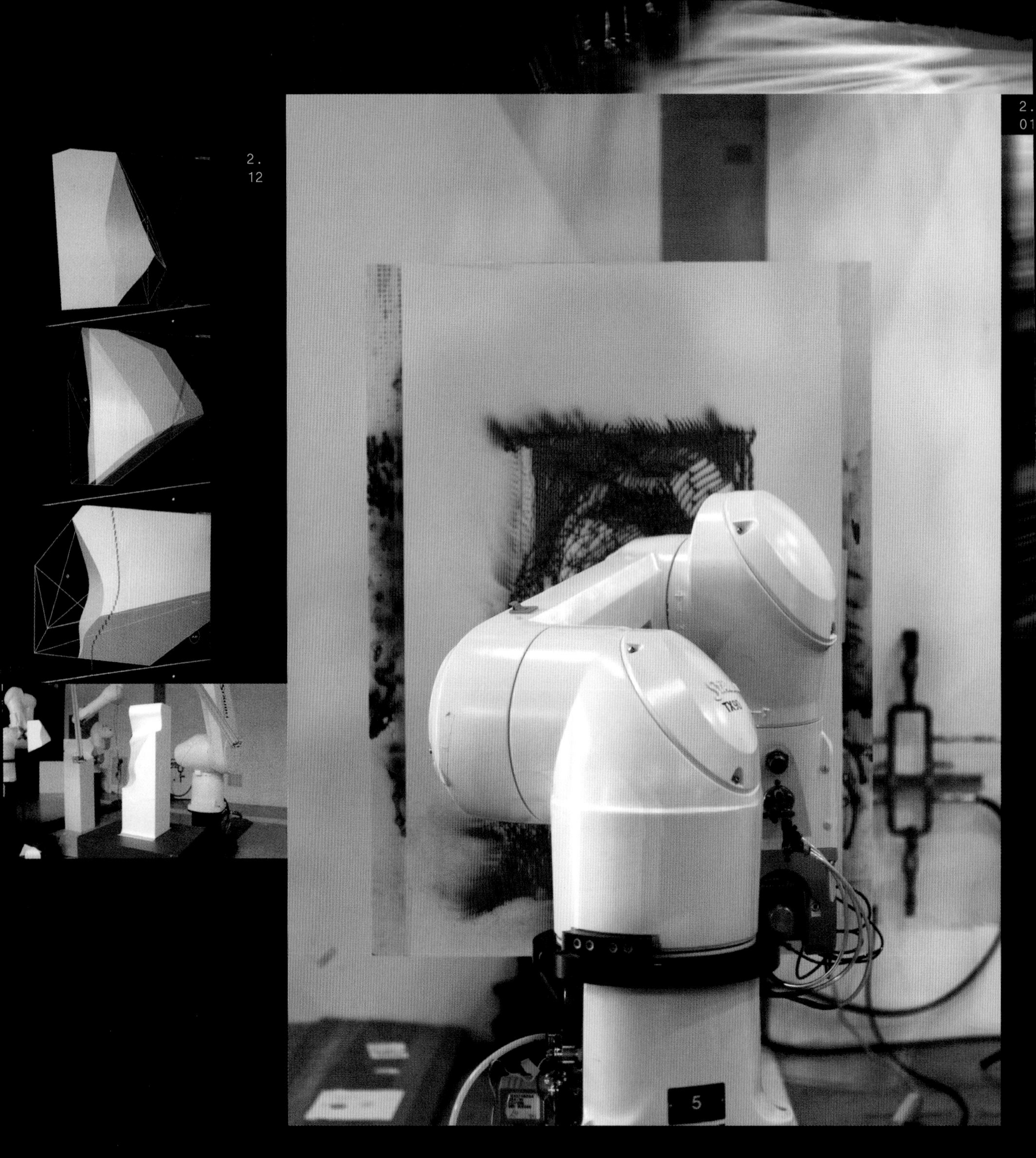

and subtractive processes within a single workflow

2.
10

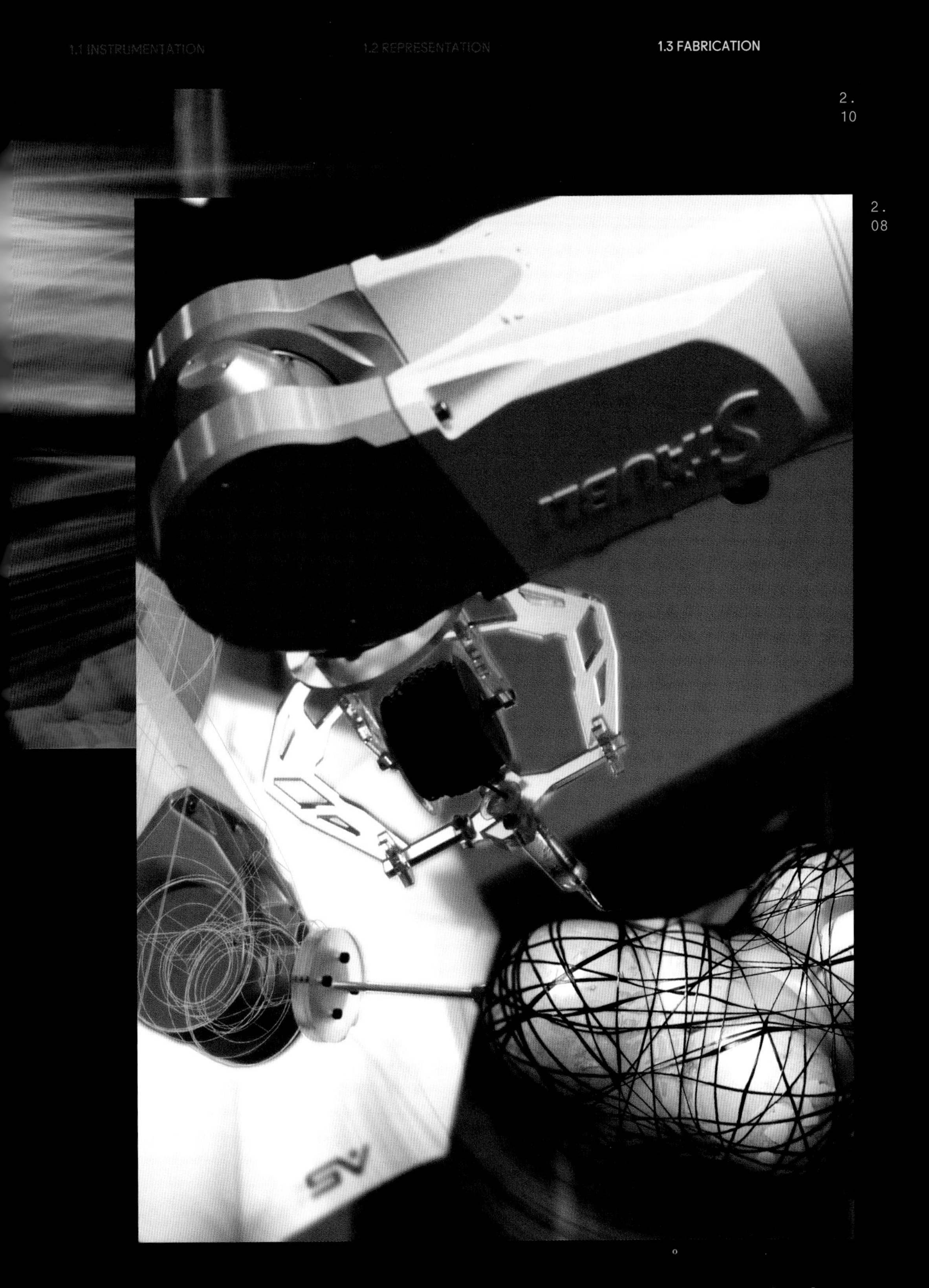

2.
08

allow materials to be removed and reapplied

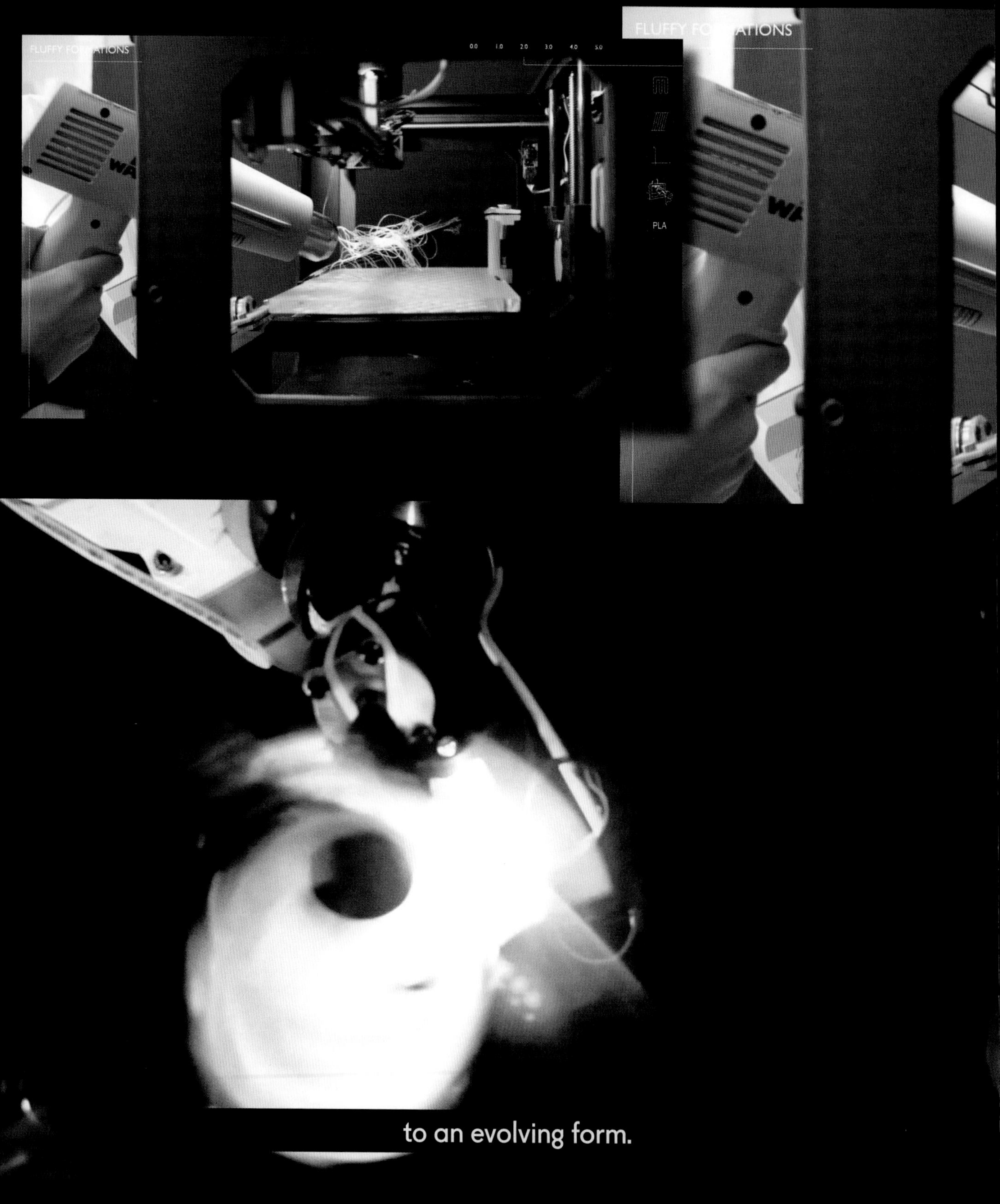

to an evolving form.

0.0
1.0
2.0
3.0
4.0
5.0
PLA
2.
13
2.
06
2.
14

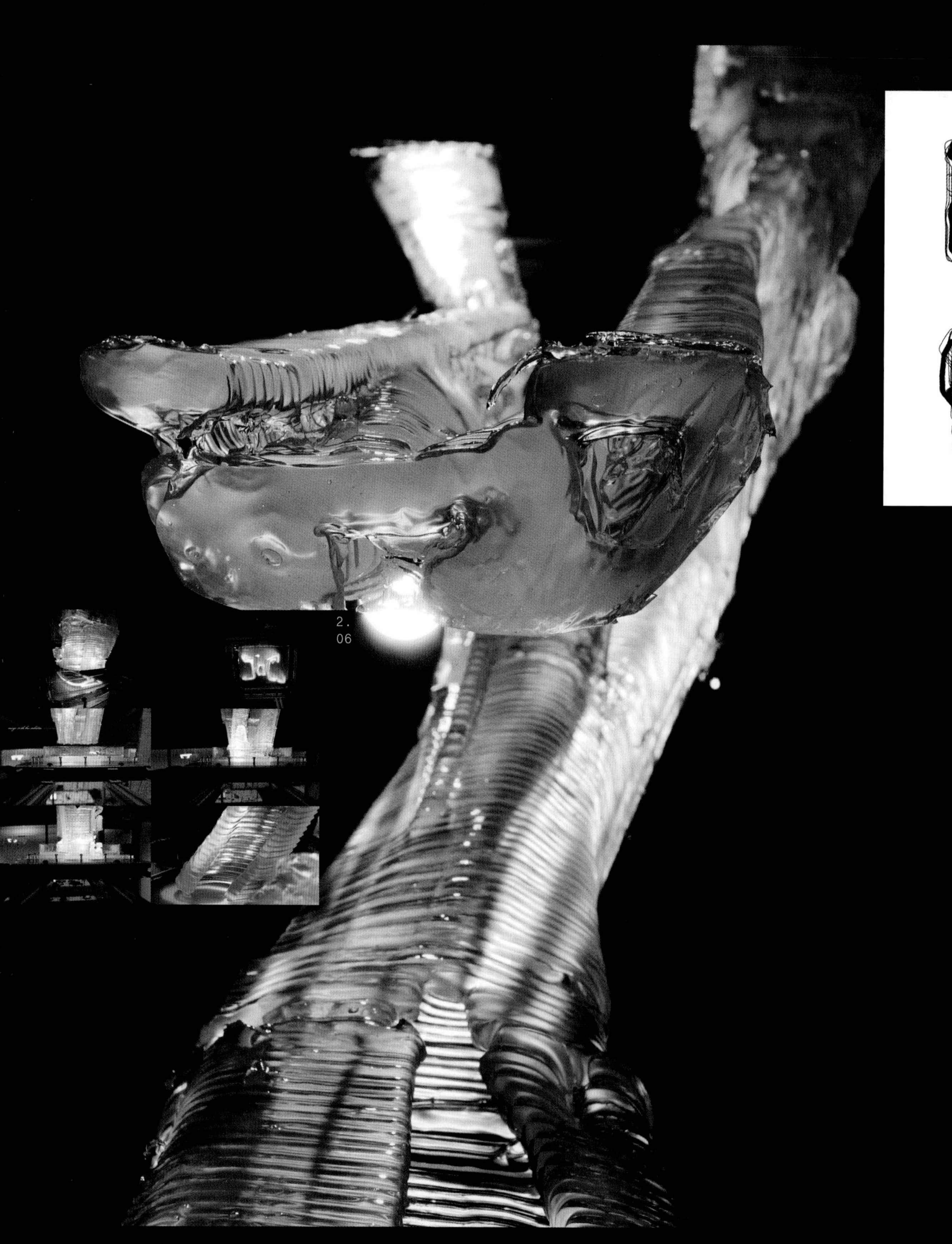
2.
06
2.
06

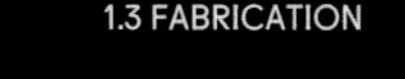

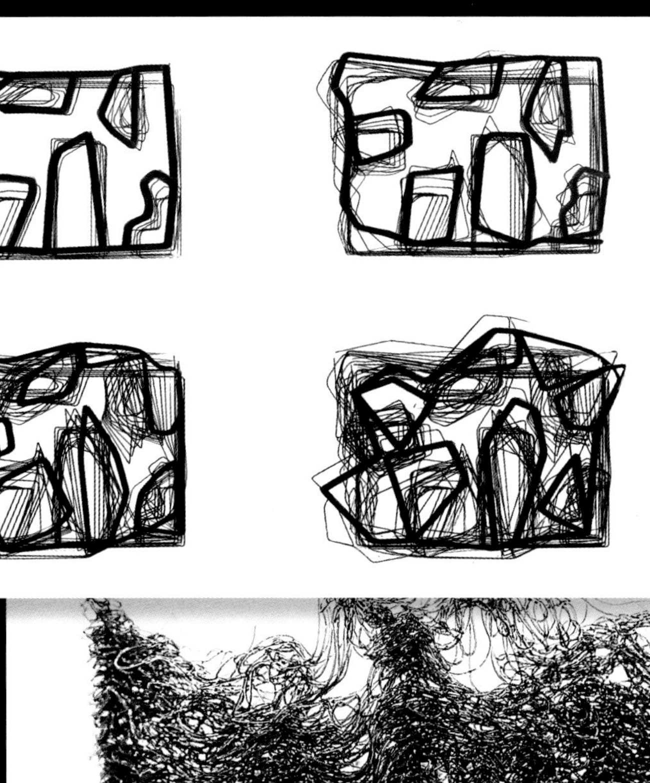

2.
19

2.
19

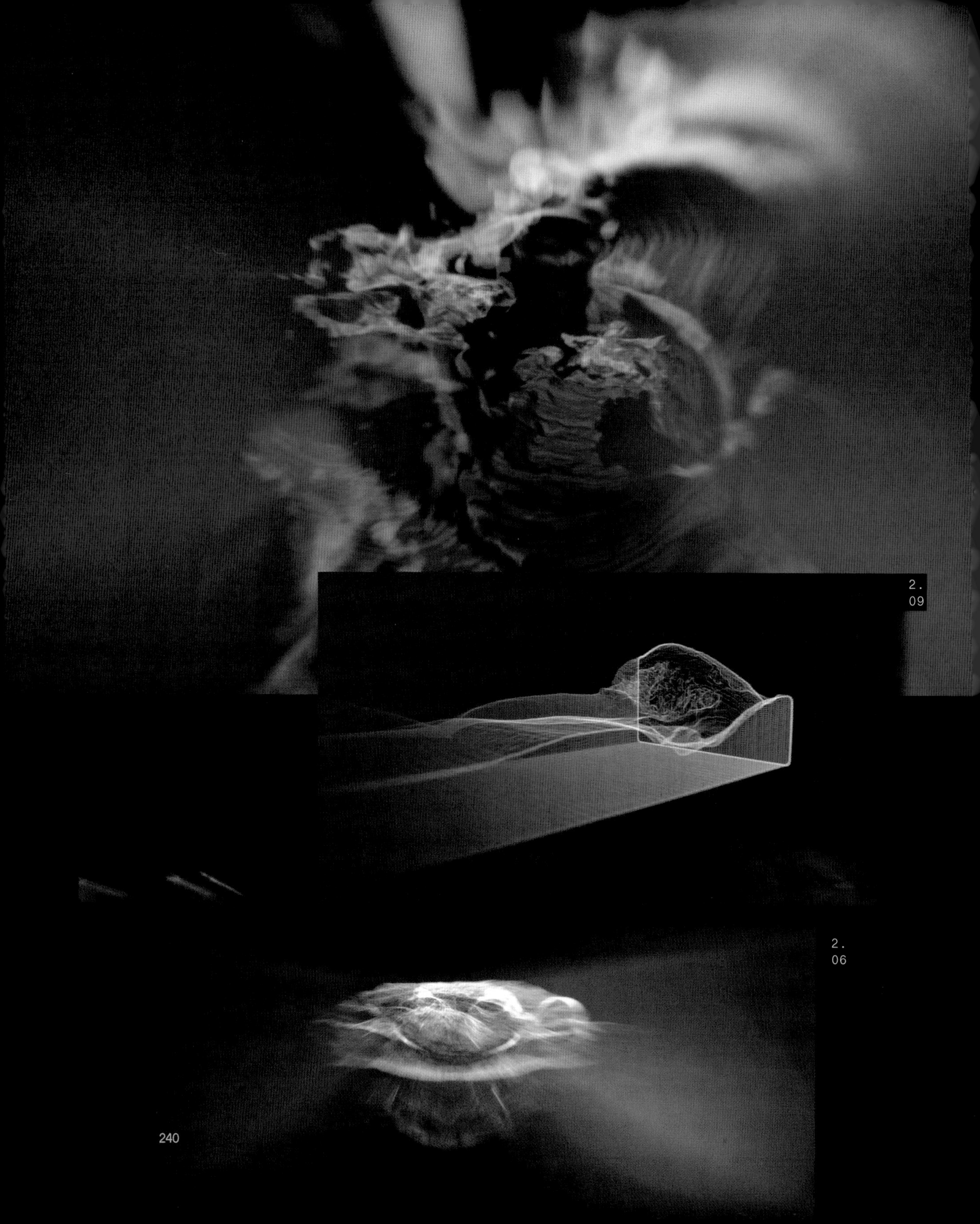
2.
09
2.
06

2.
06

Image-Based Fabrication

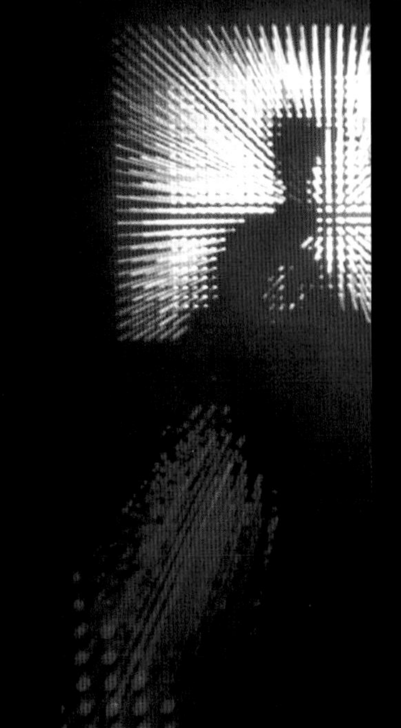

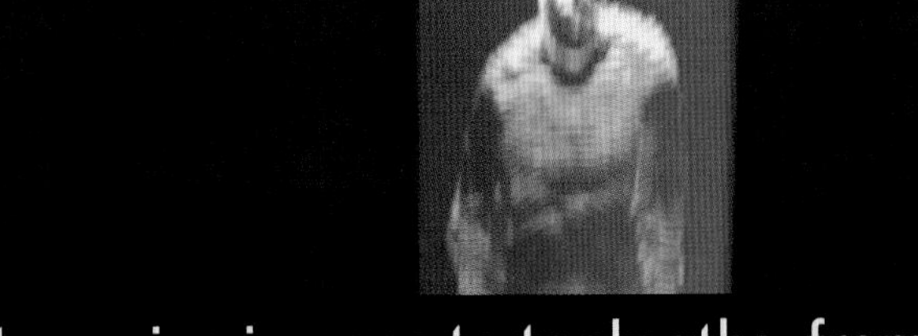

Streaming images to toolpaths, from real-time

scanned data to texture mapping, shifts conventional

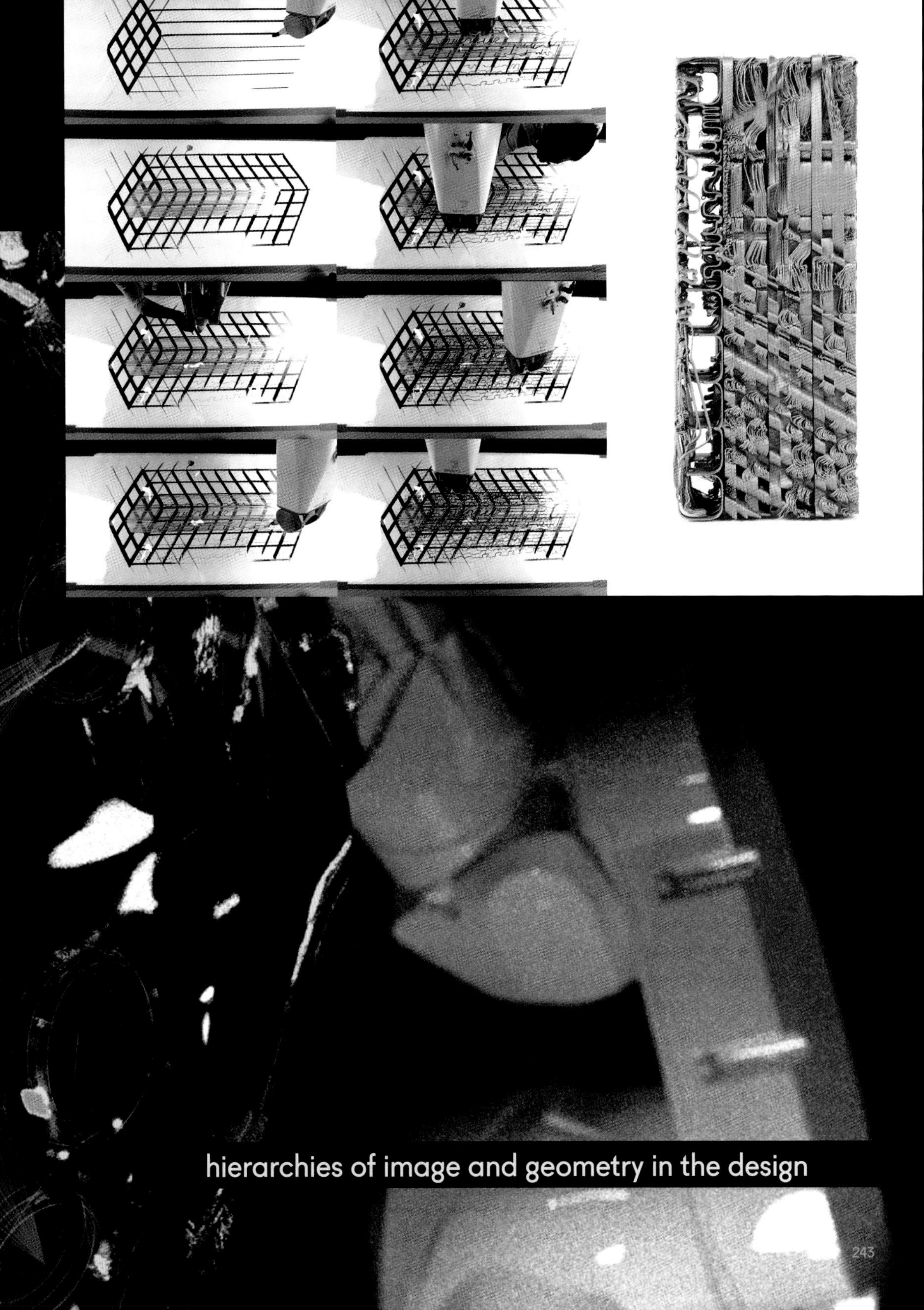

hierarchies of image and geometry in the design

and fabrication of physical artifacts. Continuous

2.
06

2.
06

representation of the object integrates the use of

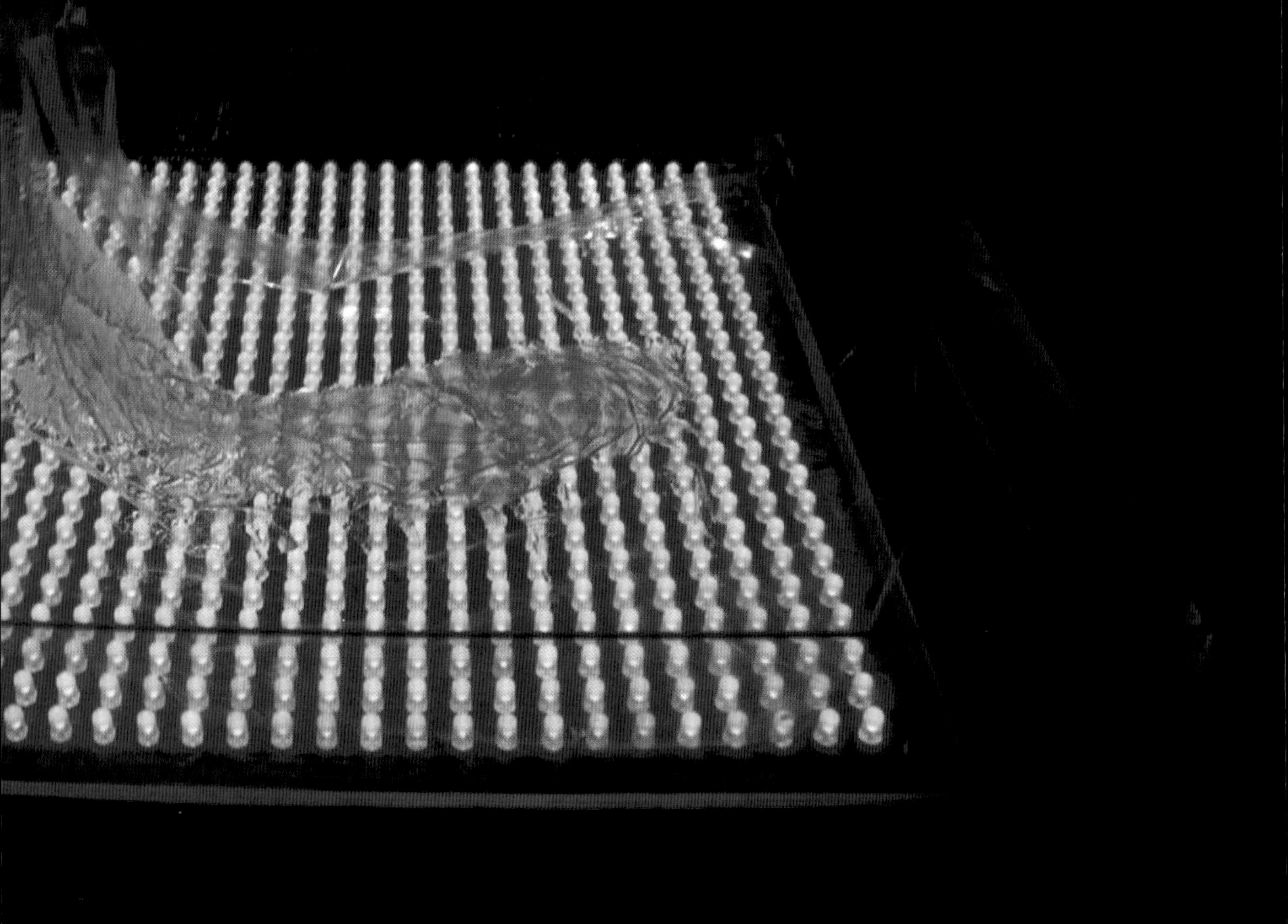

data-rich images rather than relying on 3D modeling.

Multiresolution Fabrication

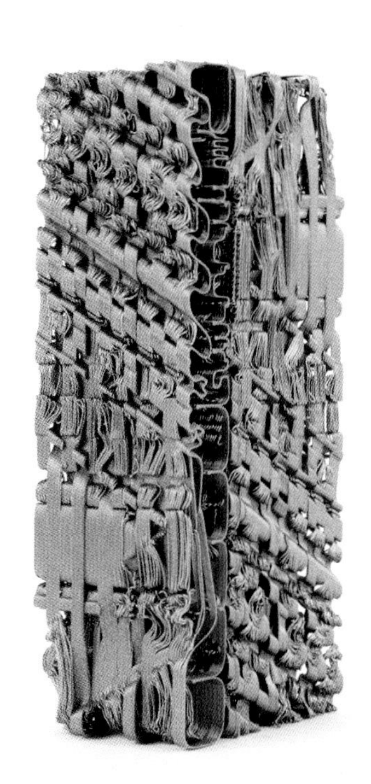

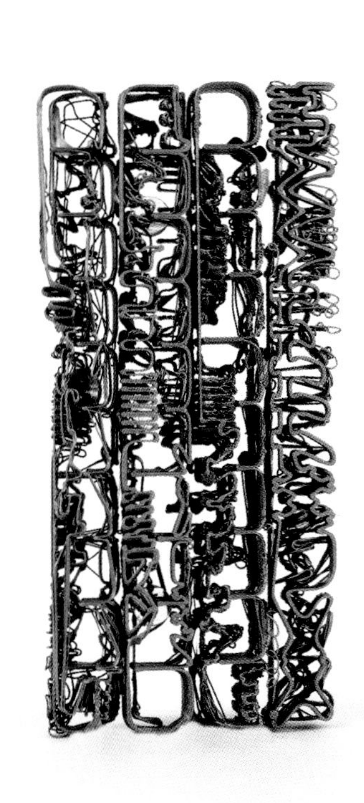

2.
19

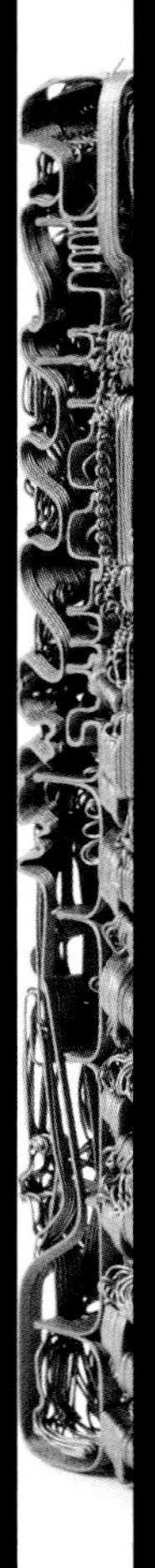

In place of layered manufacturing, robotic deposition

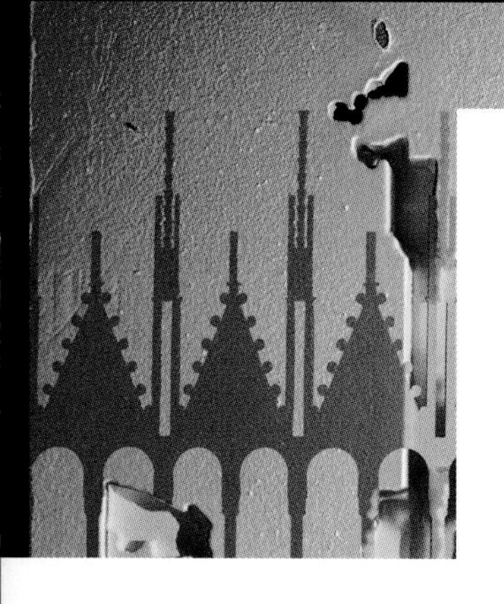

printing offers a new type of multiresolution fabrication.

Direct user intervention and varying levels of material

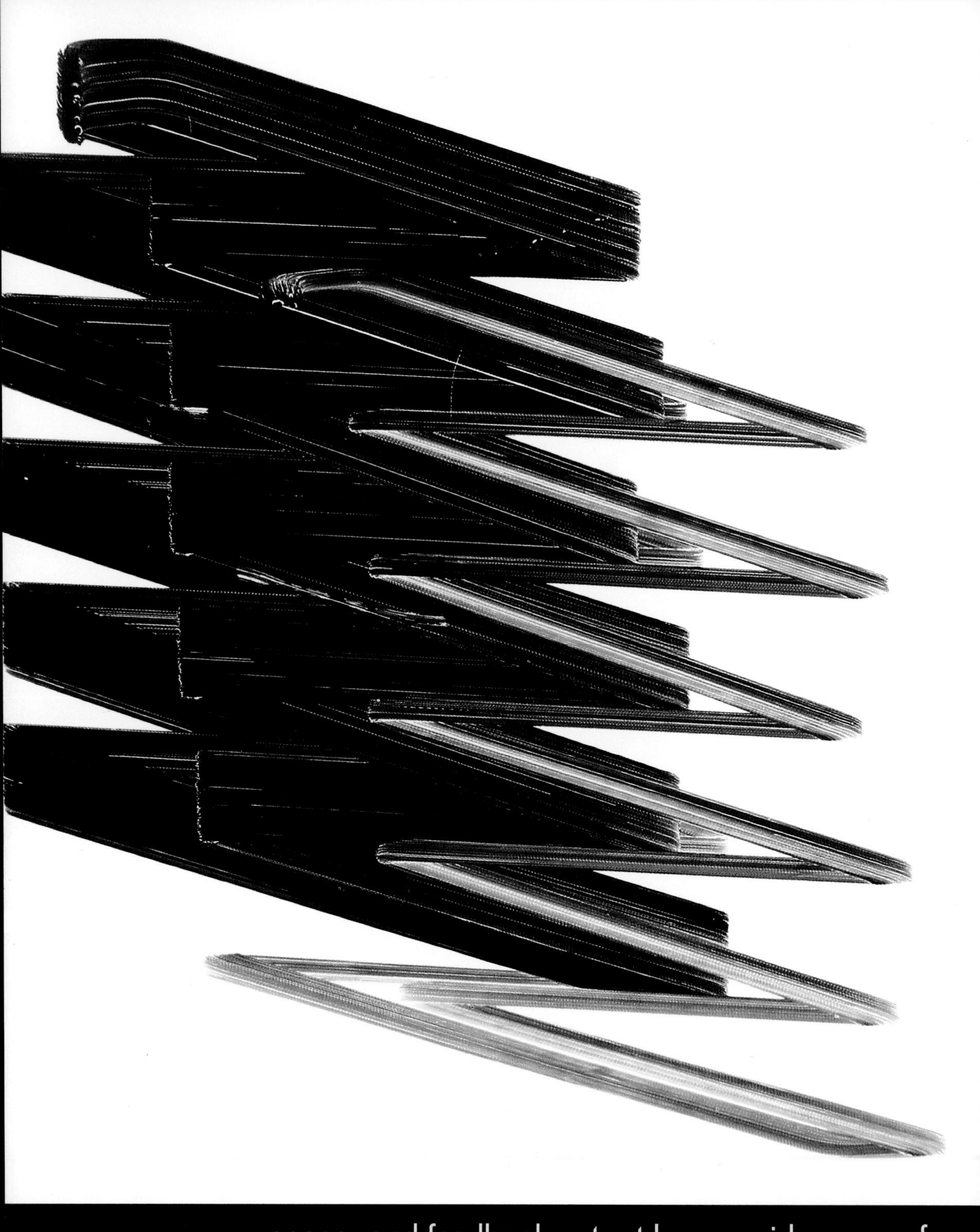

agency and feedback output have a wide range of

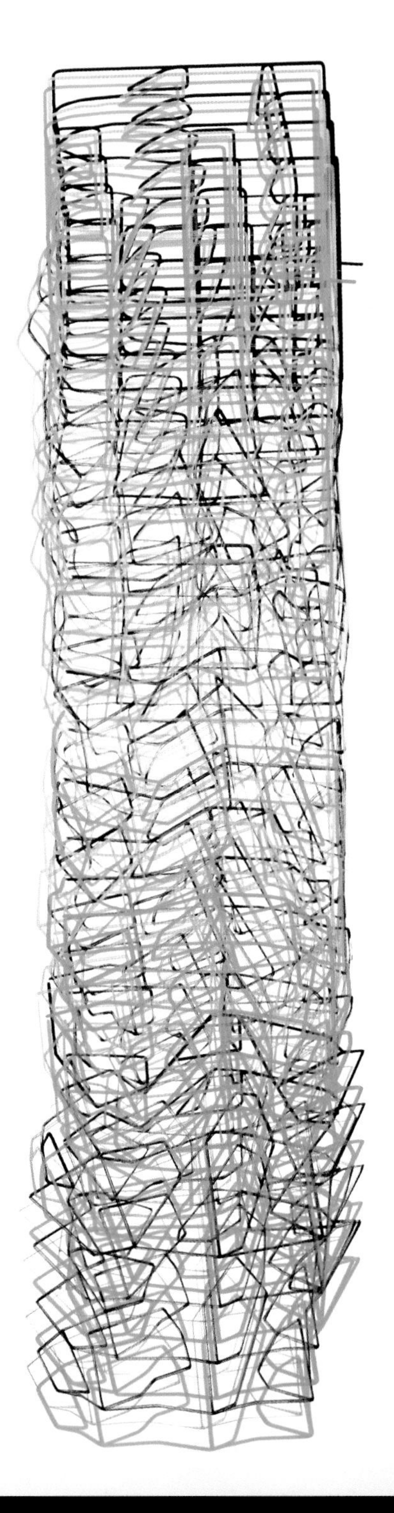

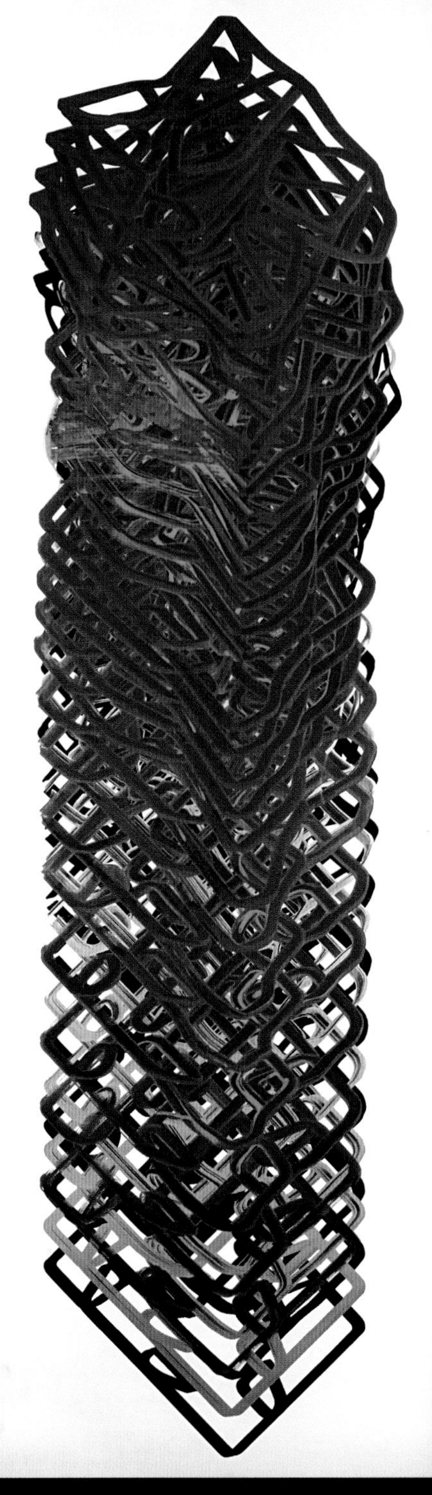

material behaviors, possible resolutions, densities and

2.
19

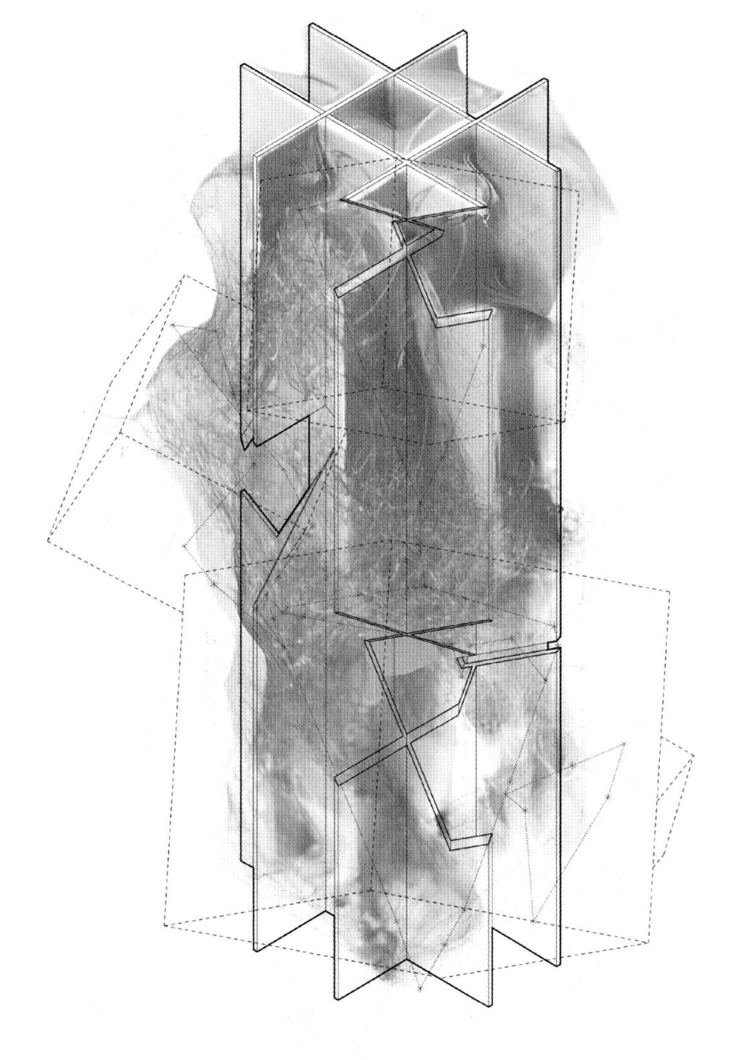

Computational Materials
Scaffolds and Templates
Transitive Materials

2.
05

Material computing explores the potential for developing "materials that compute," and directly linking robotics to material processes, including additive free-form fabrication. Techniques of moldless additive fabrication combine with real-time scanning and embedded sensing to break down distinctions between processes of design and production. The use of reversible material processes introduces new forms of material agency within non-linear formative processes. These workflows operate beyond simple cause and effect to test ideas against materials and materials against ideas. In this improvisational approach robots come to operate from within the material field (rather than acting upon inert materials) via techniques involving scaffolds and templates and transitive materials.

Scaffolds and Templates

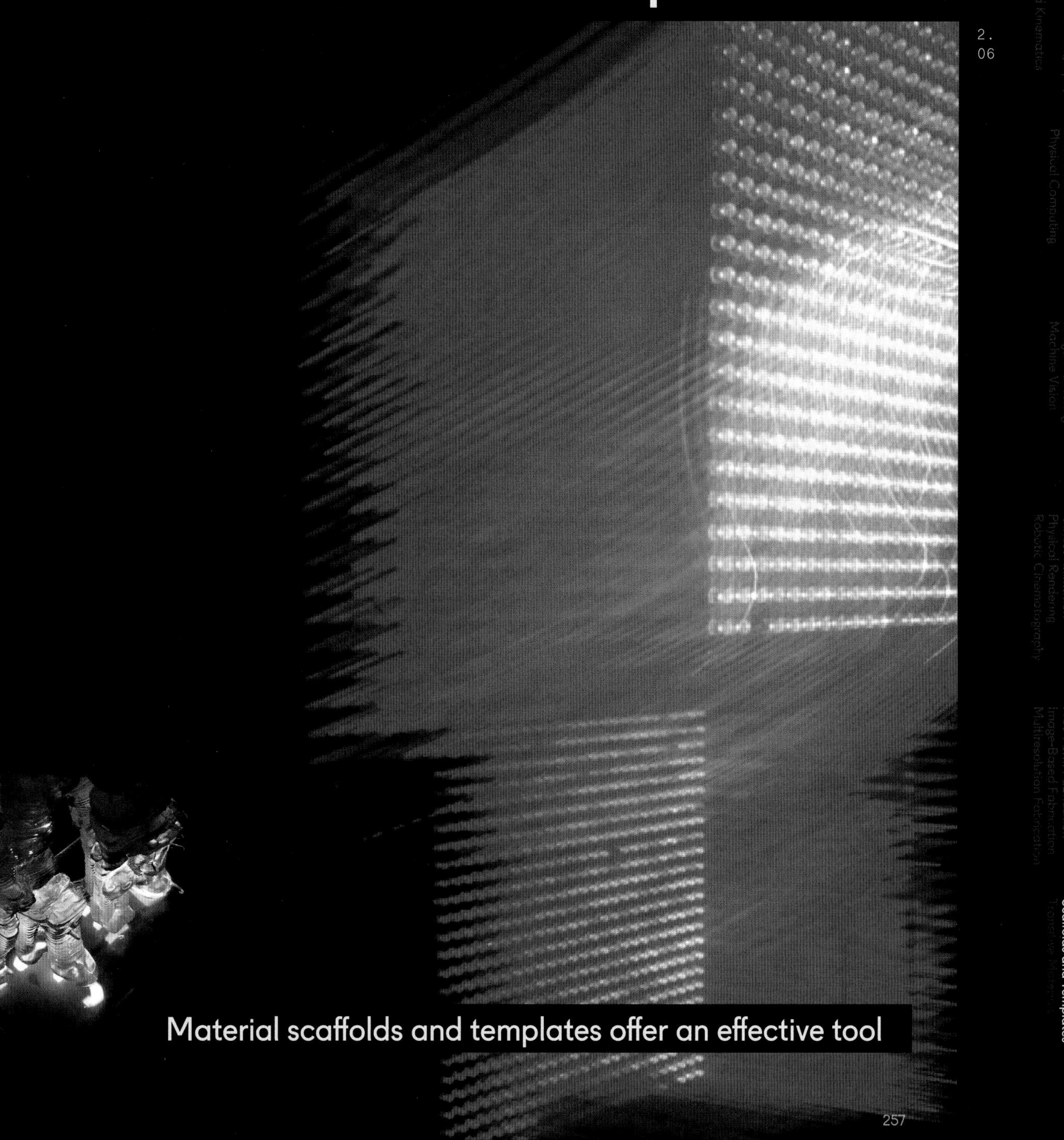

Material scaffolds and templates offer an effective tool

to probe kinetic behavior and structural morphology

of polymers. The use of preforms emphasizes the

pre-visualization between initial conditions and a

dynamic shaping environment.

2.
05

2.
14

2.
11

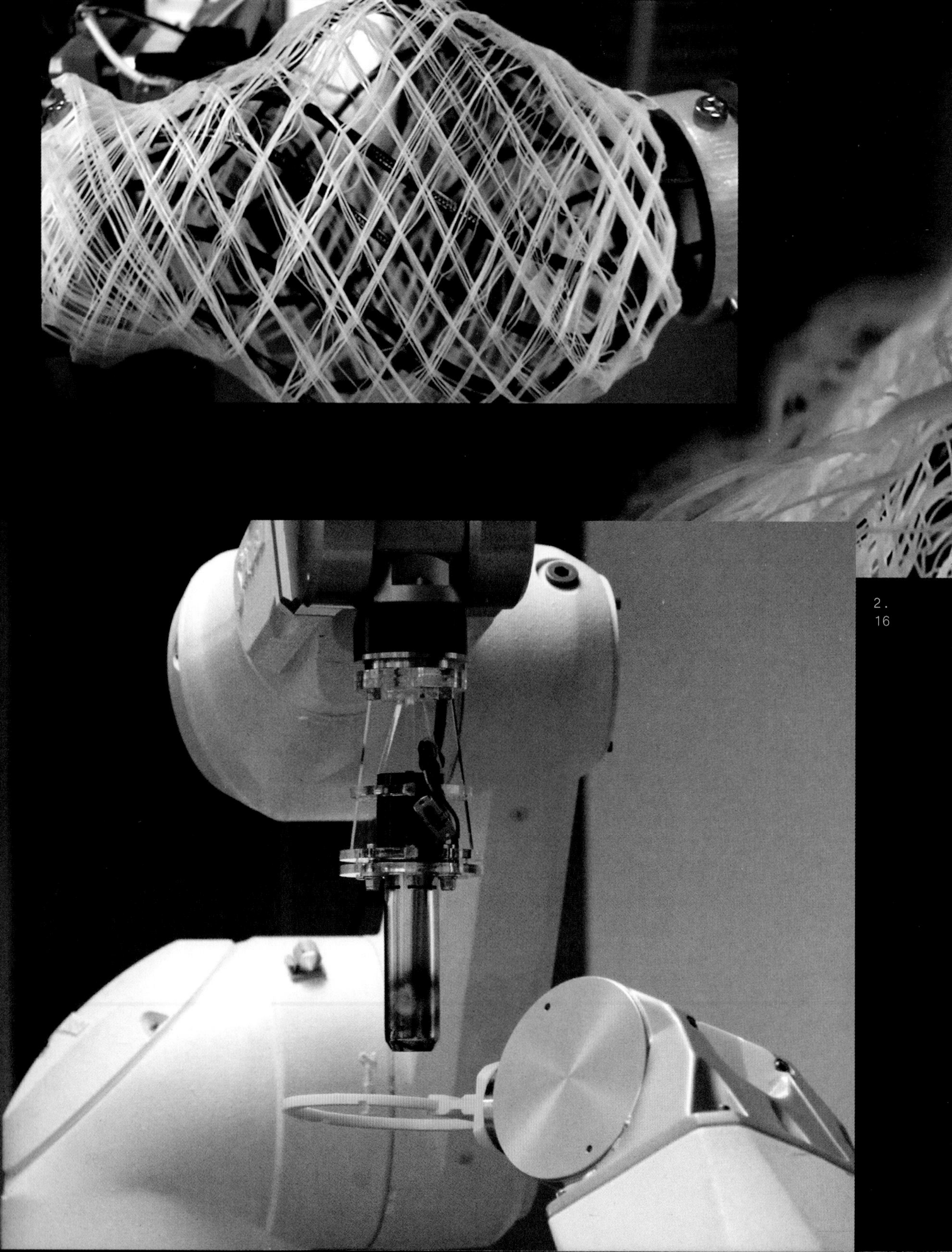

2.
16

2.
13

2.
19

2.
06

Transitive Materials

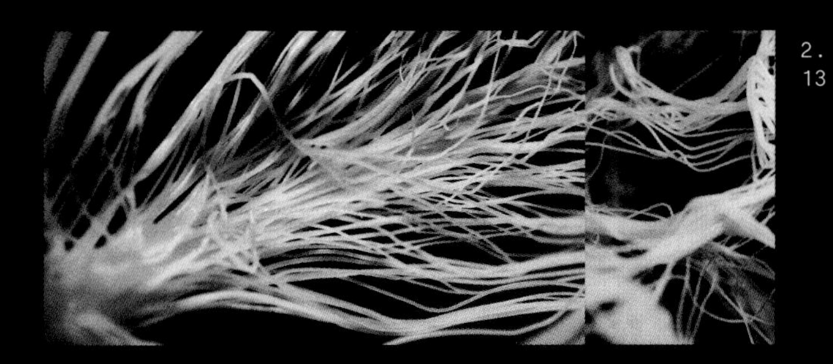

2.13

Smart, shape-changing materials that alter their properties

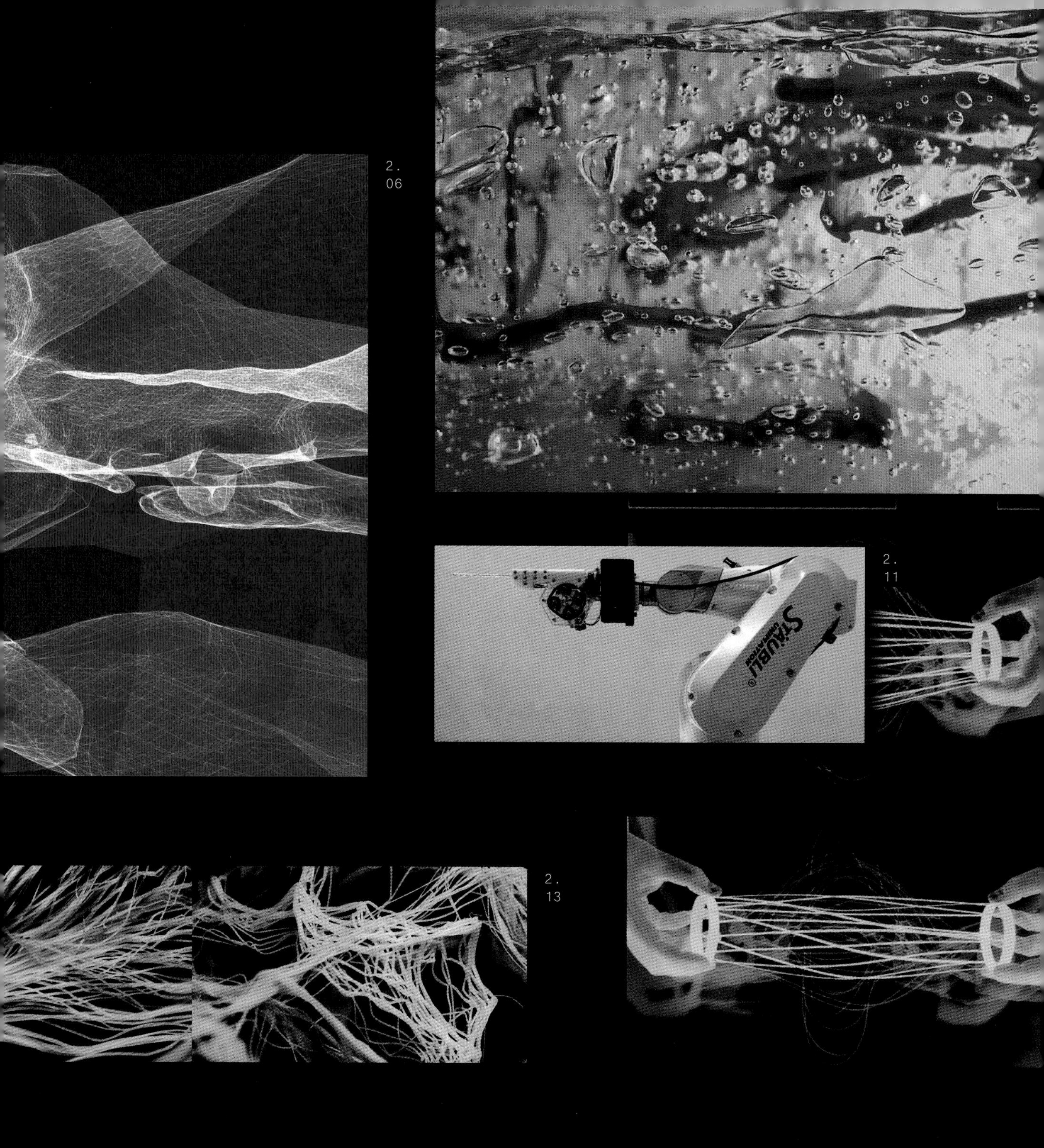

2.
06

2.
11

2.
13

in a controlled fashion offer the possibility of coupling

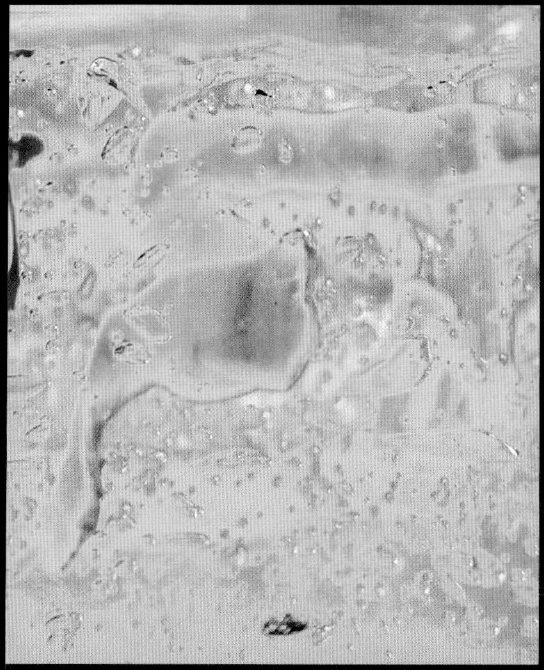

2.
11

2.
13

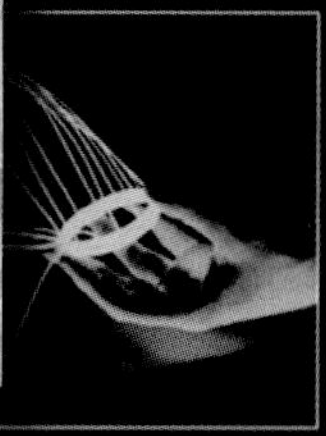

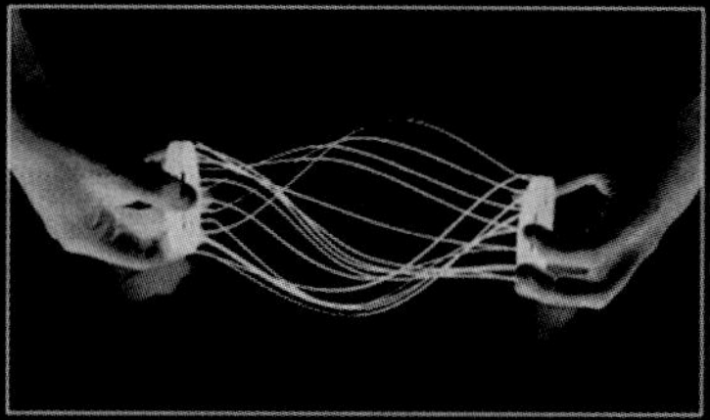

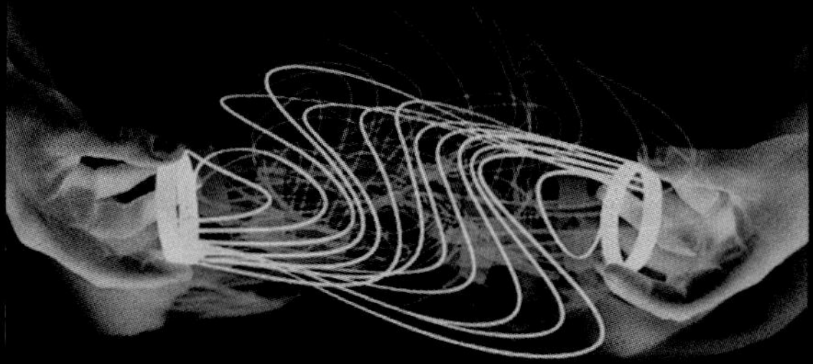

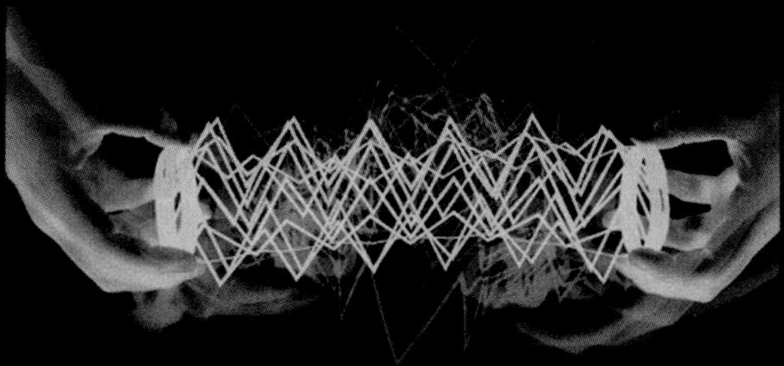

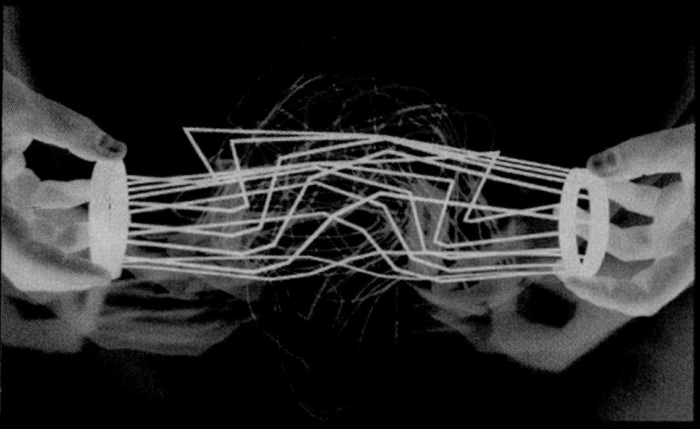

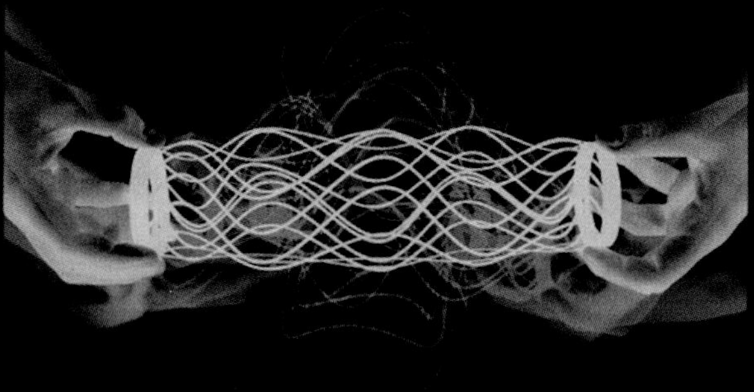

input, output, sensing, processing, and interaction.

The interplay of information and physical processes is

2.
17

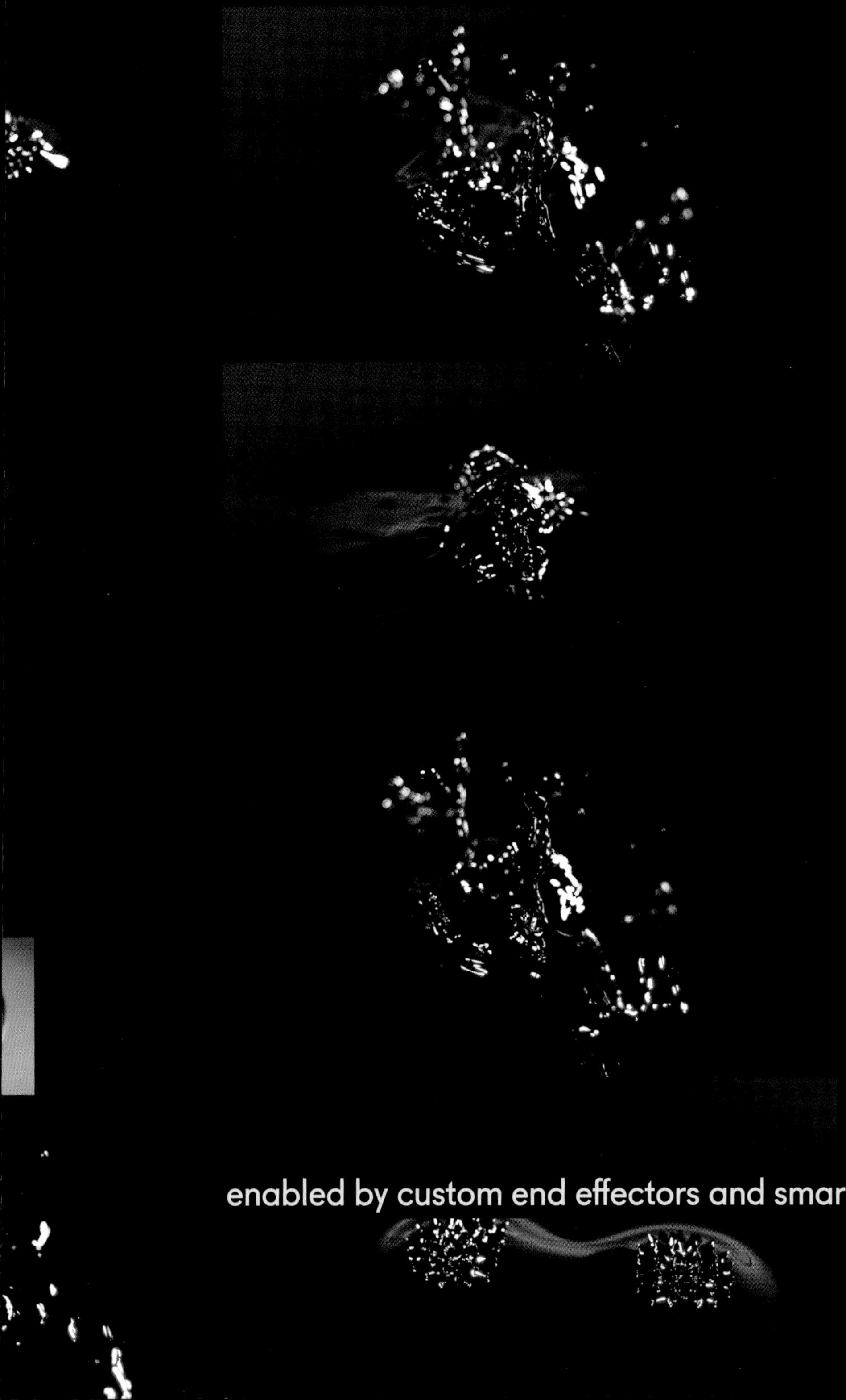

enabled by custom end effectors and smart tooling.

2—
PROJECTS

2.01 B1TS+B0TS

Instructor: Devyn Weiser
TAs: Nicholas Barger, Jeff Halstead, Brian Harms, Jonathon Stahl
Robot House: Nazareth Ekmekjian, Brandon Kruysman, Jonathan Proto, Jake Newsum
Seminar: SCI-Arc 2011–2013
Credits: Viola Ago, Anass Benhachmi, Erin Besler, Kyle Branchesi, Scotty Zane Carroll, Lung Ch Chang, Nan Yen Chen, Talin Ebrahimi, Tom Farmer, Jack Gaumer, Paniz Golkar, Mina Jun, Kirstin Wehrenberg-Klee, Saana Koivusalo, Wenxin Lin, Tyler Martin, Lily Nourmansouri, Marta Piaseczynska, Joseph Ramiro, Laylee Salek, Austin Samson, Klemens Sitzmann, Paul Stoelting, Paul Trussler, Peter Vikar, Jakob Wilhelmstatter, Michael Woodruff, Chao Yan

B1TS+B0TS develops robust processes for synchronous control of multiple six-axis robot arms allied to a range of retooled painting and drawing media, from scanners to industrial airbrushes. Without pretensions to transforming painting as a medium, this enterprise is in a lineage of art practices and artists involved with ideas of the serial, the machine, and the procedural, from Andy Warhol to Sol LeWitt, as well as the contemporary production of such artists as Kerstin Brätsch, Albert Oehlen, and Garth Weiser. It does not belong or aspire to the tradition of "machine art" and "technological automatism," as in this project robots and other mechatronic tools are seen simply as part of expanding the instruments and techniques of representation, specifically drawing and painting, by moving between analog and digital modalities.

For Devyn Weiser, Robot House is part of a larger conceptual apparatus—"the idea that becomes the machine that makes art."[1] New digital/physical workflows embody a series of translations in which well-known aesthetic tropes come to be seen in new ways and conventional representational techniques are redeployed to generate new forms. Reversing hierarchies of object and image, patterns, computer raster screens, motion paths, scanned bodies, and objects are hacked, shredded, and reused. Real-time motion-based imaging is used to break down and reintegrate data streams and challenge the status of image and object.

B1TS+B0TS breaks conventional models of computing and robotics by shifting the frame or focus from the extensive to the intensive. In the paint-based works, air-driven and viscous materials combine with precision and high-resolution motion control to support speculation on authorship, conventions of representation, new forms of composition, and new geometries. With a variability of motion ranging from the imperceptibly slow to the invisibly fast and the repetitive, this body of work gives a different sense of speed and space. The encumbrance of the instrument creates obstacles to natural movements associated with painting.

At the other extreme, works encode complex feedback loops between programmed and un-programmed motion sequences, basic shapes, and paint. For example, in "Feed Forward," two cameras record the drawing of nested circles using instructions that exchange viewpoints and reverse motion paths. This and other works demonstrate the idea that inputs do not equal outputs and that paradoxically, as Bruno Latour has observed, "where there is the most artifice and complete manufacture of the image is where the most unexpected and surprising outcomes occur."[2] Compared to the naïve material realism of elaborate software workflows that go directly from pixel to plot, 3D print or other output in a closed and largely pictorial mode, B1TS+B0TS argues for a new relation to the real. Just as painting remains the most analog form, this physicality is seen to offer channels for reconsidering digitality via superposition and non-correlation of media.

1—Sol LeWitt, "Paragraphs on Conceptual Art," Artforum *(June, 1967).*
2—Bruno Latour, "Visualization and Cognition: Drawing Things Together," Knowledge and Society Studies in the Sociology of Culture Past and Present, *6 (1986), 1–40.*

39, 40, 41, 42

134

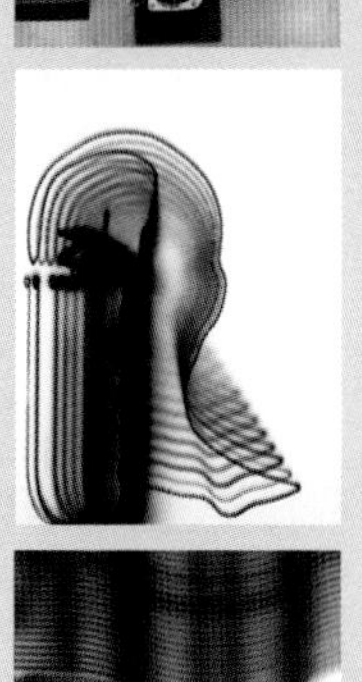
70, 173

39, 41, 42

39, 41, 42
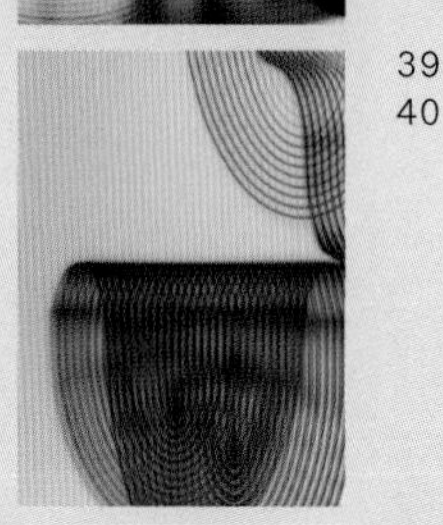
39, 40
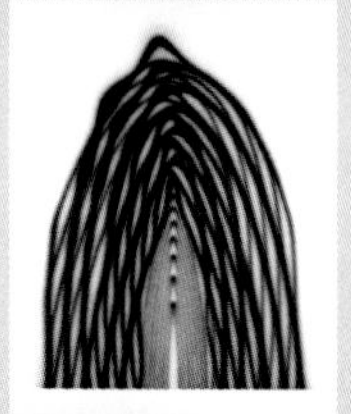
70, 173
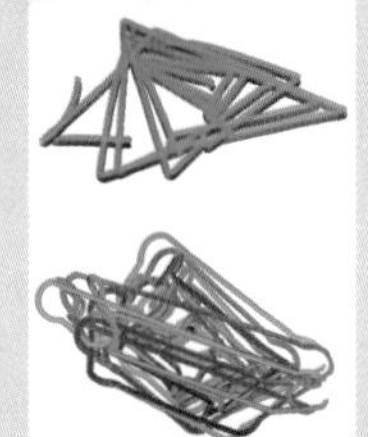
70, 173
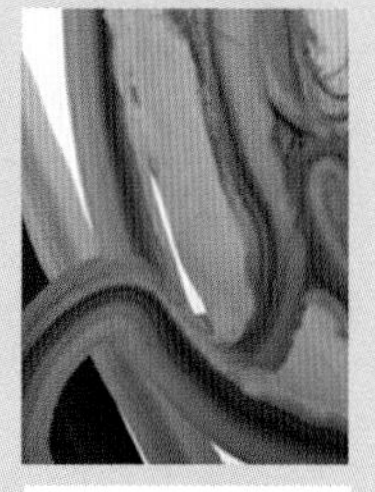
134

64

63, 64

2.02 SYNCHRONOUS OBJECTIVES

Thesis Advisors: Peter Testa, Devyn Weiser
SCI-Arc Graduate Thesis 2011
Credits: Curime Batliner, Brandon Kruysman, Jonathan Proto

Synchronous Objectives invents new control models for multi-robot collaboration, including motion path generation, end effector integration, and synchronization of multiple robots in space. The thesis engages Robot House as a next-generation digital design platform by moving away from pure computational 3D modeling towards a model where the synchronization of movement and forces allows for designing in real-time. Seventeen thought experiments or "takes" exploit the inherent complexities in contemporary design protocols and argue for a flexible and reconfigurable apparatus to speculatively prototype design ideas.

A significant contribution of this project is the development of esperant.0, a customizable control model for collaborative robotics. As a software plug-in to Autodesk Maya, esperant.0 supports the generation of g-code for the movement control of Stäubli robots while providing commonly used animation techniques. ¡Charla! written in Python and integrated within esperant.0, supports a higher level of control and precision in the synchronization of multiple Stäubli industrial robot arms. Initially implemented through low-level electronics, ¡Charla! gives "voice" to the autonomous robot arms within Robot House. The system tracks the position of multiple objects, machines, and tools in space. Communication between robots in the form of basic inputs and outputs not only helps avoid collisions, but also gives designers an accessible route to end-of-arm tool integration.

Synchronous Objectives shows the potential of allowing designers to program motion in Autodesk Maya and integrating this familiar and complex toolset into the Robot House workflow. The keyframe approach to the use of industrial robots creates a flexible platform that allows designers to animate the physical world and provides precise control over six-axis industrial robot arms.

41, 73, 213

41, 75, 99, 157, 158

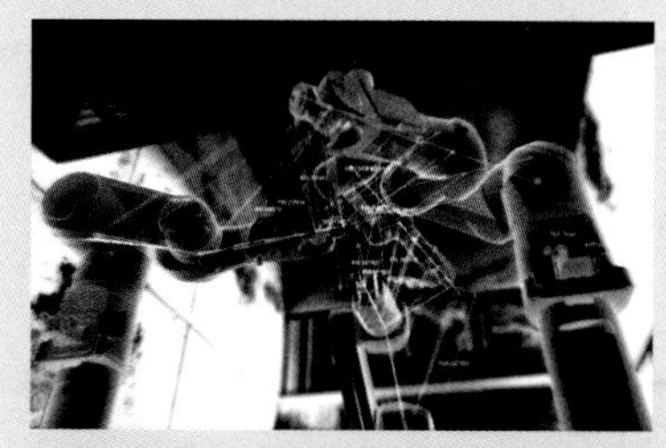

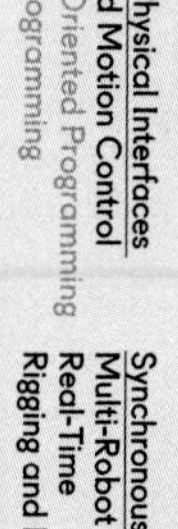

118, 119, 227

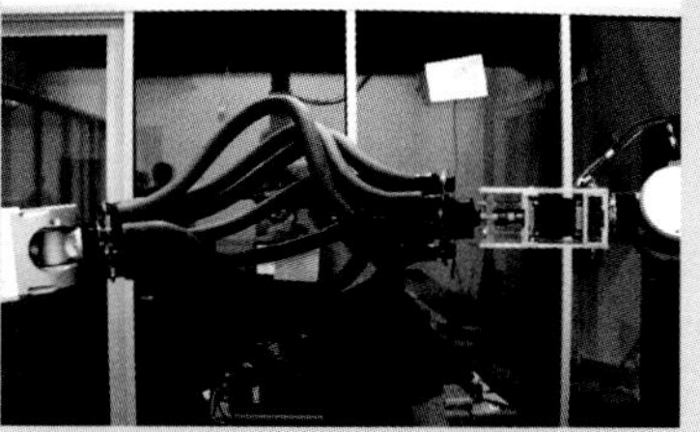

75, 135, 136, 137

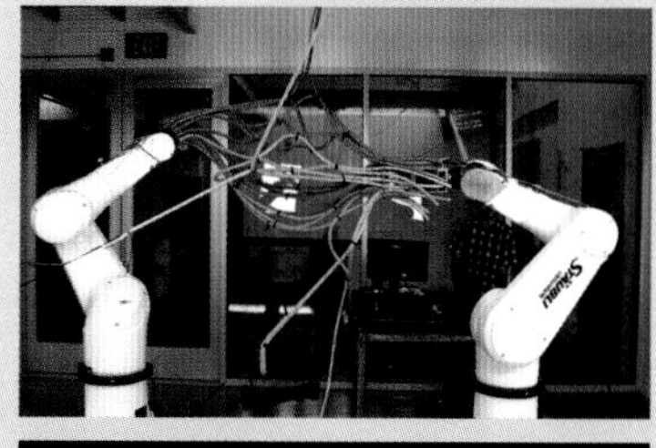

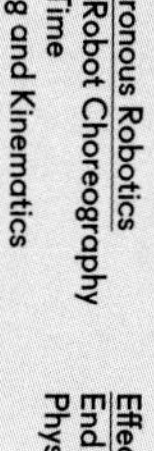

83

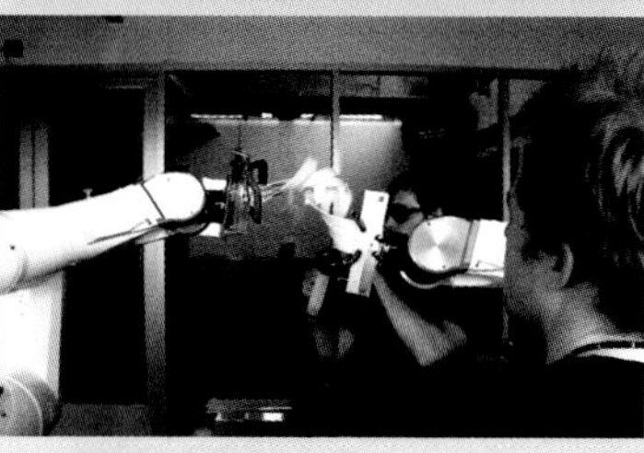

83, 157

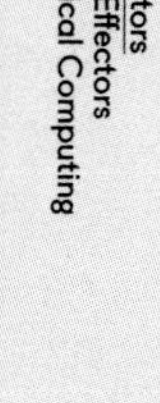

100, 101

208, 209, 210

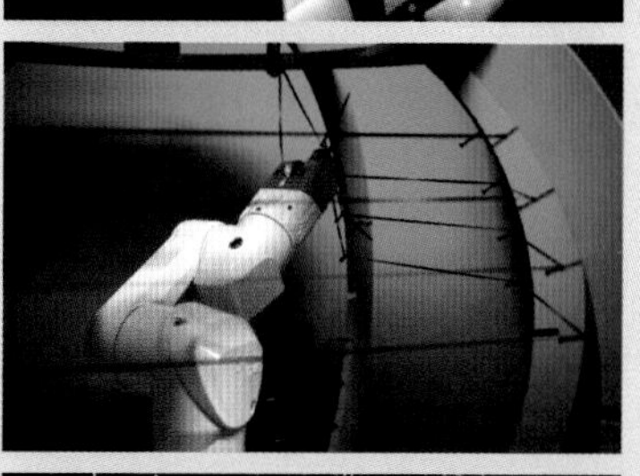

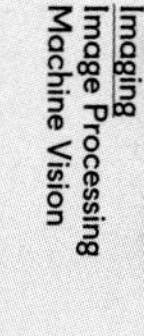

41, 208, 209, 210

208, 209, 210

Fictioning
Object Animation
Physical Rendering
Robotic Cinematography

41, 206

41

Augmented Fabrication
Free-Form Fabrication
Image-Based Fabrication
Multiresolution Fabrication

41, 208

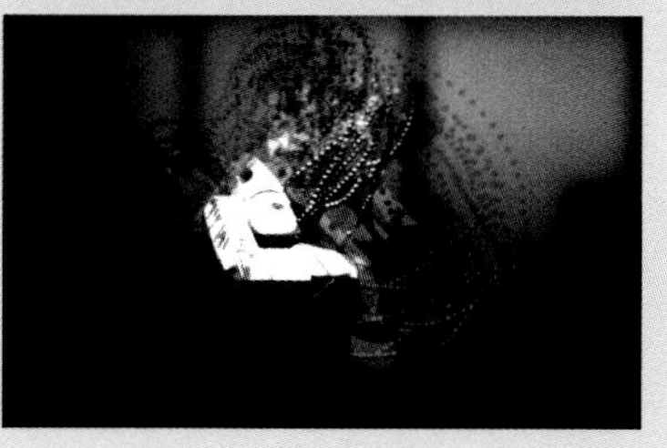

41, 206

Computational Materials
Scaffolds and Templates
Transitive Materials

2.03 sPHYSICAL

42, 120, 159

Instructor: Peter Testa
AT: Jonathon Stahl
Robot House: Nazareth Ekmekjian, Brandon Kruysman, Jonathan Proto
Studio: SCI-Arc 2012
Credits: Erin Besler, Eugene Kosgoron, Siim Tuksam, Peter Vikar

121

sPhysical, one of the earliest projects realized in Robot House, focuses on the complex exchanges and feedback across the digital/physical interface. As the project team notes, in this work material agency is expressed through the conceptualization of "rigging matter"—the idea that dynamic material processes might act as an external stimulus or control model for robotic motion. By crosslinking and overlapping digital and physical processes, sPhysical playfully exploits paradox and slippage between highly precise robot systems allied to indeterminate material processes. In this way the non-correspondence between geometry and matter is foregrounded and exploited. Unlike industrial robot cells, the six relatively small-scale robot arms of Robot House allow designers to work inside the movement space and subvert the automated logic associated with large, heavy-payload robots. Indeed, the interplay of animation, cinematography, and fabrication using multiple small-scale robot systems working in close proximity and in collaboration with human designers anticipates developments in the field of robotic manufacturing and the future construction industry.

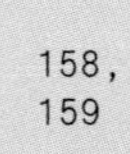

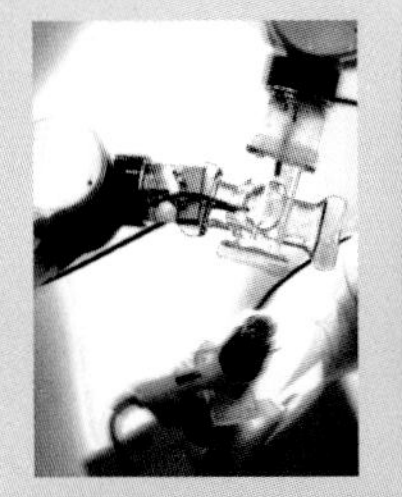

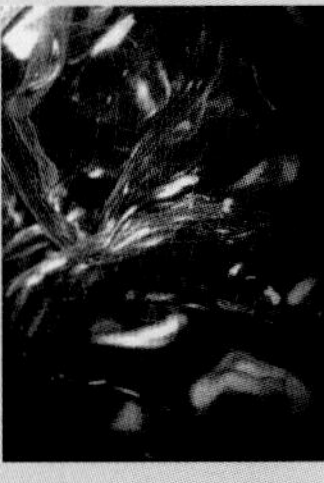

83

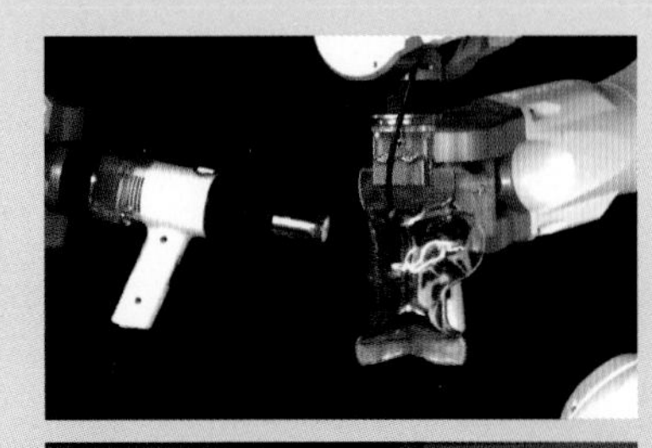

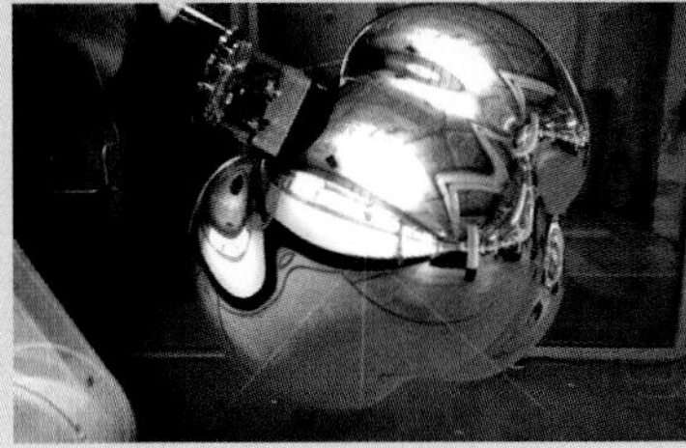

83

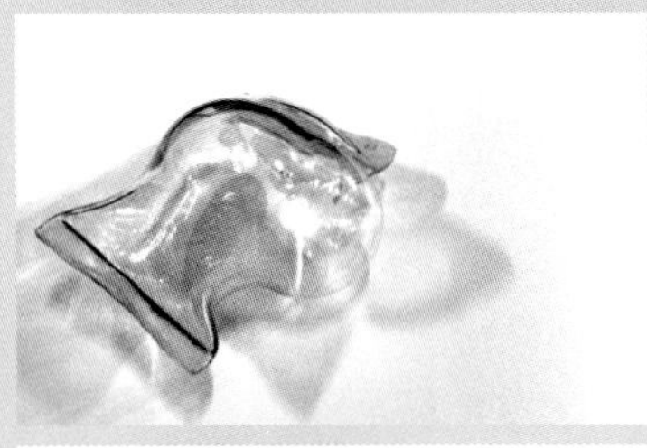

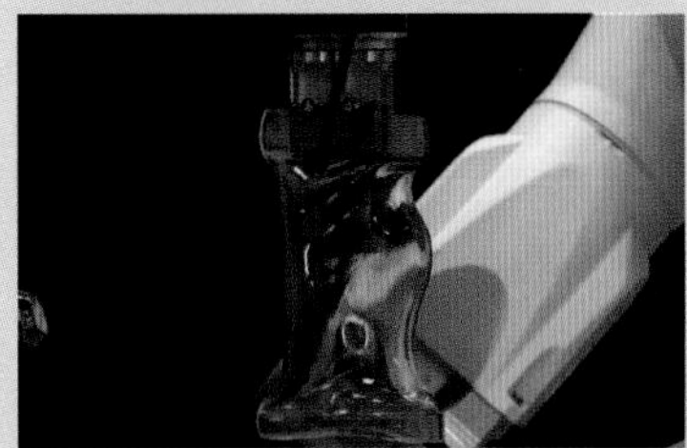

83

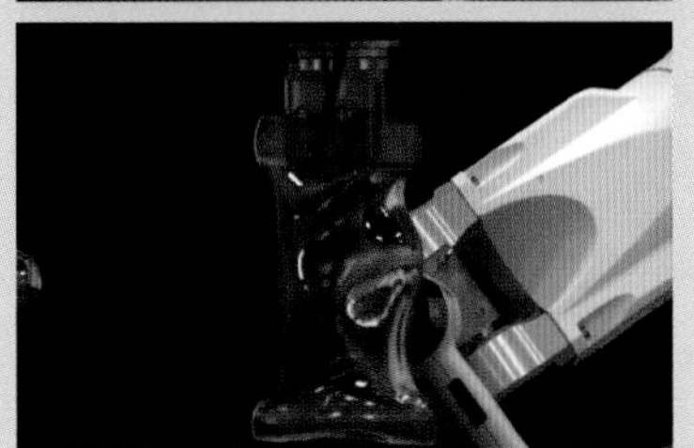

83

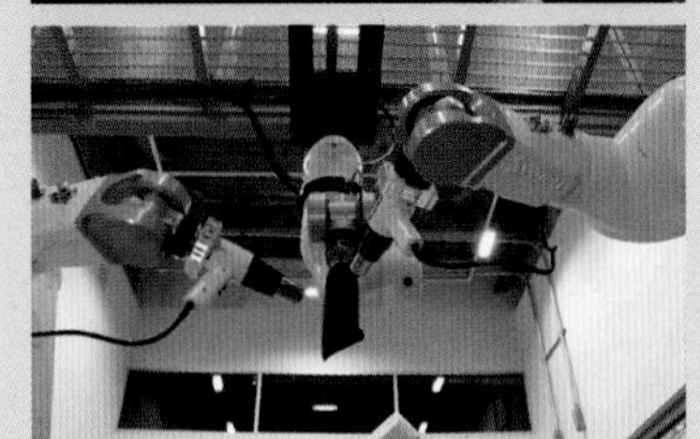

156

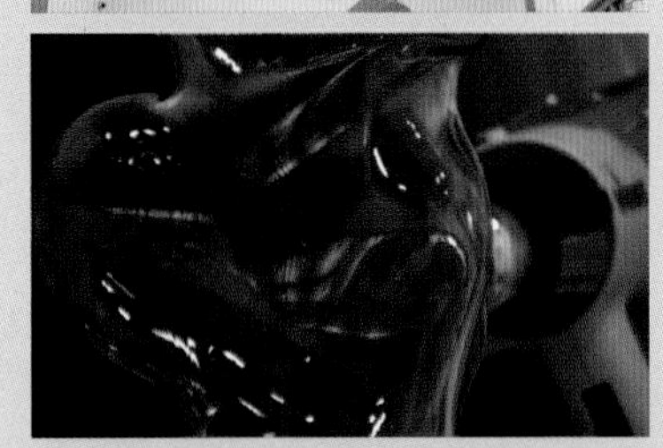

158, 159

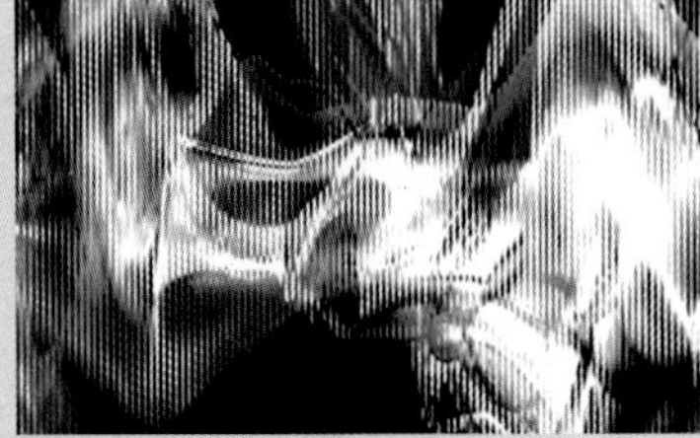

2.04 APPROXYMOTION

Instructor: Peter Testa
AT: Jonathon Stahl
Robot House: Nazareth Ekmekjian, Brandon Kruysman, Jonathan Proto
Studio: SCI-Arc 2013
Credits: Peter Vikar

Approxymotion, a motion-based forming protocol,enables computational geometry to take form in physical space.

Traditionally, in architecture forms are transferred from paper or virtual space to building through fixed shaped molds or as the assembly of elements. Approxymotion shifts these translational protocols by effectively setting the mold in motion, while maintaining the parametrics inherited from a digital model. Sequential and controlled corner-cutting algorithms and processes that play a key role in Computer Aided Geometric Design (CAGD) are combined with robotic motion such that each step of the system consists of a convex combination. The result is a motion form that computes between the initial motion input, the build geometry, and its material properties. The nested "corner-cutting" system, from rough to smooth layers, displays a gradient condition—from the accuracy of robotic motion control to the averaging behavior of the elastic net. Issues of fidelity and misregistrations arising from translational discrepancies between digital and physical modalities represent new design protocols. In this way Approxymotion demonstrates the potential for synchronous robotics to advance new approaches to computational geometry and form making.

42, 258

42, 173, 179

Digital/Physical Interfaces
Animated Motion Control
Object-Oriented Programming
Visual Programming

42, 77, 78, 173

179

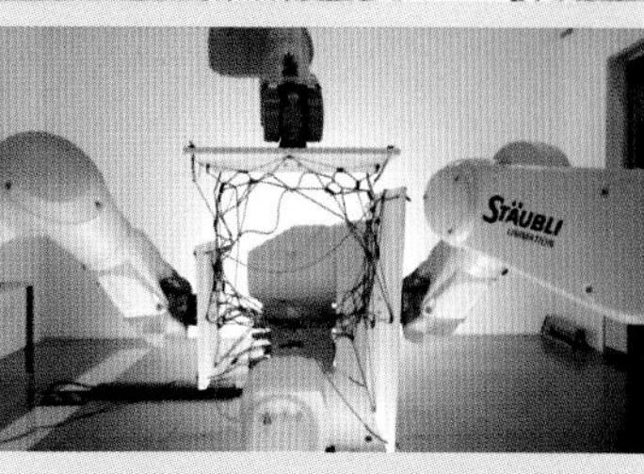

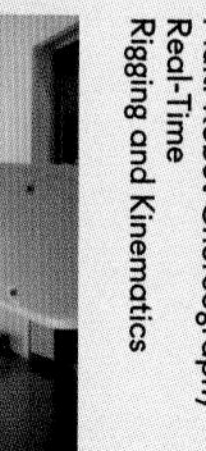

77

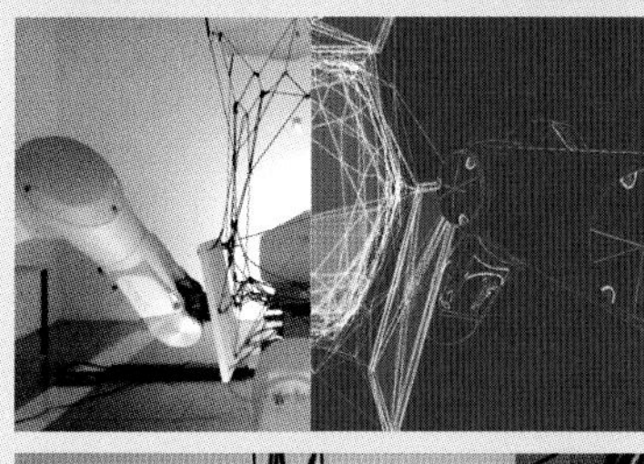

231

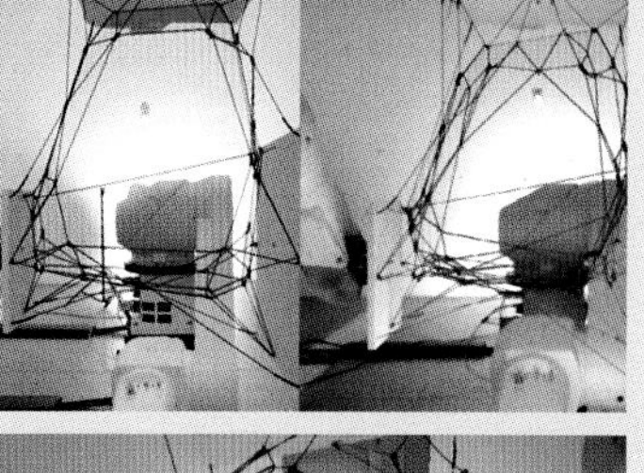

Effectors
End Effectors
Physical Computing

102, 103

179

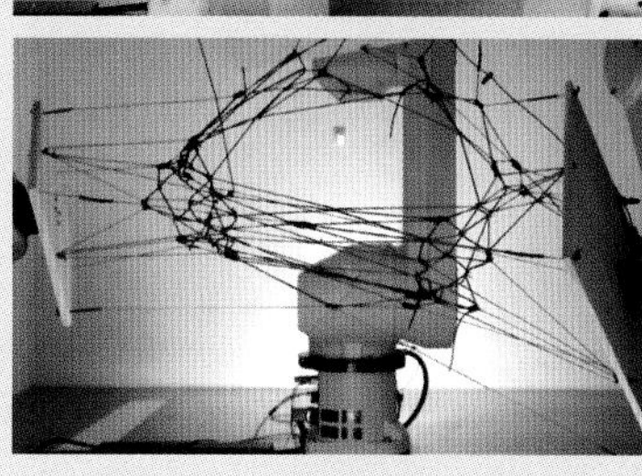

Imaging
Image Processing
Machine Vision

77

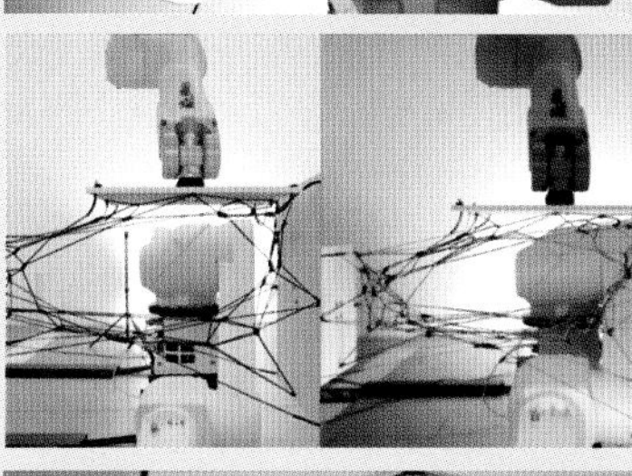

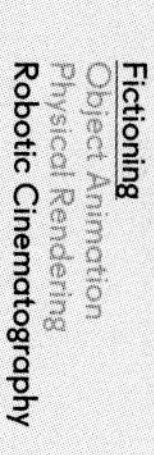

Augmented Fabrication
Free-Form Fabrication
Image-Based Fabrication
Multiresolution Fabrication

2.05 GLUSION

Thesis Advisors: Peter Testa, Devyn Weiser
Robot House: Nazareth Ekmekjian, Brandon Kruysman, Jonathon Proto SCI-Arc Undergraduate Thesis 2013
Credits: William Hu, Haleh Olfati, Jasmine Park

Glusion exemplifies a non-standard aesthetics in which design is controlled via protocols that are developed empirically. Most significantly, the work inverts the relationship between material form and geometry, as the form is the outcome of programmed and unprogrammed instrumentation between robotic motion and material deposition rather than geometry. In this process, other notations, toolpaths, templates, and scaffolds supersede drawings in defining form.

Glusion uses synchronous robotics, rheological materials (materials that can change their physical state very quickly in response to a stimulus), and motion-based shaping logics to develop these design and fabrication protocols. This project may be defined in relation to both material behavior and robotic motion in a morphological process that can vary its form from a single strand to a solid mass. Rheological material, hot melt glue, is broken down into its essential properties through manipulation of density and layering in relation to gravity, as well as centripetal and centrifugal motion using dynamic scaffolds. A recursive motion path produces a seemingly limitless range of material gradients, densities, and textures. Parameters such as reach, speed, and distance further define this dynamic shaping environment with an interest in complex patterning.

The incorporation of secondary fiber elements and nested figures allows for the creation of complex surface topologies. Moving from homogeneous materials to multi-materials and from single- to multi-stepped processes shifts the range of the work towards the complexity and scale of architectural elements and layered enclosures. Such layered and multidimensional shaping logics combining hard and soft elements extend to the use of inflatable forms and bulbous subcutaneous scaffolds that form convex surfaces, gradient structures, and apertures. Ultimately the mandrel or formwork gives way to automorphism in which strands stack and fuse. A catalog of these material behaviors offers the basis for controlled patterning, structure, and form.

227

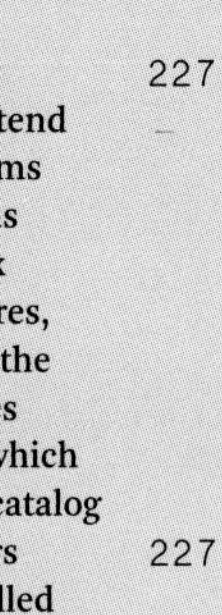

254, 255
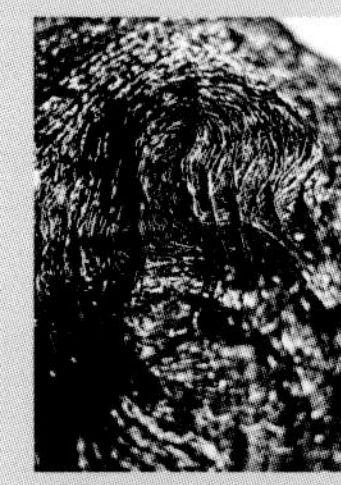
227

44, 45, 87, 180
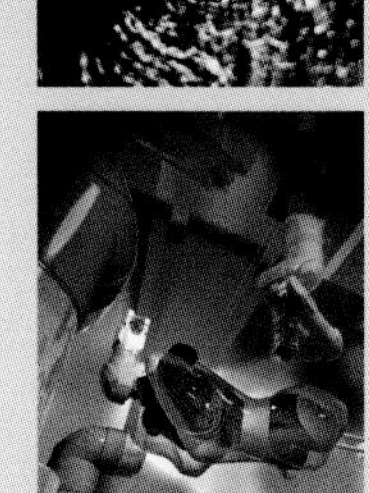
227
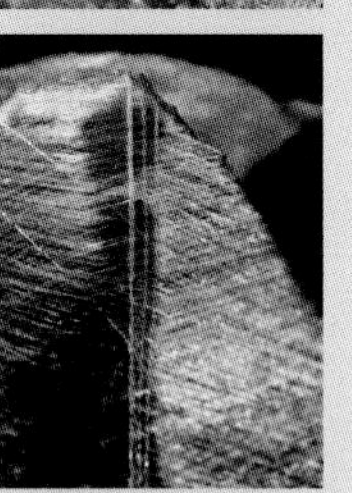
262, 263

86

122, 123, 226

180, 226

230, 231
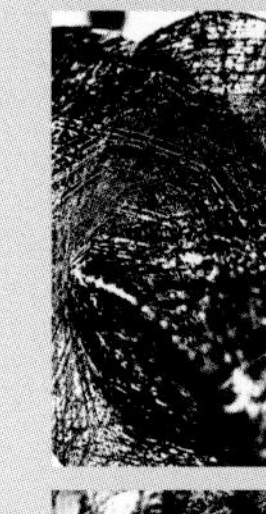
230, 231
258, 259
230, 231

139

230, 231

230, 231

2.06 PHANTOM GEOMETRY

Thesis Advisors: Peter Testa, Devyn Weiser
Robot House: Nazareth Ekmekjian, Brandon Kruysman, Jonathan Proto
SCI-Arc Graduate Thesis 2012, Gehry Thesis Prize
Credits: Kyle von Hasseln, Liz von Hasseln

Beginning with this project, a number of innovations have been realized in Robot House that challenge the limitations of current methods for deposition-based 3D printing that use only the XYZ positioning space. In addition to the implementation of six-axis robots, Phantom Geometry creates a series of non-linear workflows, interactive software interfaces, end-of-arm tools, material technologies, and shaping logics that advance over established protocols of digital fabrication and 3D printing.

Phantom Geometry is a full-scale dual robot system that uses ultraviolet light from a modified digital light-processing (DLP) projector to continuously and selectively cure resin until streaming data takes physical shape. The real-time workflow challenges conventional techniques of representation and production methodology. The process is non-linear and interruptible, and it does not rely on periodic flattening to 2D. As its name implies, the visual assembly of data is drawn in physical space at full scale, so it occupies augmented space but is not yet materially incarnated—resident data can be used to generate a photographic artifact, or to create material form through the selective polymerization of proximal photoresponsive resin.

Phantom Geometry investigates a design paradigm centered on the material reification of light: light is the medium for data in this system. This paradigm questions the supremacy of the 3D digital model, and the static flattening and stacking logics inherent to typical fabrication workflows. Innovations in material processes and deposition techniques are supported by experimental image capture and processing that does not require a 3D digital model. Robot House allows for the careful collection and display of these types of information and material processes, including motion-based photography and dynamic layer imaging the designers refer to as "projected tomoscopy."

Using a purpose-built digital/physical interface developed in Touch Designer, this system of fabrication relies upon native, real-time feedback and feedforward mechanisms. The light being transmitted from the projector is accessible in real-time, and geometry may be modified during production. The image can be from any local or remote source. Fidelity to the original image or form is also open to interpretation and modification. Significantly, any image manipulation that can be performed has direct physical consequences. This new digital/physical workflow opens the possibility for linking scripting and generative digital design techniques to material form.

From tailored organic resin chemistry allowing open processing with UV light to hacking a DLP projector and rescripting off-the-shelf animation software for motion control of industrial robot arms, Phantom Geometry brings together a vast array of techniques and technologies in a novel workflow. In this demonstration project a large networked object is produced by moving a robotically actuated soft silicone resin vat within the intersecting work spheres of the robots allowing the object to change direction and merge with neighboring forms.

Phantom Geometry is part of a shift in architectural thinking towards the procedural, the generative, and variable material processes over the parametric. With an interest in performance, interactive real-time affects are as significant as the artifacts. Rather than system efficiency, performance is concerned with producing new perceptions and modes of visualizing new classes of objects that challenge conventional techniques of representation in architectural production. Built up from data structures, the image is no longer synonymous with its visual appearance—it has become a more complex informational and material object.

64, 212

45, 84, 85

Digital/Physical Interfaces
Animated Motion Control
Object-Oriented Programming
Visual Programming

43, 172, 228

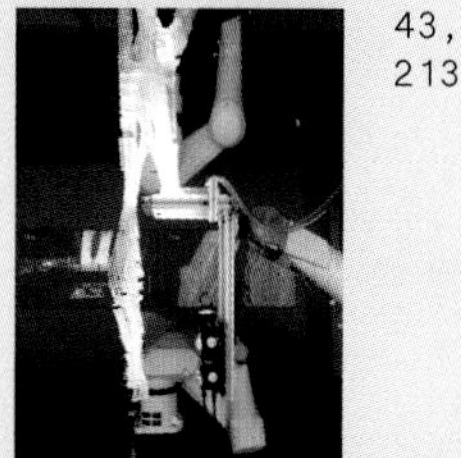

43, 213

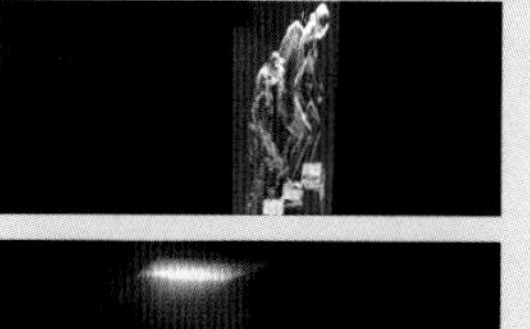

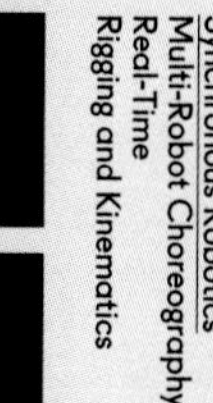

65, 225, 238

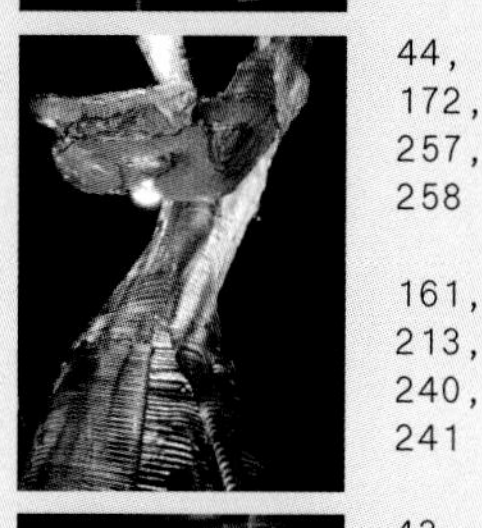

44, 172, 257, 258

161, 213, 240, 241

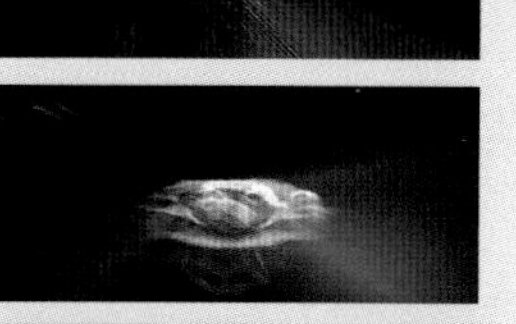

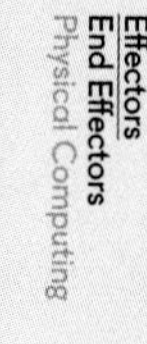

230

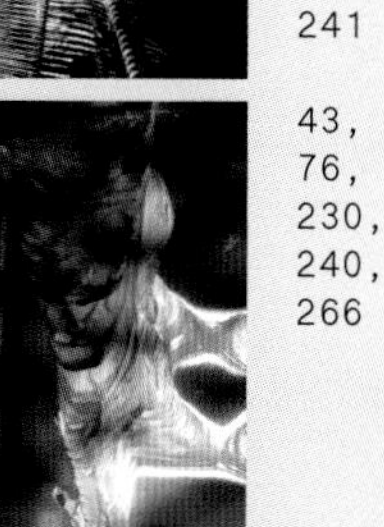

43, 76, 230, 240, 266

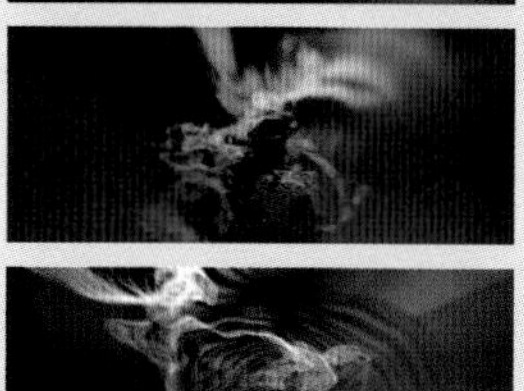

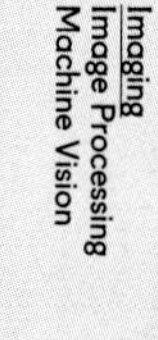

237, 238, 245

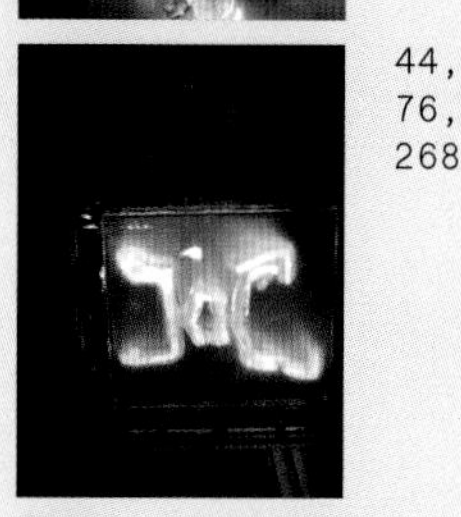

44, 76, 268

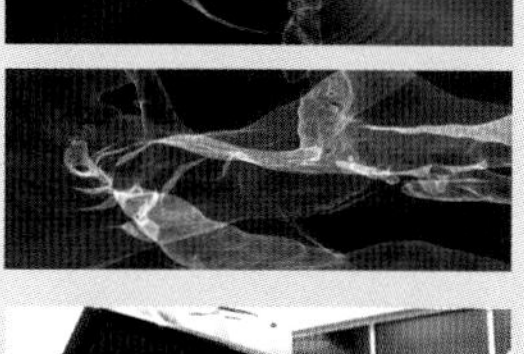

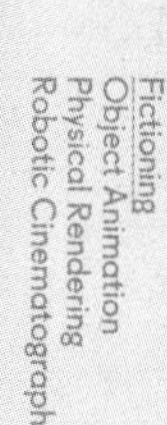

237, 238, 245

121, 178, 179

138, 190

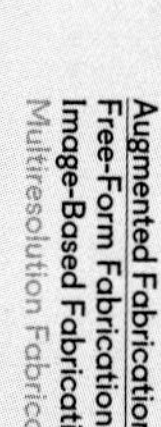

230

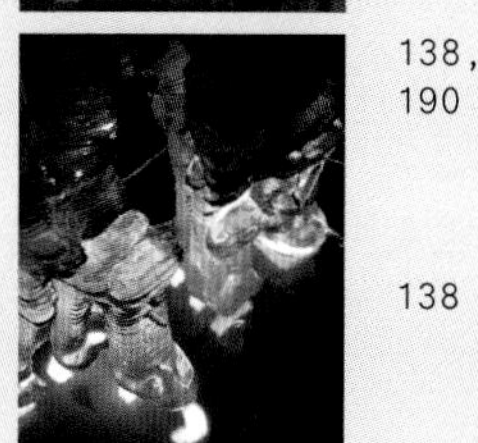

138, 190

138

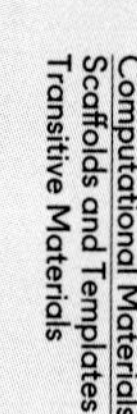

2.07 HOT NETWORKS

Instructors: Brandon Kruysman, Jonathan Proto
Workshop: SCI-Arc 2013

Hot Networks is original in exploiting cinematic techniques and advanced robotic manufacturing protocols as a mode of material production. This approach shifts the role of robotics away from processes largely focused on geometric rationalization and into the sphere of visualization and idea creation. A prototype articulates a workflow in which simulation and material studies operate in parallel.

Five industrial robot arms, with different tools and tasks, act as one apparatus. Each robot performs a separate task; one filming the fabrication sequence, one picking components, one airbrushing, one holding the work-surface, and one thermoforming. Ideas of representation are embedded into the sequence, as well as material behavior and synchronous motion and tooling. The project used heat as a way to transform plastic components in the form of piles and stacks, and also used paint as an additional process within the robotic sequence to get various levels of transparency.

The programming of the robots is designed so that their tasks are offset (meaning that when one robot moves to get another piece of material, two others work together to paint the pieces that are placed). The sequence is also designed so that the work surface is dynamic, where it has the ability to move into neighboring robots' work spheres for collaboration, while having an extremely accurate way of positioning where the plastic pieces are in space. Many calibration tests were performed with the heating sequence that associated timing with formal implications. This allowed the objects to have varied material and formal characteristics. Variation in form was a result of the timing and coordination of robots. In the Chandelier prototype, simulation and material studies were carried out in parallel, resulting in a project that extends beyond the images or the physical prototype itself.

Hot Networks was created using a custom plug-in for Autodesk Maya, esperant.0 (written in Python), to translate animated character rigs to motion paths for Stäubli six-axis robot arms. An additional Python component, ¡Charla! manages intra-robot exchange.

44, 123

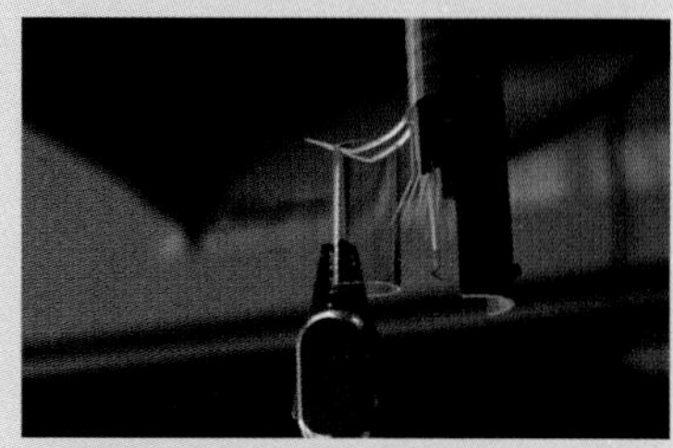

88, 174

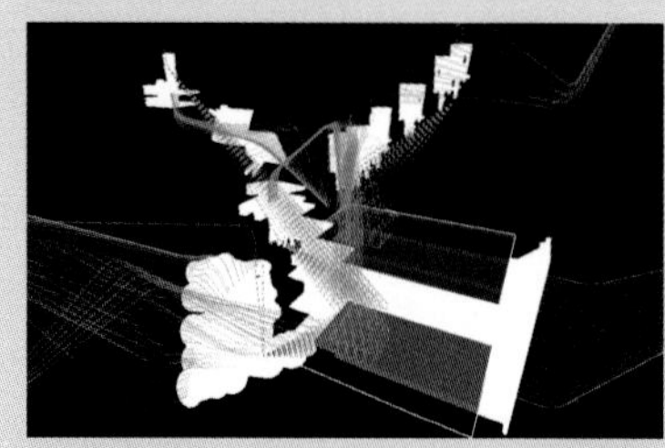

44, 123

44, 123, 232

44, 123

44

160, 161, 174, 181, 214, 260

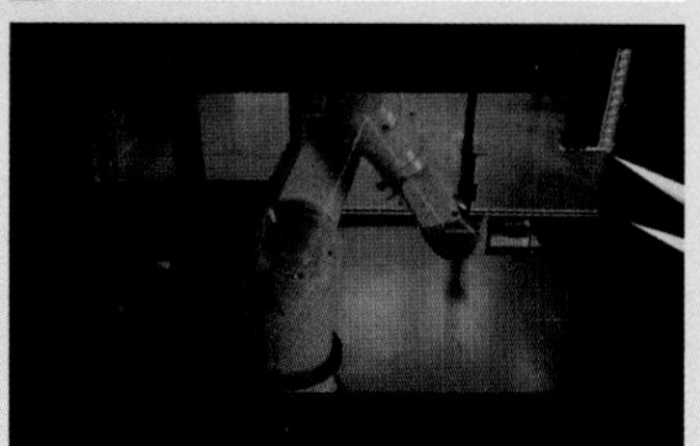

44

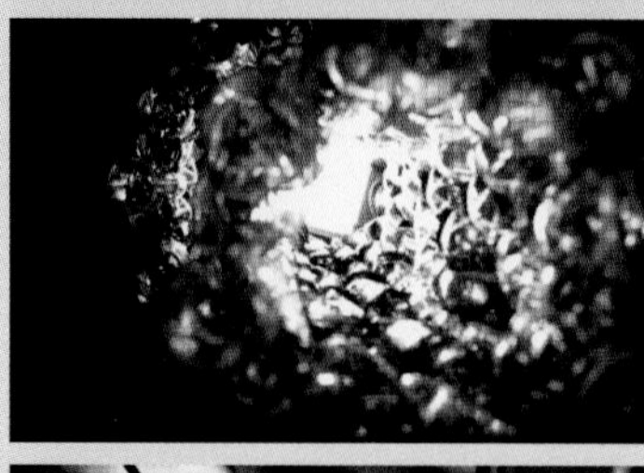

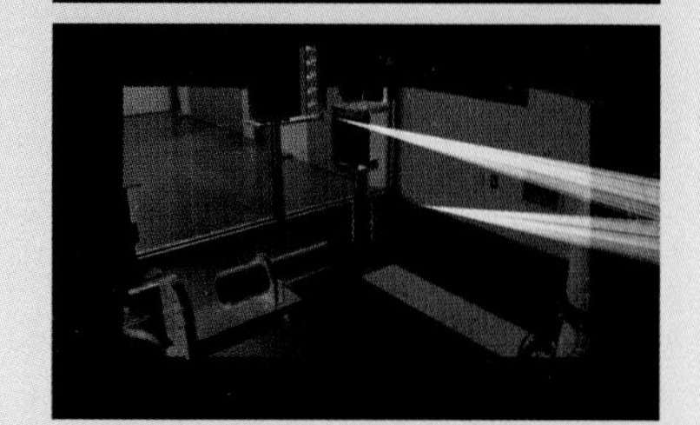

44

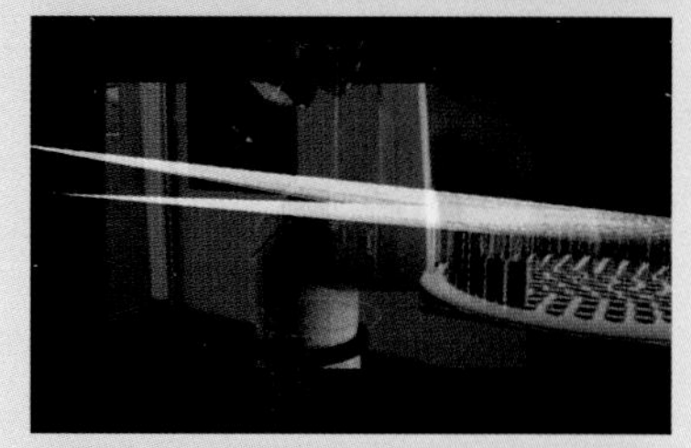

44

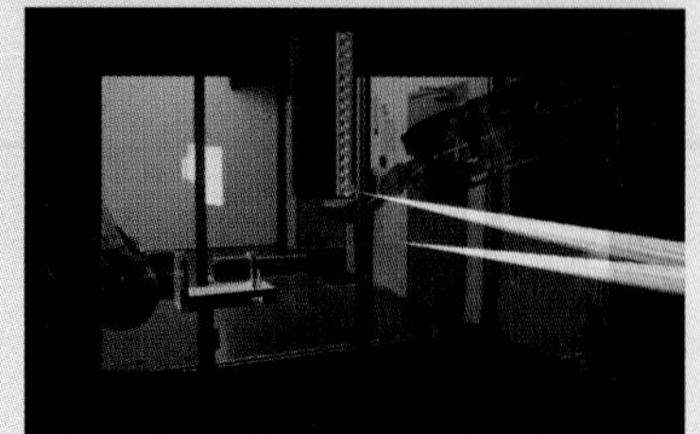

2.08 AUGMENTED FABRICATIONS

Instructors: Brandon Kruysman, Jonathan Proto
Workshop: SCI-Arc 2013

119, 124, 140, 141, 162, 214, 215

Virtual prototyping combining simulation, emulation, and fabrication is expanded in this project to incorporate cinematic techniques and mixed reality modeling. In this process Automated Tape Laying (ATL) techniques from the composite industry are adapted to six-axis robots as a flexible manufacturing process. A real-time overlay system employs an external screen in collaboration with calibrated cameras, showing path procedure, patterning strategy, and the virtual end-of-arm tool prototype composited into the footage with an actual robot. Match moving in combination with compositing techniques allows for virtual prototyping in digital fabrication scenarios, overlaying both virtual and physical objects through precise calibration of cameras. In this experiment, different robotic cell configurations and end effectors could be tested virtually. Kruysman and Proto describe the attributes of the system in the following terms:

"The custom animation-based robotics platform has provided a unique understanding of the translation between architectural representation and production. Through a time-based approach to motion control using very precise feedback algorithms, a model for robotics has been created that opens up new possibilities for architectural representation, speculation, and visualization with the ability to juxtapose and combine the virtual and physical worlds. In this interface, objects are not just one-directional, virtual objects are not simply translated into the physical world, but rather exist in a non-linear exchange between both."[3]

3—Brandon Kruysman and Jonathon Proto, "Impossible Objects," Architectural Design *84 (2014): 106–11.*

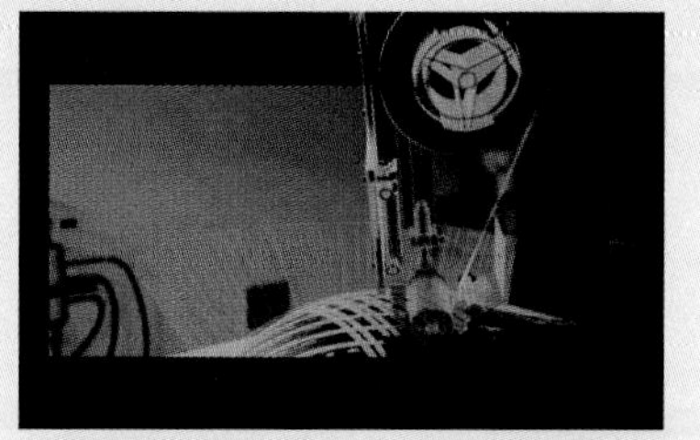

46, 47, 175

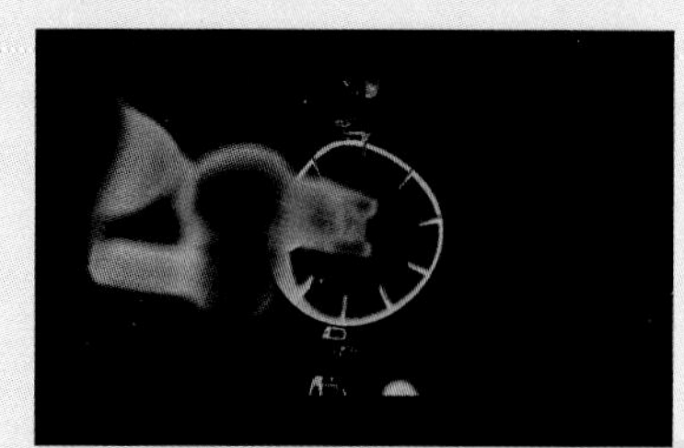

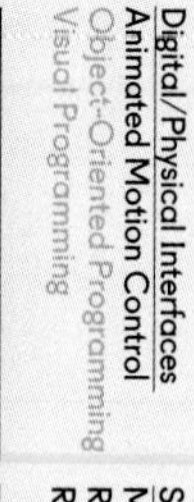

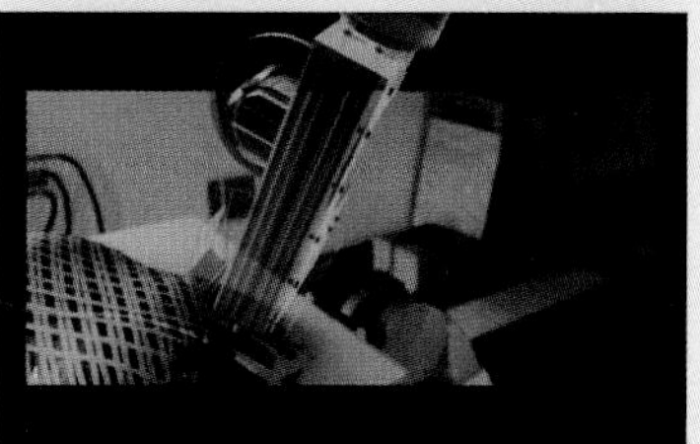

46, 47, 86, 87, 162

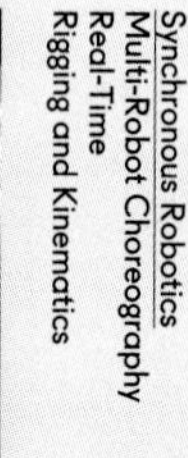

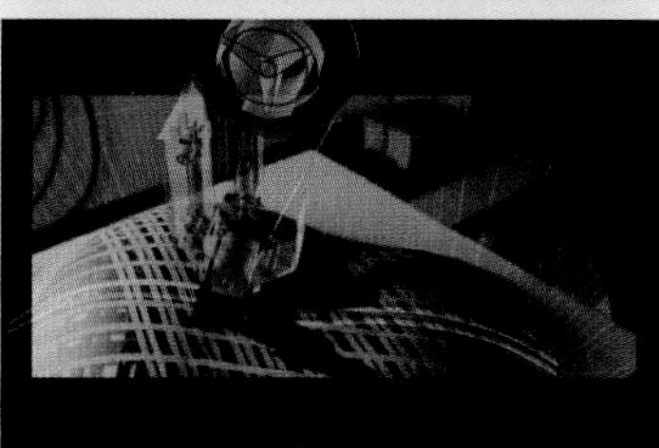

46, 47, 175

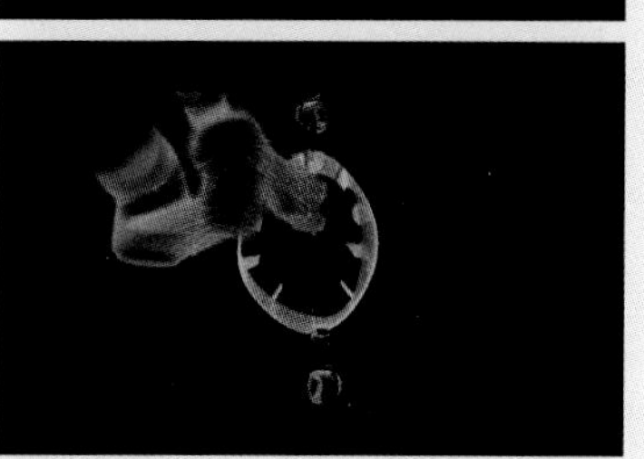

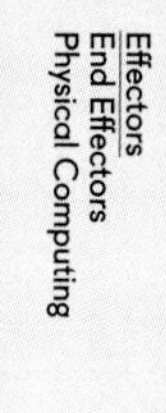

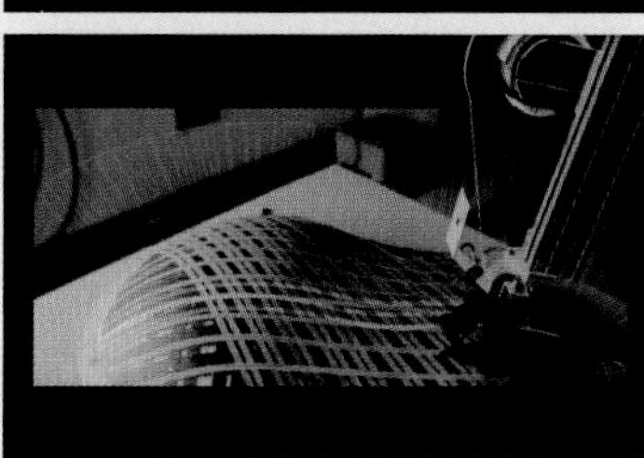

46, 47, 260, 261

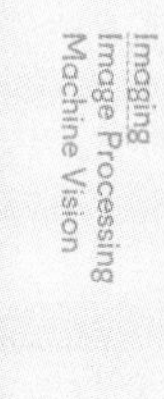

46, 47, 175, 232

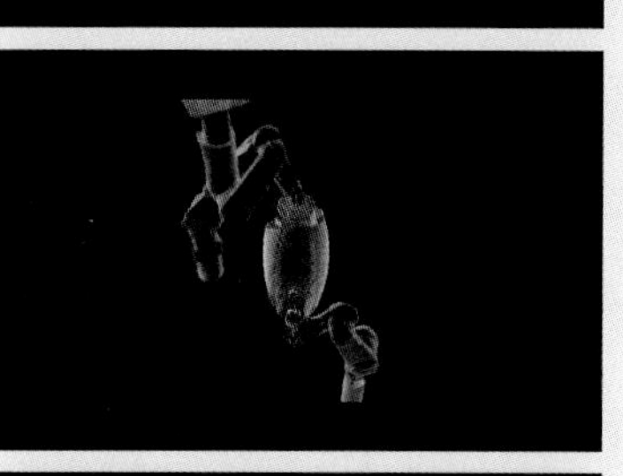

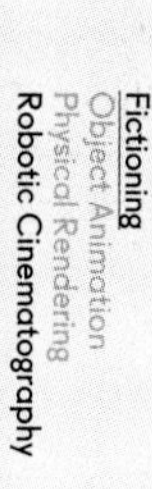

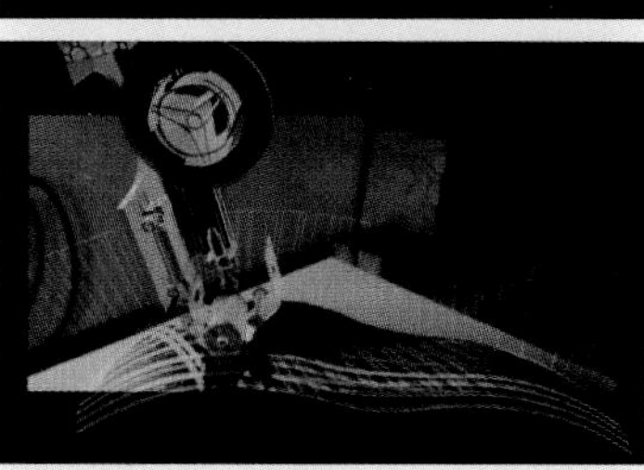

46, 47

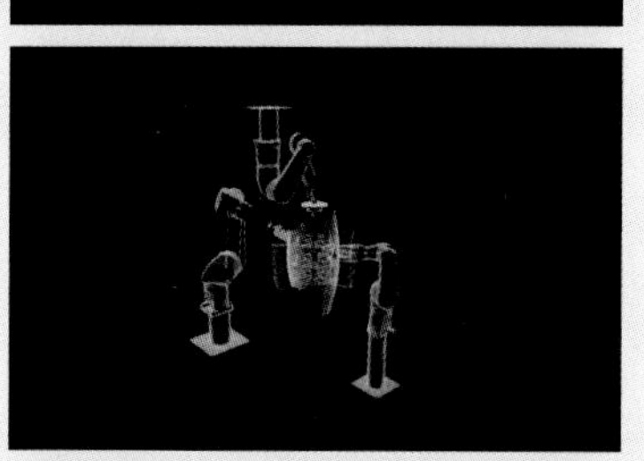

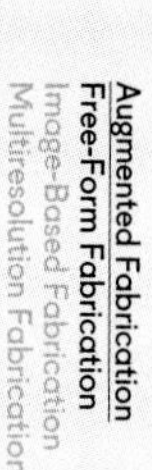

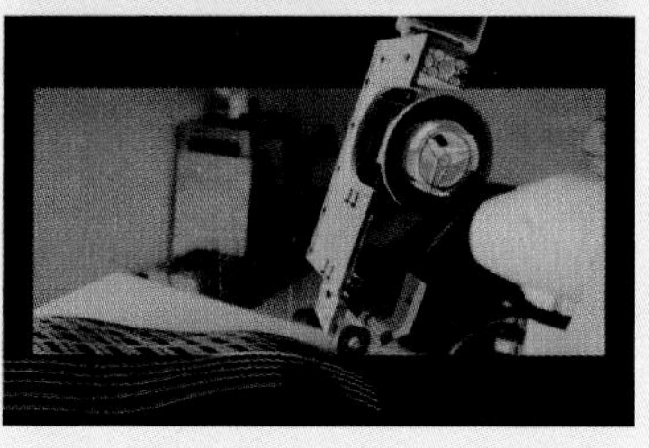

46, 47, 175

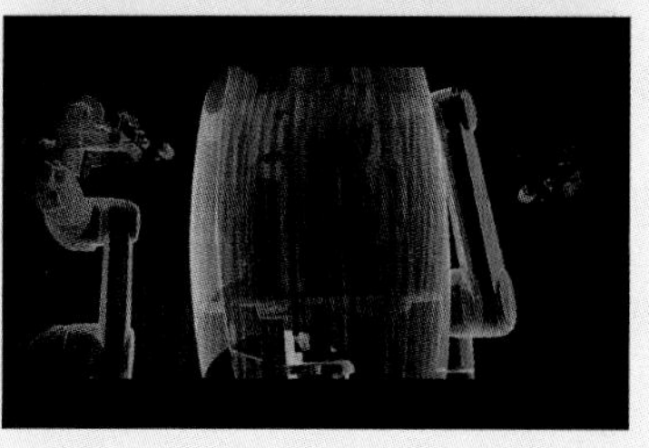

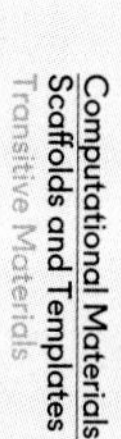

2.09 EYE, ROBOT

Instructors: Brandon Kruysman, Jonathan Proto Seminar/Workshop: SCI-Arc 2012-2013 Credits: Viola Ago, Simon Alvarez, Philippe Arias, Daniela Arriagada, Matthew Asfaw, Al Ataide, Nicholas Barger, Anass Benhachmi, Yuying Chen, David Eskenazi, Antonio Follo, Jack Gaumer, Brian Harms, William Hu, Zhexiong Hu, Jung Huang, Chris Jimenez, Haejun Jung, Rangel Karaivanov, Andrew Kragness, Kervin Lau, Chheng Lim, Ryan Tyler Martinez, Alex Phi, Mehrzad Rafeei, Somayyeh Ramezani, Rafael Ruiz, Naomi Scully, Maria Setaro, Scott Starr, Peter Vikar, Shitong Zhang

Eye, Robot focuses on the intersection of computation, robotic fabrication, and cinematography. Projects explore robotic motion control as a creative medium for designers through the use of the custom robotic animation software platform, designed for Robot House. Kruysman and Proto stress the designer's newfound ability to design motion, program, simulate, and speculate all at the same time.

"This type of animation space suspends the distinction between simulation, speculation, and 'the real'. Long-exposure photography in combination with robotic motion control is pushed to its limits. Projects focus on tracking and precise positioning of objects in space using synchronized robots, programmable cameras, as well as moving images on a large screen. Influenced by bullet-time photography and virtual cinematography techniques, the experiments use a combination of animation and automation to suspend an object in motion with programmable cameras. Using a plasma television playing a 60,000-frame-long section cut animation, the robot pulls the movie through space while synchronized to the shutter of a single lens reflex (DSLR) camera controlled by the robots. The resulting short movie stitches together hundreds of photographs, each a ten-second-long exposure."[4]

4—*Brandon Kruysman and Jonathon Proto, "Impossible Objects,"* Architectural Design *84 (2014): 106–11.*

56, 142
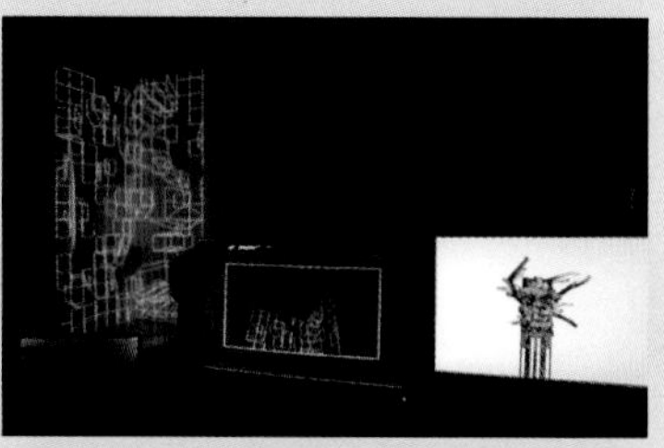
208, 209

49, 209

49

56, 89, 163

50, 56, 57, 216, 217
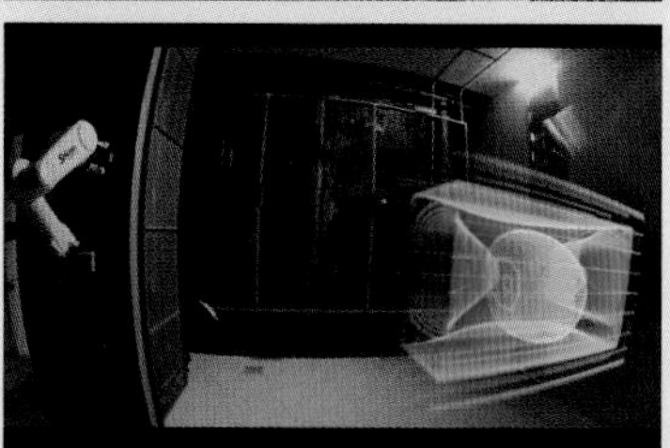
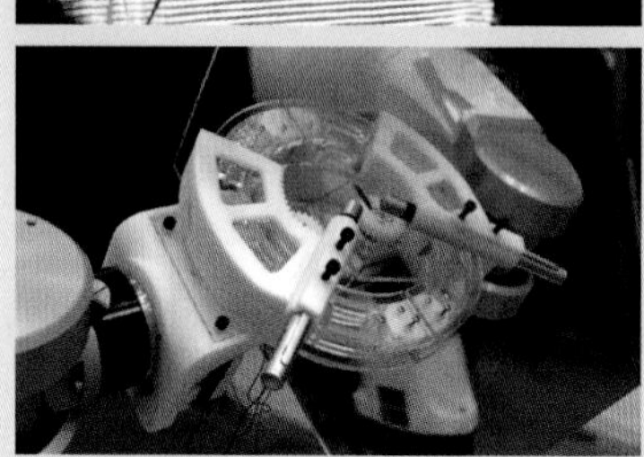
65, 126
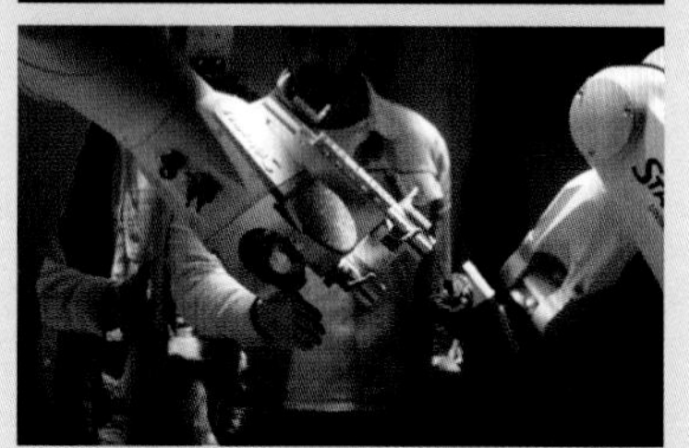
48, 163

48, 125, 126, 228

53, 163, 209
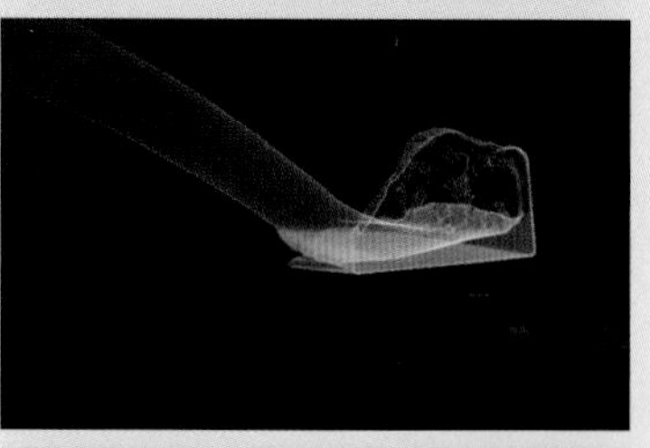
48, 66, 125, 126, 228

48, 163
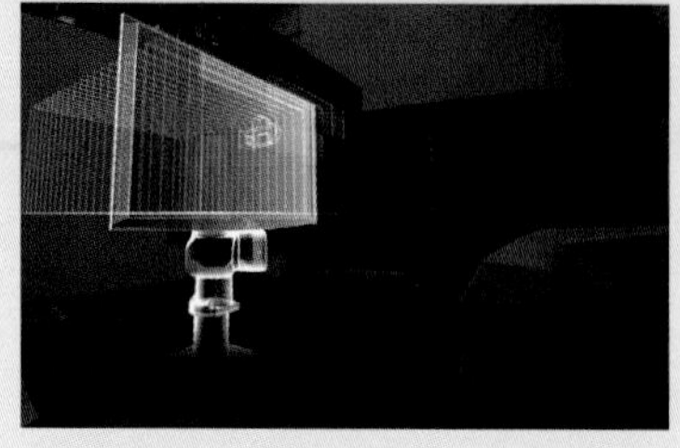
48, 65, 126
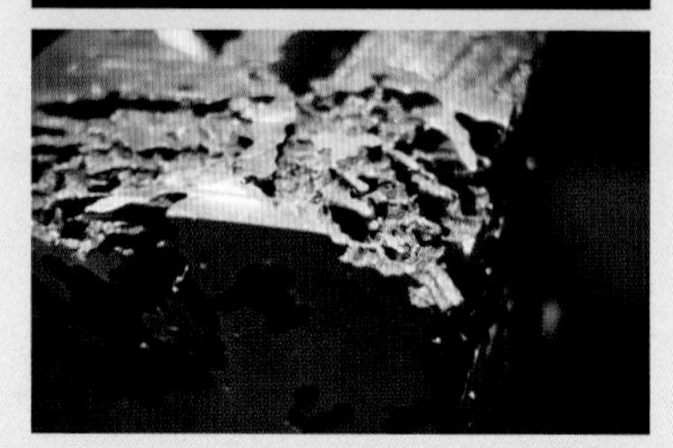

2.10 FIN.0
Instructor: Peter Testa
AT: Peter Vikar
Robot House: Nazareth Ekmekjian, Brandon Kruysman, Jonathan Proto
Studio: SCI-Arc 2012
Credits: Nicholas Barger, Evan Emery, Rangel Karaivanov, Andrew Kragness

FIN.0 instantiates a real-time prototyping workflow and interface that moves beyond 3D modeling in the computer and conventional physical prototyping. This approach has immediate application to prototyping complex curved surfaces in the automotive, aerospace, and marine industries as well as large-scale architectural envelope systems.

The idea of real-time, dynamic, adaptive form-making has long held an interest for architects. Perhaps for the first time, the hardware and software are becoming available to actualize a responsive, mutable, and reconfigurable architecture. FIN.0 embeds robotics within the physical fabric of architecture itself as a dynamic forming agent. This approach produces both a virtual and a physical artifact that oscillates back and forth across the digital/physical interface, offering new ways to visualize and make what may be best described as quasi-objects.

FIN.0 creates a real-time design and prototyping platform comprised of repertories of robotic motion, material logics, tool customization, and cinematic techniques networked into a dynamic Touch Designer interface. This physical animation and prototyping interface supports the design and evaluation of 3D spline-curve-driven surfaces within animate form. The synchronous robotics platform of Robot House supports FIN.0's real-time animation and choreography of motion and features. In FIN.0 robots are physically linked with ridged frames and flexible fiberglass splines (curves). To control this structure a Maya-based heads-up display was developed that updates the geometry and analyzes their curvature. The morphological thinking and solid drawing techniques underlying these methods have significant advantages over geometrical methods, from spline surfaces and NURBS (Non-uniform rational Basis splines) to subdivision surfaces. The system allows for the creation of highly complex surface geometry that cannot be achieved within even the most sophisticated software environments. These include, for example, surfaces resulting from intersection and overlapping splines that produce wrinkled and creased surfaces.

FIN.0's interactive spline-driven deformation of free-form surfaces lets the user sculpt and modify the surface in a number of ways, from the improvisational to the highly controlled, and repeatably. This nondeterministic approach allows the designer to toggle back and forth between form-making and form-finding. Variables extend to the surface material, and the cross-section and stiffness and fiber matrix of the fiberglass rods. These materials may be further developed with networks of sensors just as the end-of-arm tools may be fitted with force torque sensors to allow for a higher level of material agency allied to architect-designed templates and surface behaviors. The project actively shows the possibilities and limits of sculptural surfaces—allowing material to participate in the forming process.

58, 62, 90 106, 107, 164

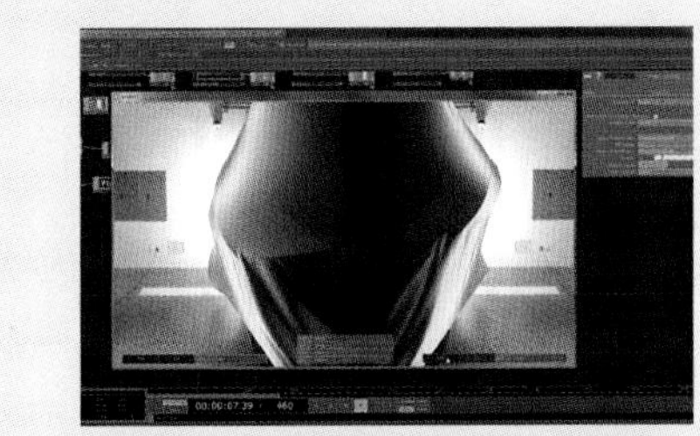

50, 80

82, 83, 143, 144

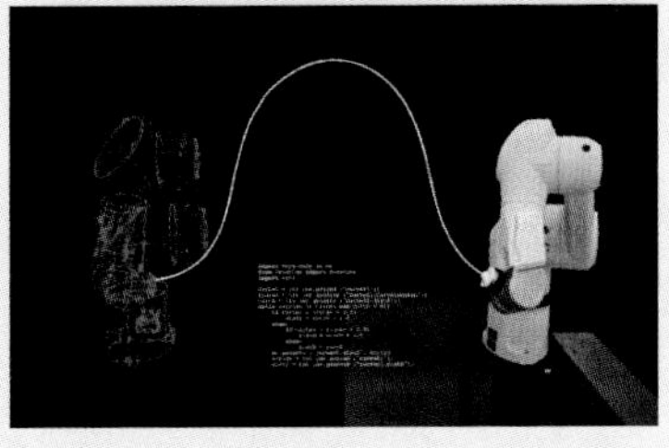

58, 90, 107

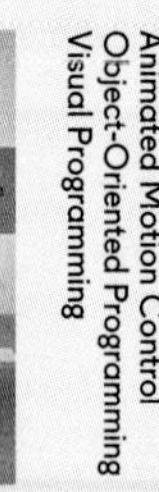

50, 81, 82, 235

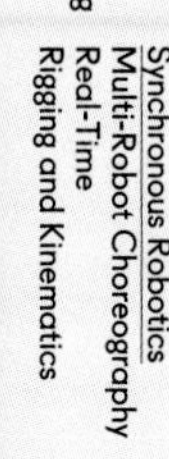

90, 126

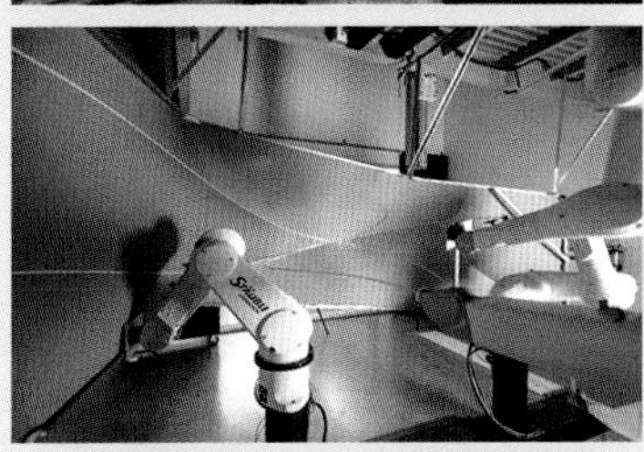

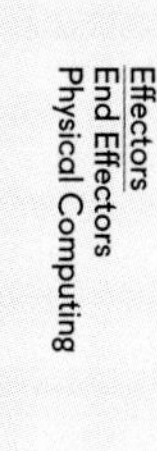

76, 77, 78, 101

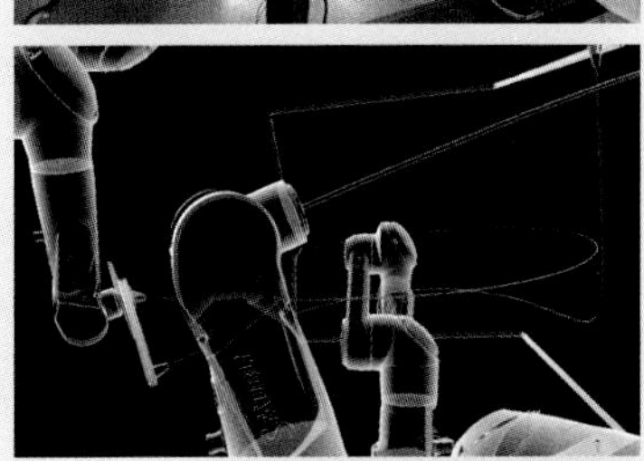

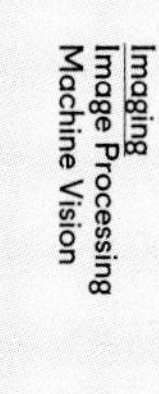

76, 77, 78, 101, 262

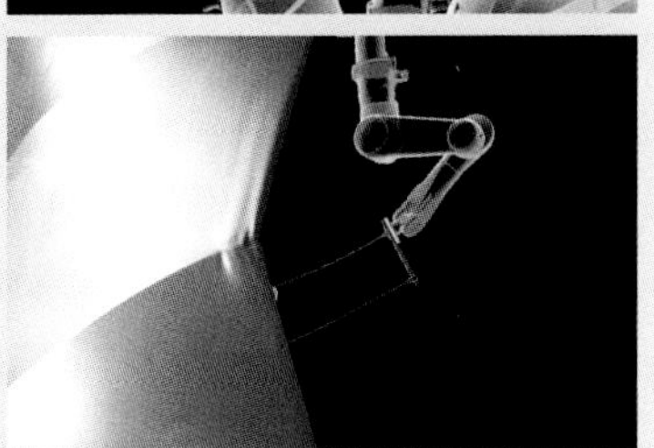

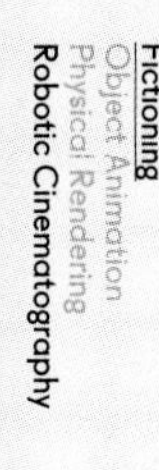

57, 59, 90, 91, 106, 107, 164

Augmented Fabrication
Free-Form Fabrication
Image-Based Fabrication
Multiresolution Fabrication

59, 78, 90, 107

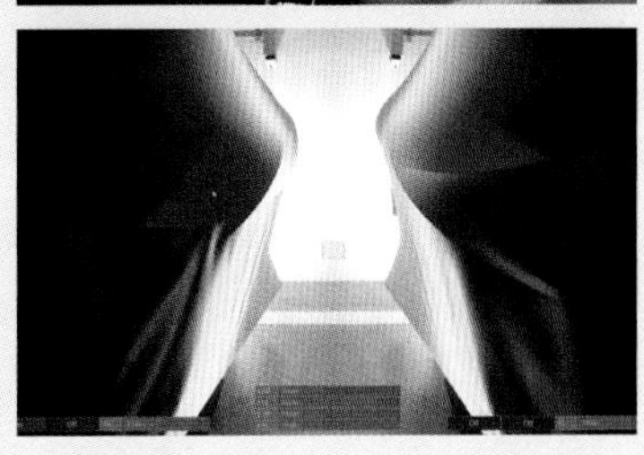

2.11 SUSPENDED DEPOSITIONS

Instructor: Peter Testa
AT: Peter Vikar
Robot House: Nazareth Ekmekjian, Brandon Kruysman, Jonathan Proto
Studio: SCI-Arc 2012
Credits: Brian Harms (Lead); Yuying Chen, Vince Huang, Haejun Jung

What if a 3D printer had an undo button? This new robotically driven printer is effectively reversible, allowing users to make changes on the fly and build objects in the physical world much like in the suspended, weightless shaping environment of the computer. This novel 3D-printing technique suspends light-curing resin in a gelatinous medium rather than using conventional structural support material during the build process. In place of solid supports, the gel substrate in the free-form printer acts as a passive but omnidirectional support material. Suspended Depositions aims to blur the line between processes of design and fabrication in the context of rapid prototyping by increasing the fluidity of the fabrication process through coordinated material and robotic processes. The project exploits feedback loops that allow the process to be used as a live generative form-finding tool as well as a method for production of designed objects.

The Suspended Depositions prototype uses a six-axis robot with a peristaltic pump and needle-thin print head on its end effector. Once deposited in the gel the material is cured by exposure to UV light. Using this method the build material can be "undone" or erased before it cures by simply reversing the direction of the pump. Another significant innovation is that by using a six-axis robot, material is deposited in 3D vector-based toolpaths. As Harms notes:

"Virtually all other printing processes use paths generated via contouring a digital model, and rely on hardening of each successive layer before being able to move on to the next. The suspension of resin in space without added support material allows the robot effector to navigate directly on and around existing objects within the Gel, as well as the ability to observe the process from any angle. The suspension of time in this process allows for tool changes, manual intervention, multimaterial deposition, live modification of the digital or physical model, and the ability to physically 'undo' the build by removing uncured resin."[5]

80, 145, 268, 269

The advantages of a six-axis robot are the increased possibilities for motion over three-axis machines. It is also possible to manually control the trajectory of the robot so as to create an object that is only partially predesigned. The ability to "go back in print time" or control the printer manually is not possible with conventional 3D printers, which generate rigid structures to prevent objects from collapsing during the printing process.

126, 127, 268

From a technical standpoint this project uses Crane (visual programming toolset specific to Robot House) to generate machine code for a six-axis robot arm, and Firefly to coordinate the functions of the end-of-arm tool. The current joint positions of the robot are streamed in real-time back to Crane in Grasshopper to generate a Forward Kinematic (FK) model of the robot in order to get the precise location of the print head. If the tip is located on a toolpath, a wireless signal is sent to an Arduino microcontroller to drive a stepper motor that acts as a peristaltic pump. The pump injects UV curing resin into the gel and turns off when the robot is no longer following a toolpath. This process sequence can be manually overridden at any time, allowing the user to effectively sketch complex forms or partially predesigned objects within a suspended medium.

164, 165, 166, 242, 243, 262, 263

5—Brian Harms, "Suspended Depositions" (Project Statement, SCI-Arc, 2013).

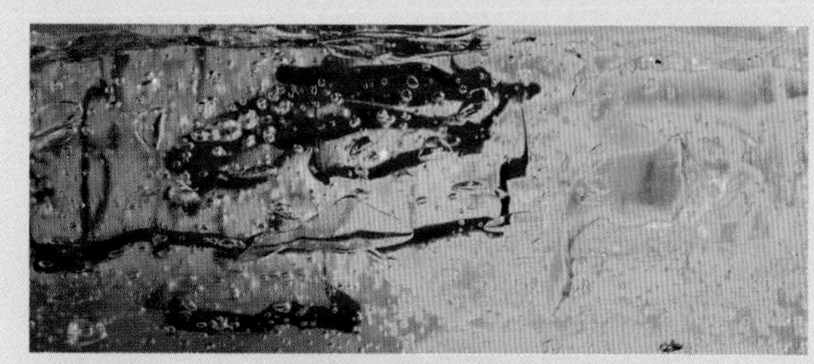

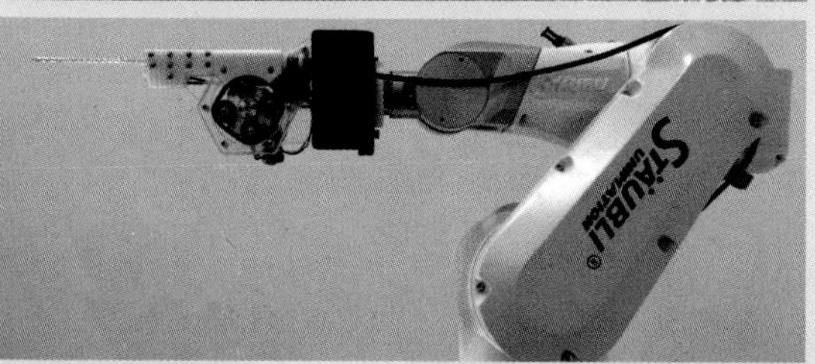

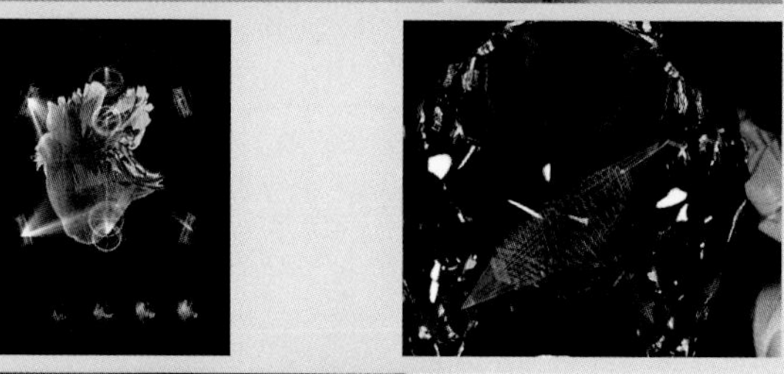

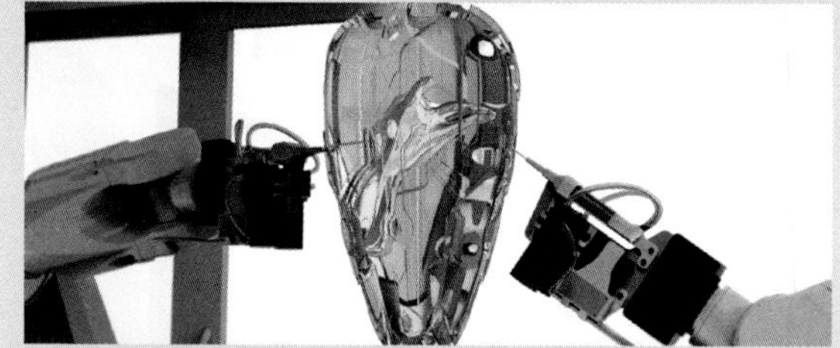

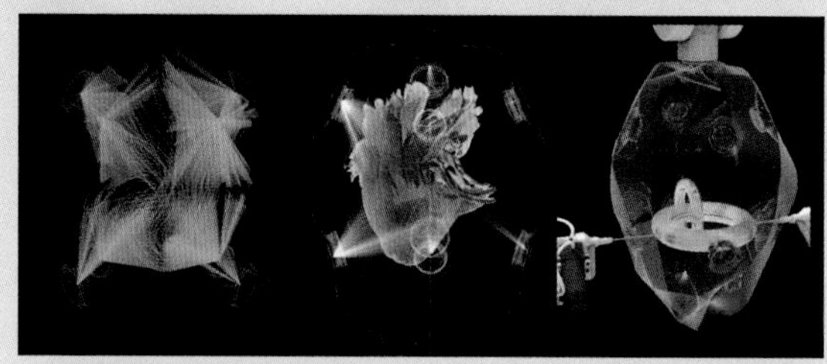

2.12 GESTURAL FABRICATION

Instructors: Marcelo Spina, Andrew Atwood
Robot House: Brandon Kruysman, Jonathan Proto
Studio: SCI-Arc 2013
Credits: Brian Harms

Gestural Fabrication develops protocol for encoding real-time motion data into robotic motion paths. The goal is to circumnavigate mediation by traditional 2D digital interfaces (mouse, keyboard, monitor), and allow for 3D input to become 3D output.

"The project posits that the coupling of projection mapping with motion can provide opportunities to explore and investigate design- and architecture-related issues as a dynamic and active process capable of informing design decisions and generating new digital geometry. The motion and slippage between object and projection are captured in the digital model and projected back onto the physical objects in real-time. The major distinction between the intentions of this project and those of typical projections (on objects in motion) is that this implementation creates an interface in which specific motion and projection combinations are not rehearsed, and the motion control is live and gestural—creating a new space for designers to operate within."[6]

Leap Motion, Grasshopper, Firefly's Leap Component, and the Crane components for Grasshopper are used to navigate Rhino and virtually "cut" through geometry. Hand movements are recorded as motion paths for a robot arm to cut Styrofoam into a user-defined shape.

6— Brian Harms, "Gestural Fabrication" (Project Statement, SCI-Arc, 2013).

59, 60, 146, 166

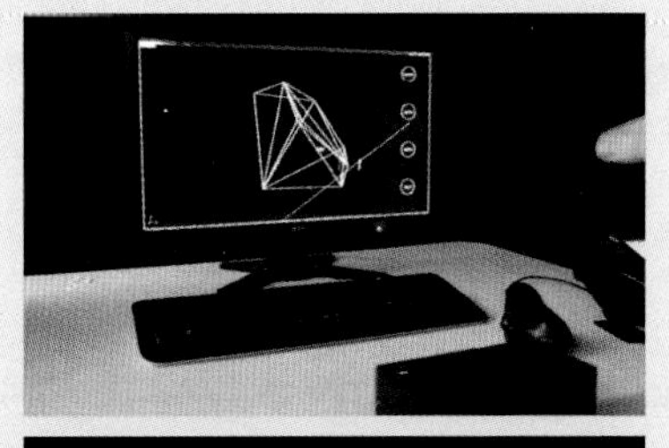

61, 109, 110, 166

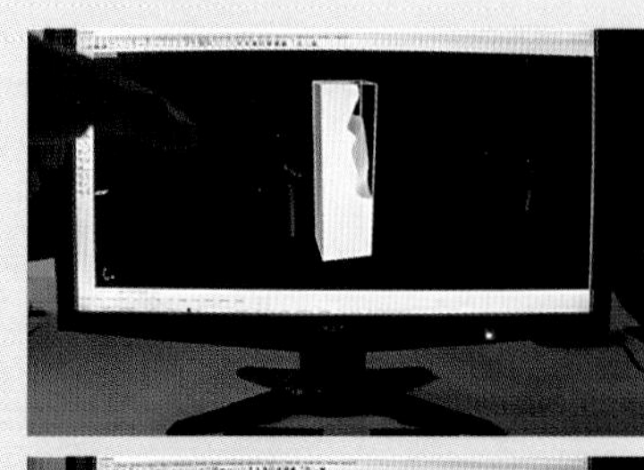

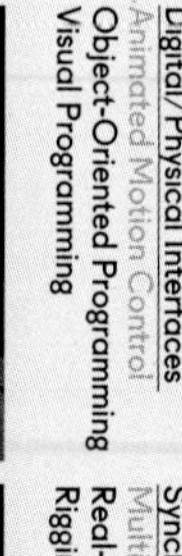

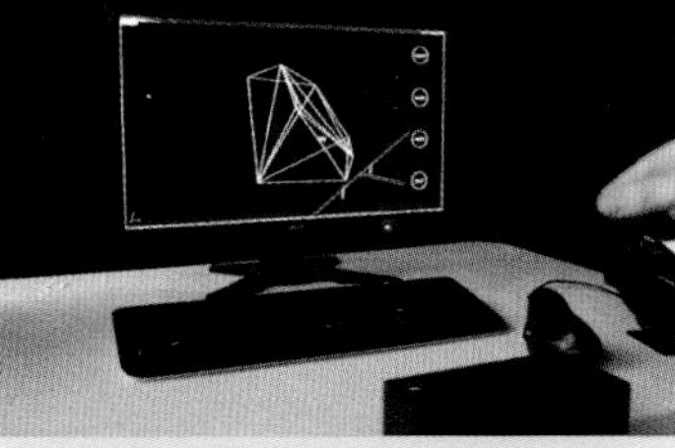

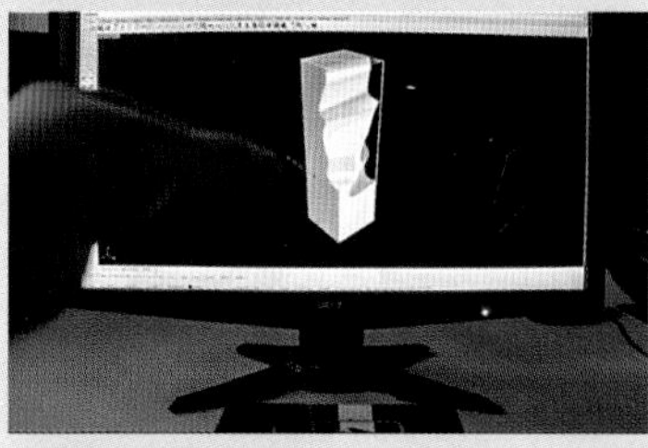

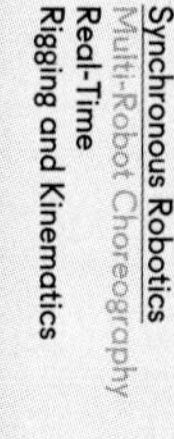

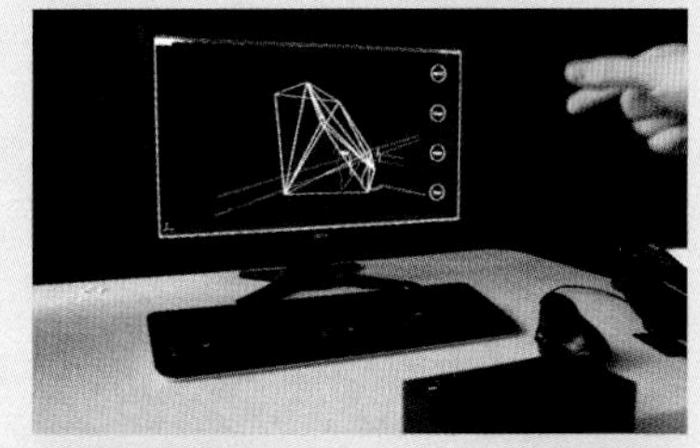

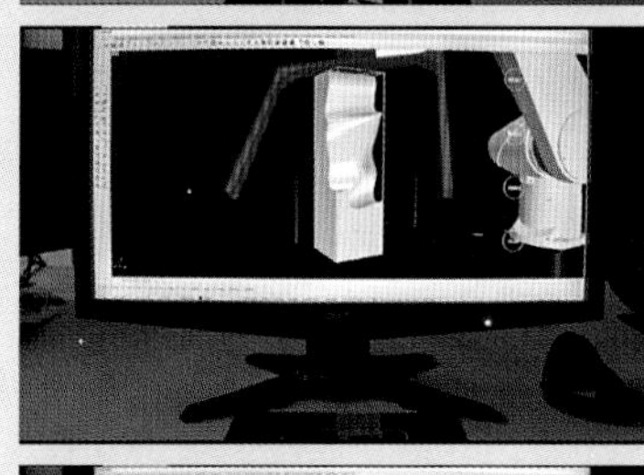

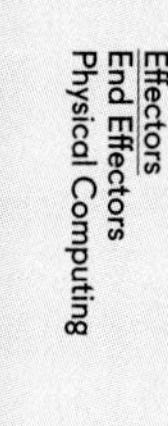

123, 146, 166, 234

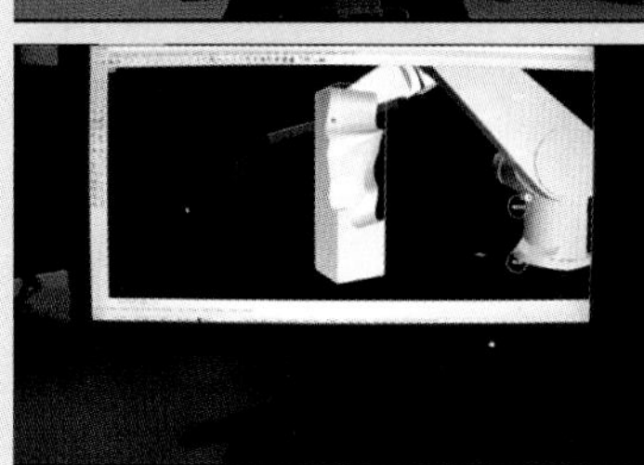

Imaging
Image Processing
Machine Vision

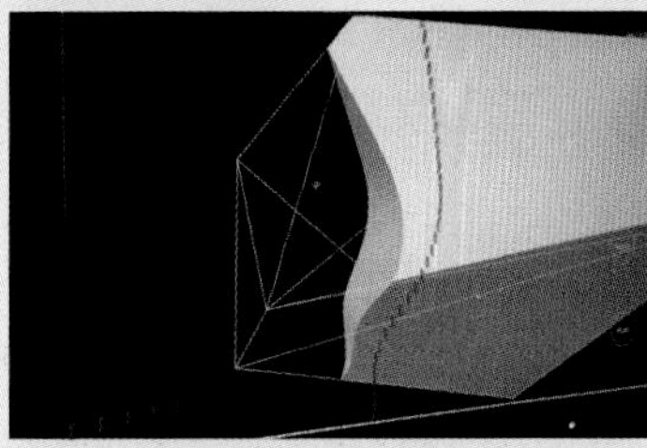

109, 110, 234

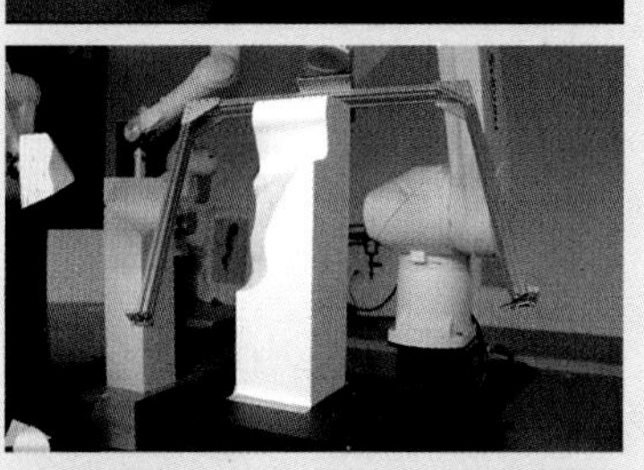

Fictioning
Object Animation
Physical Rendering
Robotic Cinematography

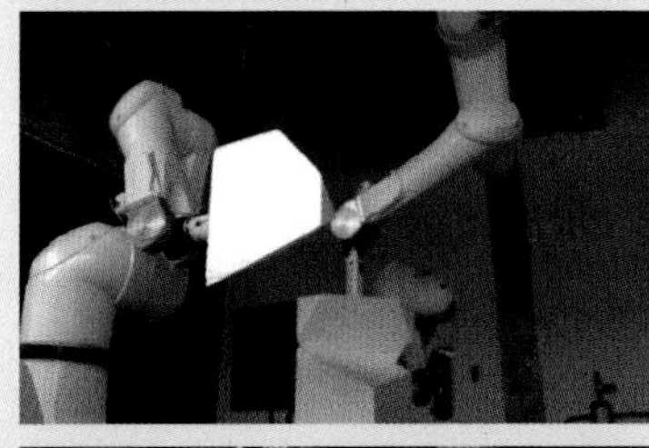

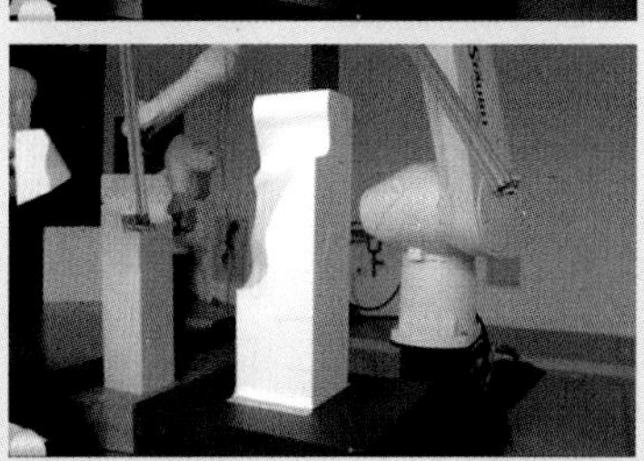

Augmented Fabrication
Free-Form Fabrication
Image-Based Fabrication
Multiresolution Fabrication

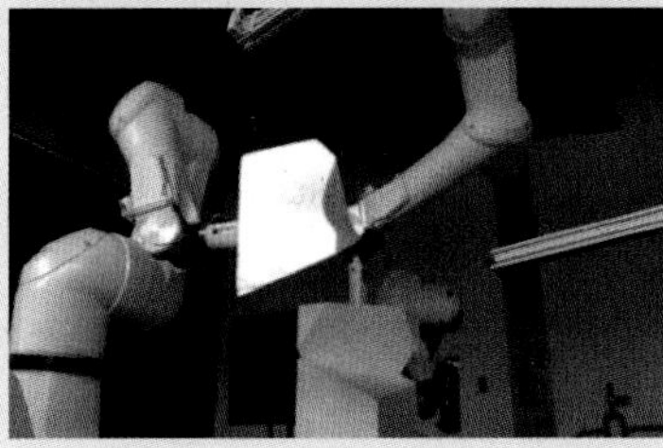

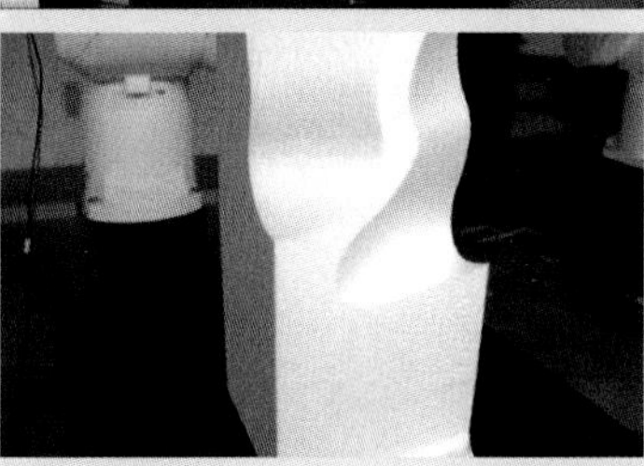

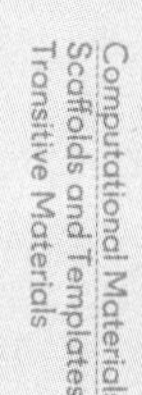

2.13 ANISOTROPIC FORMATIONS

Instructor: Peter Testa
Robot House: Jake Newsum
Studio: SCI-Arc 2013
Credits: Salvador Cortez, Cheng Lu, Avra Tomara, Nikita Troufanov

Anisotropic Formations explores the integration of robotics with vector-based 3D printing and composite filament winding. Taking inspiration from advanced composite manufacturing, and experimental application of industrial robotics, the project takes the anisotropic approach to both aesthetics and fabrication logic.

Plastic extrusion occurs in 3D space, forming fibrous geometries with extruded lines of plastic—as opposed to 2D layers. A flexible scaffold/mandrel serves as support structure for plastic extrusion paths. A custom extruder tool deposits Polycaprolactone plastic (a low-temperature re-formable polymer). The first layer, an extruded pattern, serves as a dynamic or meta-scaffold that is transformed by paired robot arms. Vector patterns are not 3D modeled in a conventional sense but generated from numeric programming of robot joint coordinates and rotation sequences.

In place of faithfully reproducing a predetermined digital geometry, the goal is to prototype geometry in physical space using machine procedures and material properties as generative agents. Starting from high-fidelity (precise extrusion of a diagonal grid) variable speeds, rotation sequences, and temperatures are used to tease out new and unexpected results from the material. The result is a series of objects that demonstrate levels of control with the variability of material agency.

167, 227, 268, 269

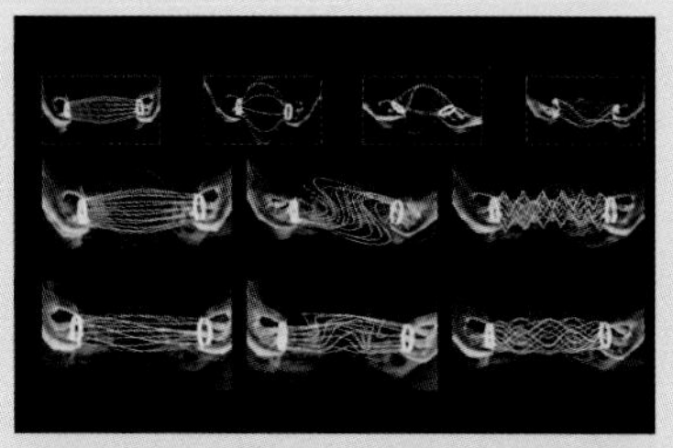

264

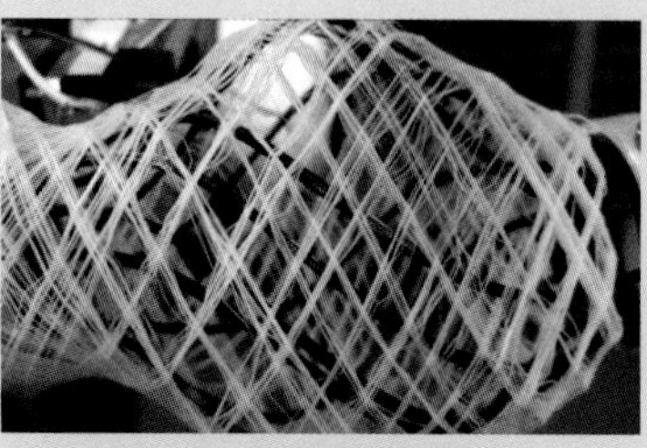

131

130

131, 267

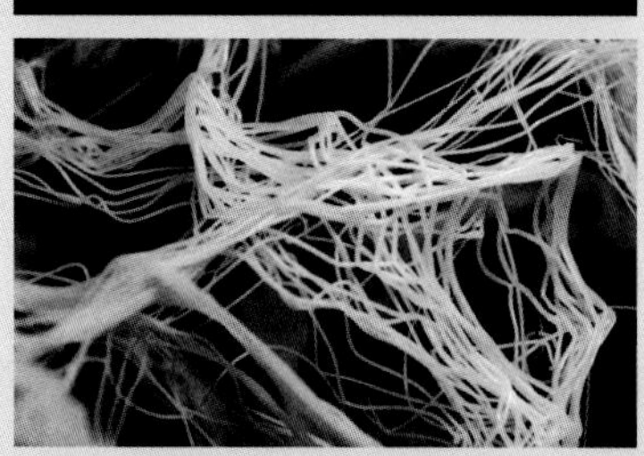

130, 228

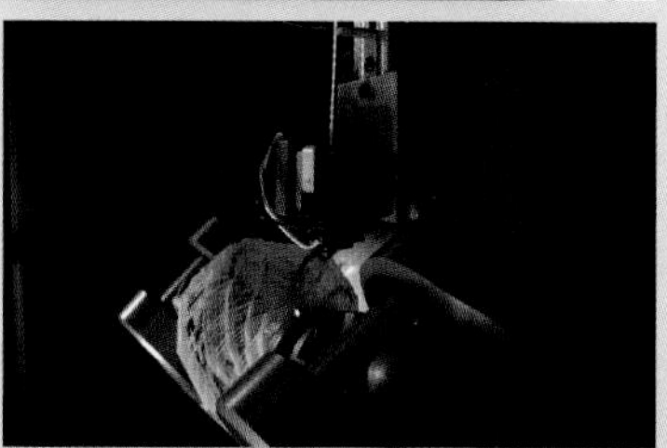

131

93, 236, 237

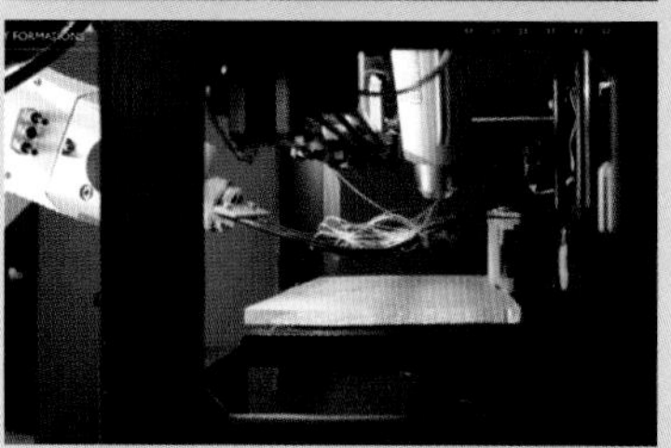

92, 93, 133, 134, 167

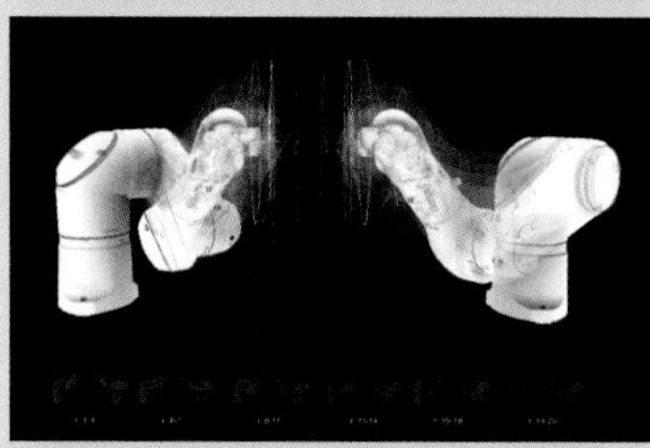

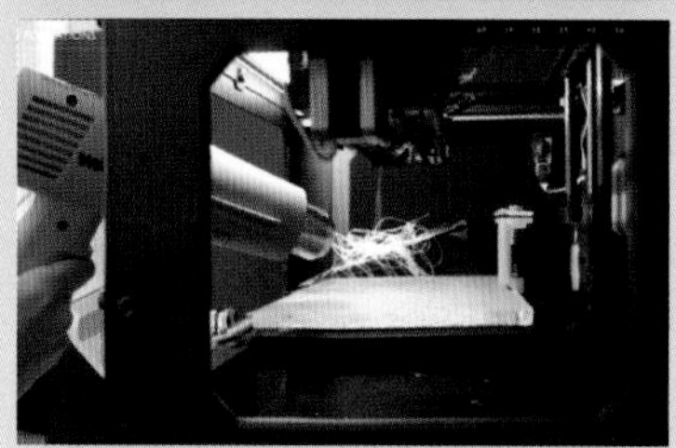

146, 147, 148, 149

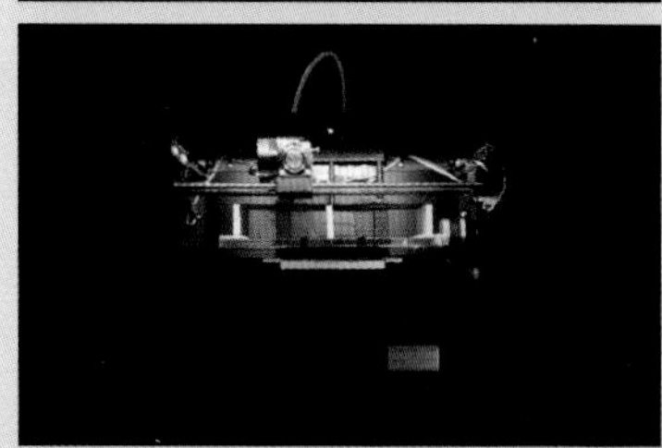

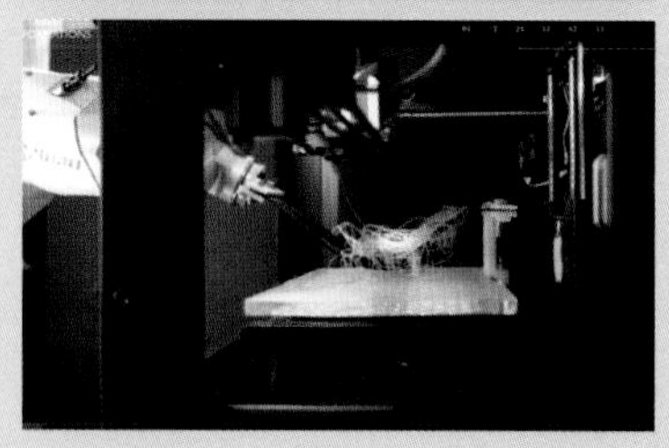

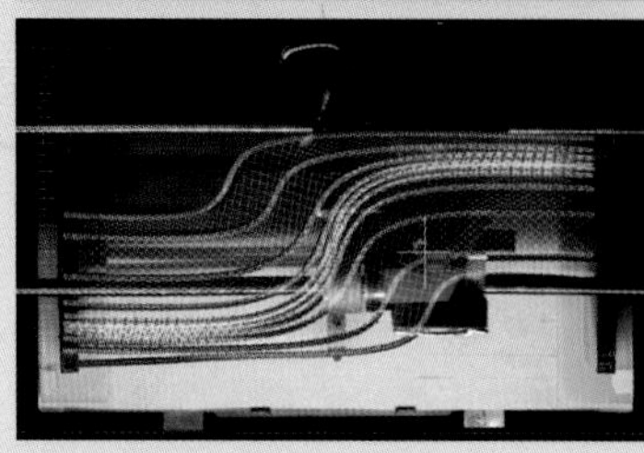

2.14 ILL-MANNERED

Instructor: Peter Testa
Robot House: Jake Newsum
Studio: SCI-Arc 2013
Credits: Kyle Branchesi, Daniel Caven, Uriel Alexander Lopez

In this augmented approach to design and fabrication, the robotic extension of the digital supports a new type of craft. Cutting back and forth across the digital/physical interface, Ill Mannered proposes improvisation technologies that have both exactness and the tactility of the designer's touch.

Speculative prototyping, informed by materials research, examines material limits in response to forces and motion. 148 Two material processes are pursued, an additive process using 3D-printed thermoplastic scaffolds, and a subtractive process involving the removal of material with a cutting tool. In this way a preform or template is strategically weakened to produce approximate forms when heated, cooled, and spun. 132, 218, 270 Material form is generated through serial repetition, moving from strand to surface and extracting strands out of surfaces.

This approach to augmented fabrication is concerned with the creation of dynamic shaping environments involving motion, heat, and pressure. 82, 184, 263, 270 Robotics becomes an essential way of mobilizing and staging dynamics and translations—just as the project becomes the point where the speculative and the vital (geometry, matter, and motion) meet. This process reaffirms the notion that form, structure, mass, energy, and geometry need to be generated, understanding 184, 219 that materials are no longer stable entities but synthetic or combinable products of design. This shift in material culture challenges ideas and entrenched assumptions concerning the relationships between matter and form.

To reposition the point of view of the designer within the motion/material construct is to 93, 117, 184, 270 challenge conventional design, fabrication, and prototyping protocols. Such a repositioning requires the invention of new instruments by which physical artifacts can be represented and produced. In this experimental setup, tools become a design medium as the architectural design output is tied to the recursive development of instruments and materials. 148, 149, 236, 237 These actuated and sensorized instruments are embedded within materials and fabrication logics at a range of scales.

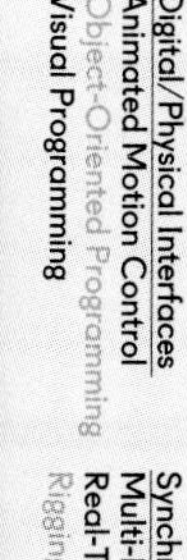

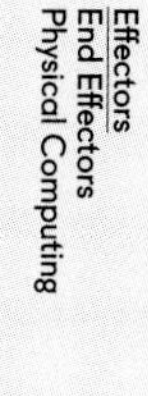

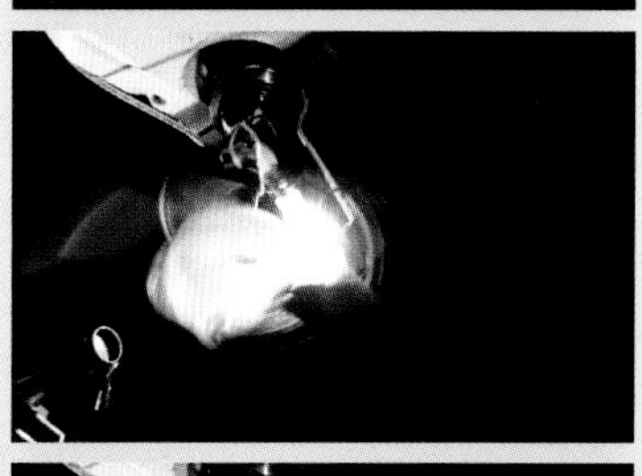

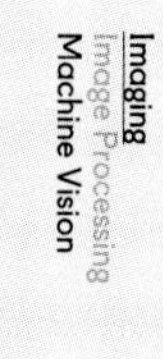

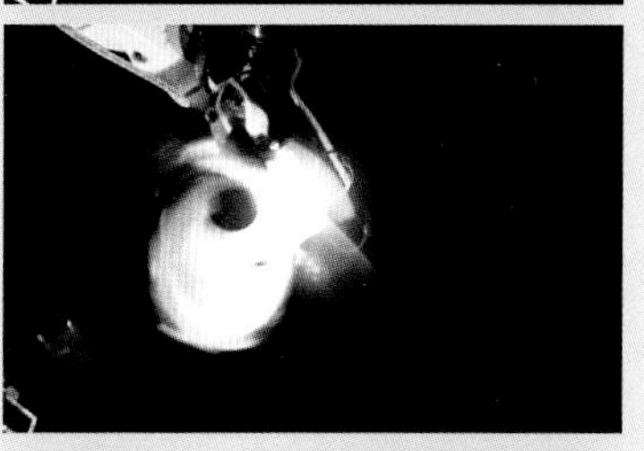

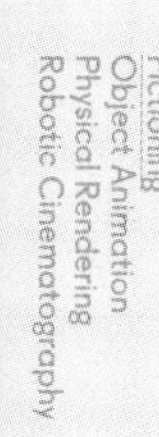

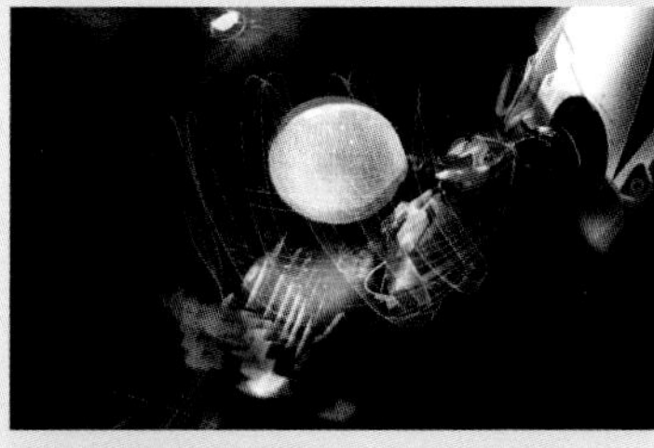

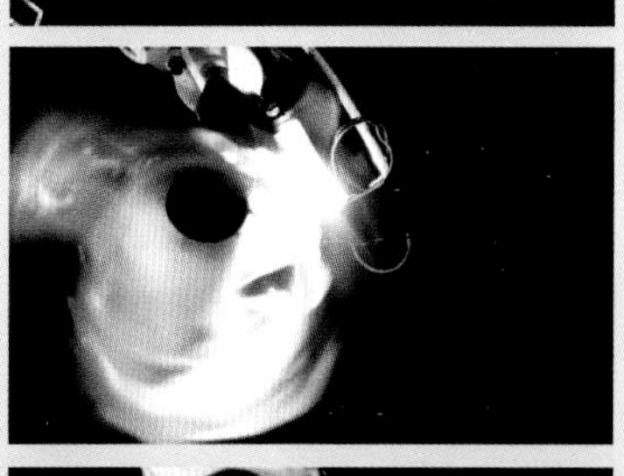

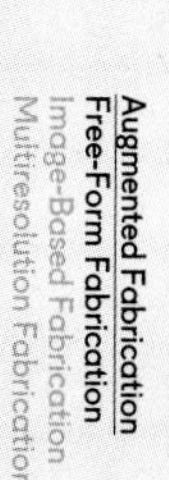

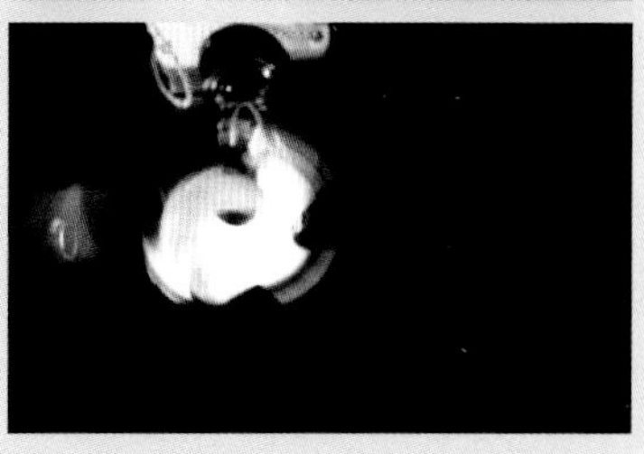

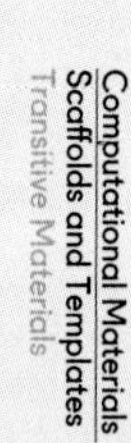

2.15 (11/1) SOL.MOTION

Instructor: Peter Testa
Robot House: Jake Newsum
Studio: SCI-Arc 2013
Credits: Jaegeun Lim, Gonzalo Padilla, Klemens Sitzmann, Jordan Squires

As robotics moves onto the architect's desktop, motion—both the real and virtual motion of parts and whole building assemblies—is being revisited. (11/1) SolMotion investigates representation and manipulation of 3D objects within a virtual/physical motion-based space. Most significantly the work develops a set of techniques that use time as a visible and malleable fourth coordinate (XYZT).

"With a focus on time and timing this project develops computational and visualization methods to produce architectural images of higher dimensional spaces. Synchronous robotics offers unprecedented control over establishing the elements of perspectival space and mobile viewpoints that in this case become generative design variables for creating new images and geometries in relationship to time. Going further, this project incorporates the techniques of slit scanning and bullet time to capture the object in multiple positions in space. Slit-scan images are re-cut and composed in time after the image data has been collected. Post-processing techniques manipulate an object's relationship to time; controlling time as an object affords new ways to understand a geometric primitive [irreducible geometric object] and its motion.

"The object of study is a 400 mm cube—a scale that allows pieces of the cube to be moved without interrupting their range of motion. (11/1) SolMotion refers to Sol LeWitt's 'Incomplete Open Cubes' as a catalog of instances. The project variously makes use of three Stäubli TX90 robots choreographed in synchronous and asynchronous motion. A fourth Stäubli RX160 robot arm is used with a digital projector and digital video camera to capture video footage for post-processing. By keeping the primitives minimal it was possible to show the potential impact of controlling motion, time, perspective, and frame rate... These methods for working with motion are uniquely architectural in the way that they are measured and manipulated. For example the light scan image sequence has, latent in a single image: primitive, motion, frame rate, sectional time geometry, sectional time rate, trajectory, and direction. The distance between the frames is analytical rather than visual, meaning there are more images in a sequence than needed to show motion, yet useful for showing geometry in time."[7]

The project is accessed with software and robotic tools that have particular constraints, interfaces, and techniques for creating, editing, and exchanging media documents. (11/1) SolMotion raises provocative questions regarding the status of drawing, coding, and modeling, with implications for the representation and production of architecture.

7—*Jordan Squires, "SolMotion" (Project Statement, SCI-Arc, 2013).*

184, 185

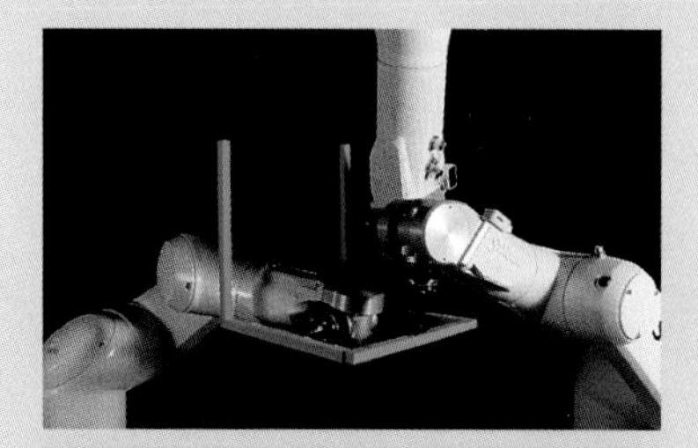

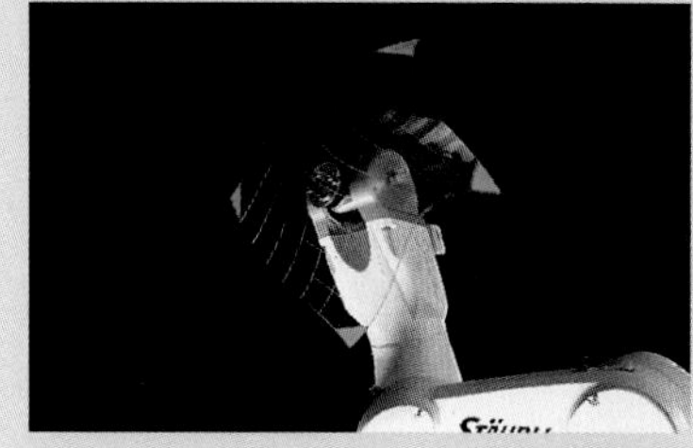

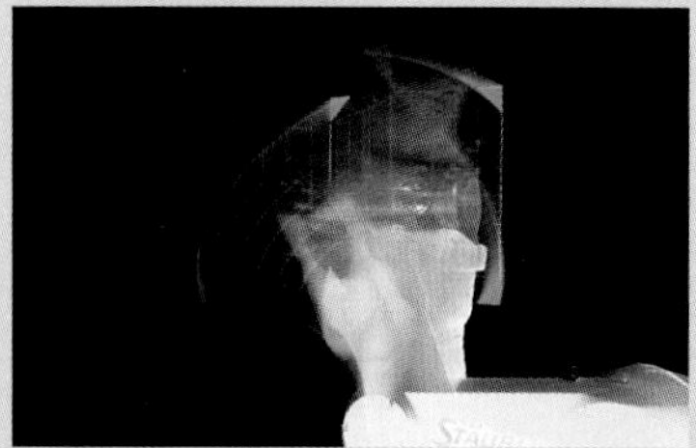

92, 150, 151, 185

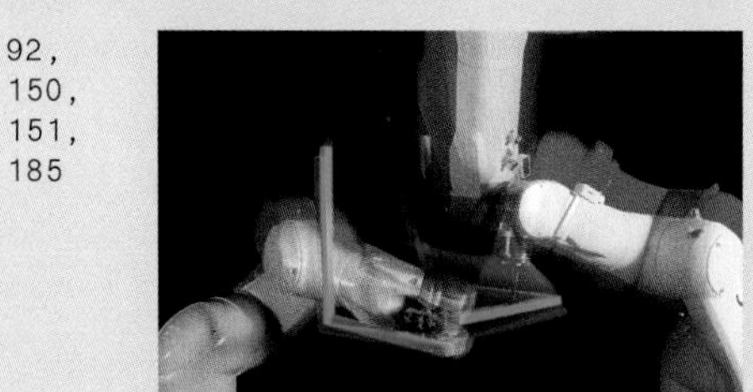

79, 108, 109, 192, 193, 194

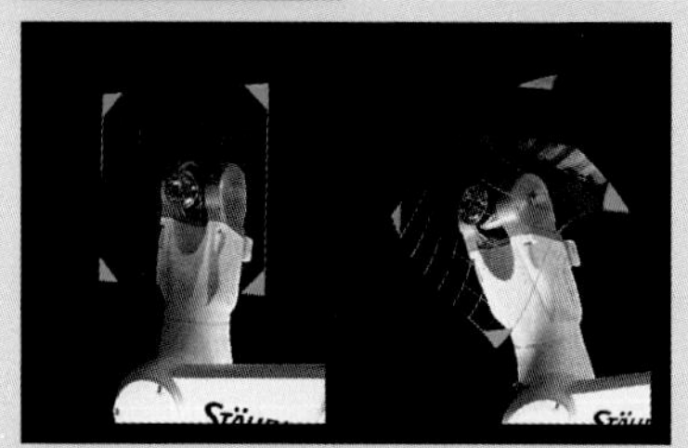

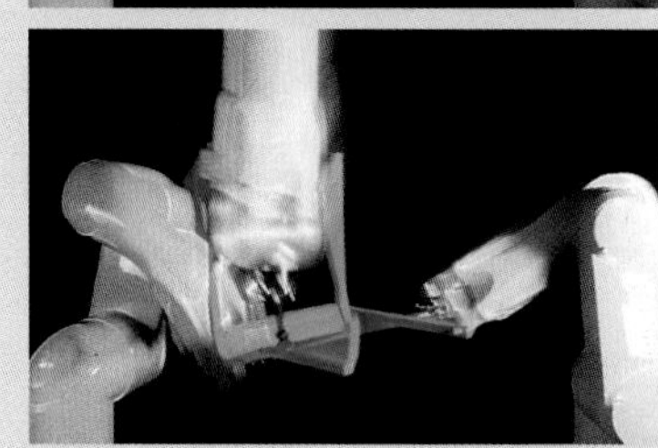

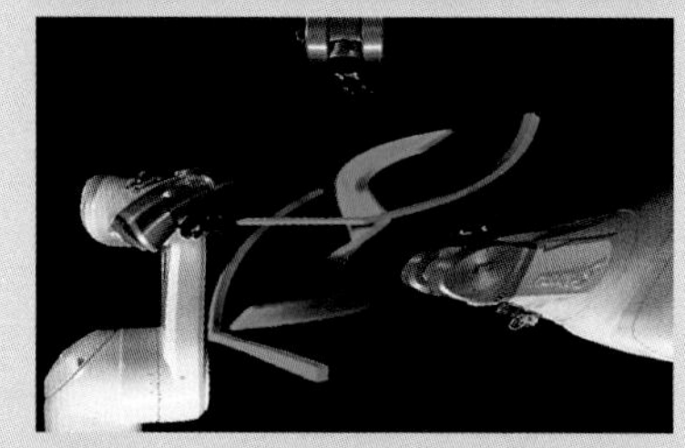

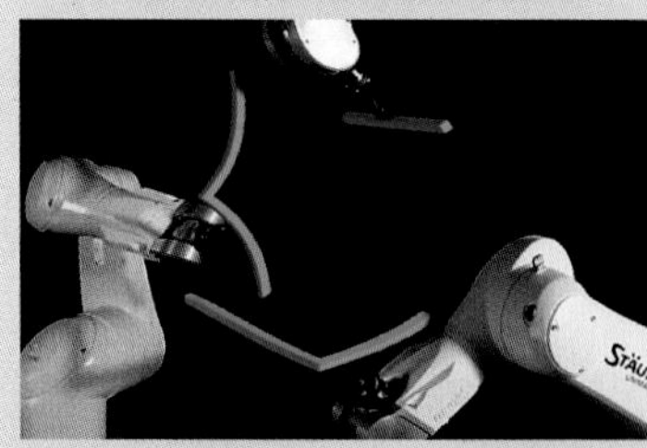

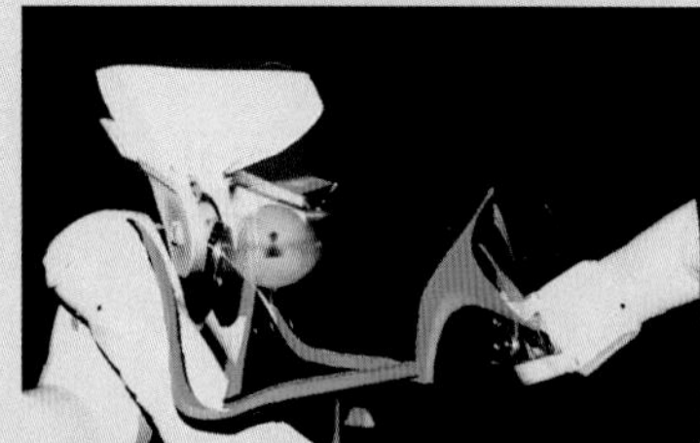

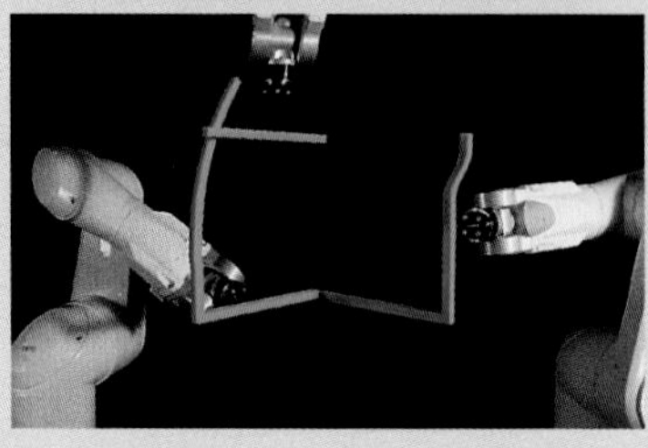

92, 150, 151, 185

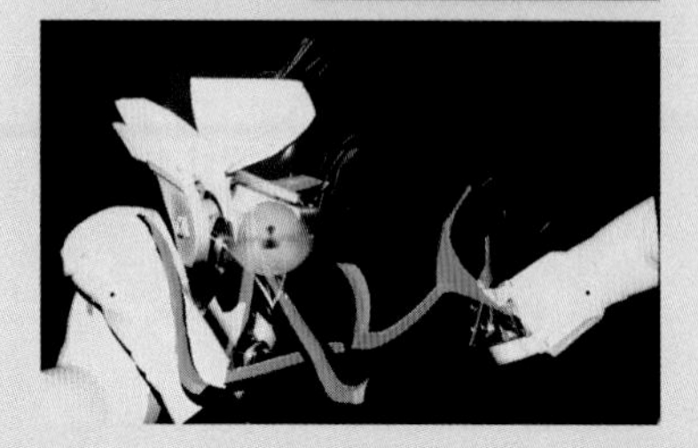

2.16 LOOP HOUSE

Thesis Advisor: Devyn Weiser
SCI-Arc Undergraduate
Thesis 2014
Credits: Uriel Alexander Lopez

186, 264

With a focus on design technique and looping feedback, the project aims to make the benefits of a dual digital/physical workspace accessible to designers. Working from a procedural (sequential or rule-based) understanding to a generative one, the work interrogates the use of digital/physical armatures (in the form of six-axis robots) in an attempt to articulate a syncretic design methodology (one in which disparate elements are combined). To test this conceptual framework the project proposes a "Loop House" or workspace/interface that can produce objects that are the result of a simultaneous engagement of both procedural and generative workspaces, with the added agency of real-time material input. Empirical data is gathered by having a number of individuals produce objects through the "Loop House." Analysis includes observation of produced artifacts and instrumentation with the interface.

"If a series of objects from a particular user are self-similar and exclusively so from the whole, it might be concluded that the procedural side of the workspace has priority. Conversely, if across many different series the objects are alike, it is possible to conclude the generative algorithms have control over the user. Loop House is part of a larger series of works that are initiating a convergent methodology—a new dialogue with architecture, taking advantage of inherent material qualities combined with rapid calculation and precision."[8]

8—Uriel Alexander Lopez, "Loop House" (Project Statement, SCI-Arc, 2014).

132, 133, 151

151

61

186

62, 186

52, 151

61, 151

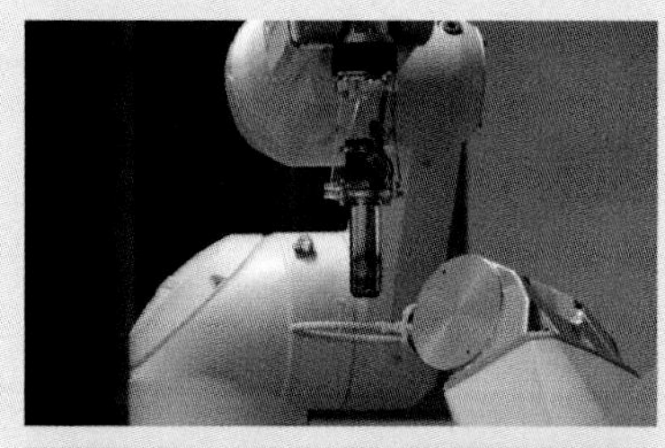

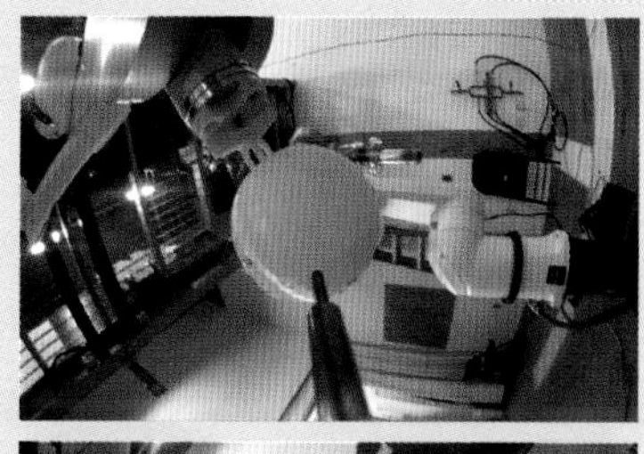

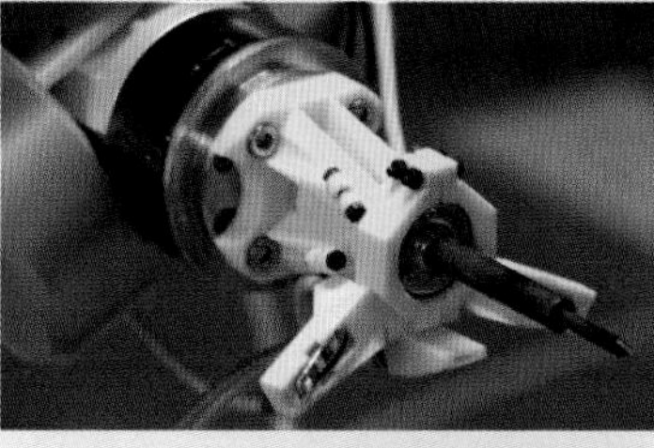

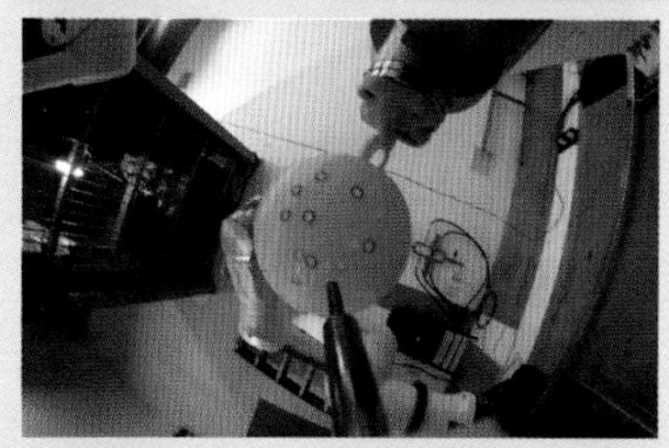

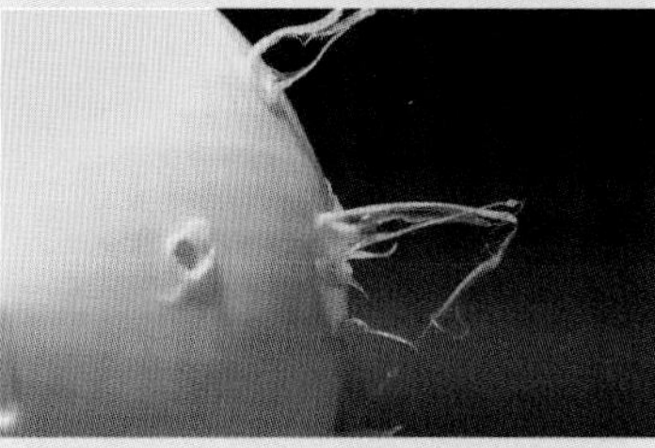

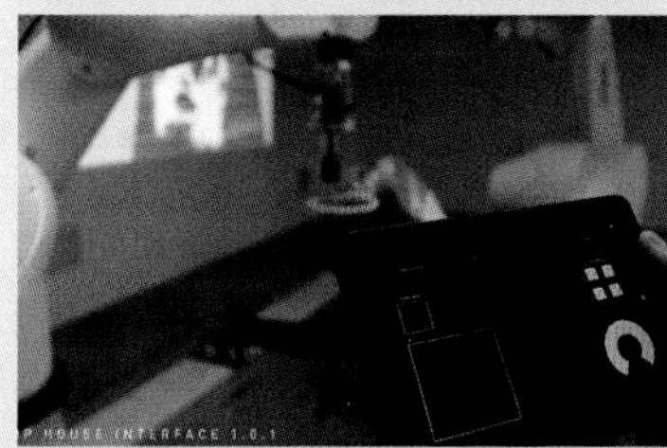

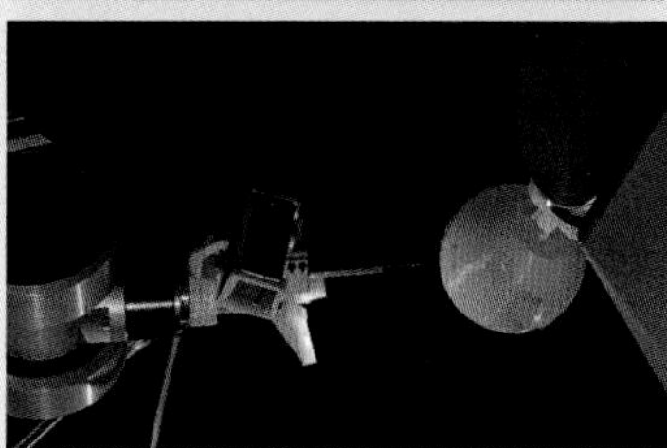

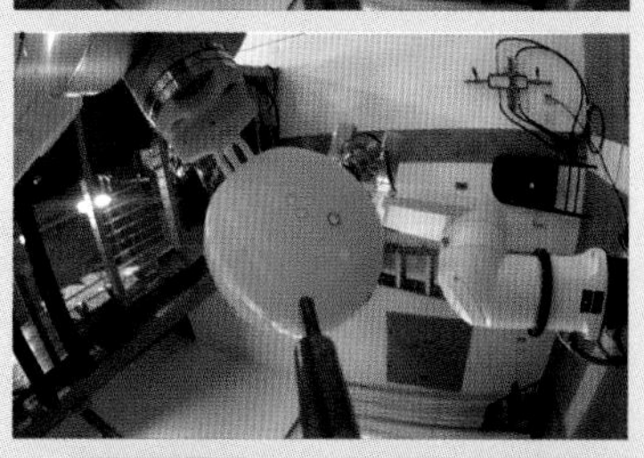

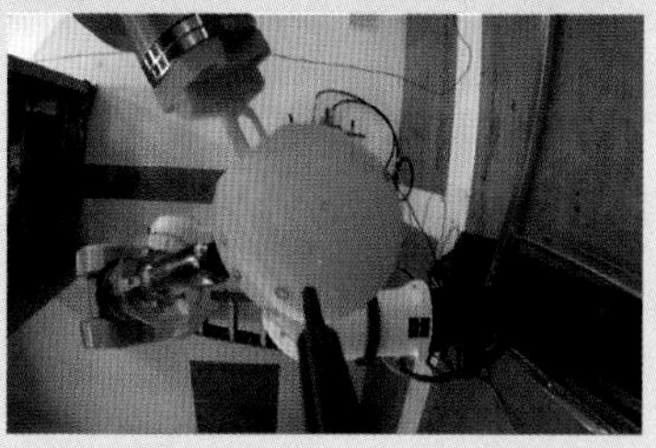

Digital/Physical Interfaces
Animated Motion Control
Object-Oriented Programming
Visual Programming

Synchronous Robotics
Multi-Robot Choreography
Real-Time
Rigging and Kinematics

Effectors
End Effectors
Physical Computing

Imaging
Image Processing
Machine Vision

Fictioning
Object Animation
Physical Rendering
Robotic Cinematography

Augmented Fabrication Free-Form Fabrication
Image-Based Fabrication
Multiresolution Fabrication

Computational Materials
Scaffolds and Templates
Transitive Materials

2.17 REAL-FAKE

94, 95, 186, 187, 270, 271

Instructor: Peter Testa
Cinematography: Josh Krohn
Robot House: Jake Newsum, Curime Batliner
Seminar: SCI-Arc 2013 & 2014
Credits: Juan Baez, Daniel Caven, Salvador Cortez, Seyed Ehsan, Chuchen Feng, Oksana Griticai, Brian Harms, Vince Huang, Kenichi Kabeya, Koho Lin, Ehsan Moghaddam, Gonzallo Padillia, Pooyan Rouhi, Abhishek Sakpal, George Smyrlis, Avra Tomara, Uri Wegman

Real-Fake represents a series of theoretical installations inventing and disrupting connections between computation and physical things. Taking as a point of departure the advanced motion control interface of Robot House, projects construct pairings of digital and physical motion carefully recorded using dual-channel and high-speed video. The project begins within what can be understood as a conventional domain of mimetic representation, only to develop a more complex exchange between the mimetic and the generative, the projective and the diagrammatic, to produce new formal logics and objects.

This research program conceptualizes a new "photic materiality" by conjoining the virtual camera in a 3D imaging system (Maya) that is embedded within a software interface with a high-speed video camera (ICD OS 4K) attached to a six-axis robotic arm. The ultra-compact camera outputs 3840 x 2160 pixel resolution at 1,000 frames per second. While the virtual camera remains unconstrained by physical restrictions, the robotic systems introduce other spatial effects. Projects exploit this post-photographic and post-animation space as a modeling, visualization, and fictionalization platform.

187, 196

94, 95

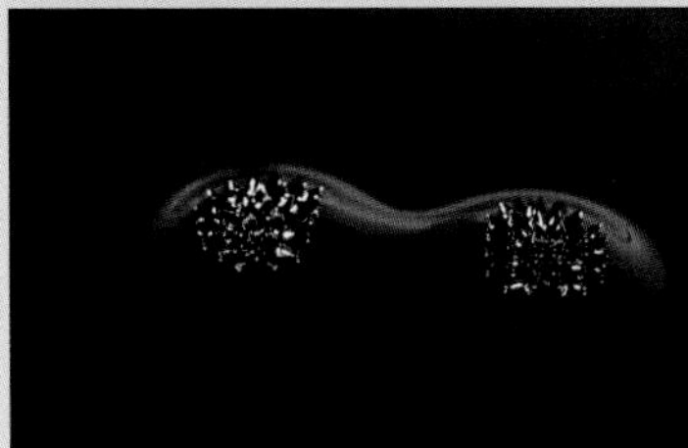

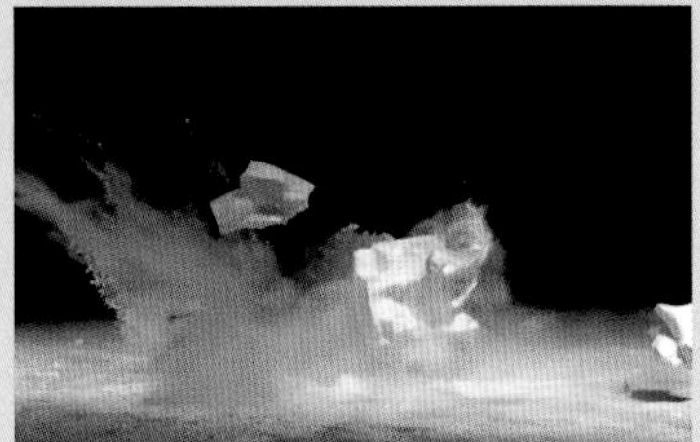

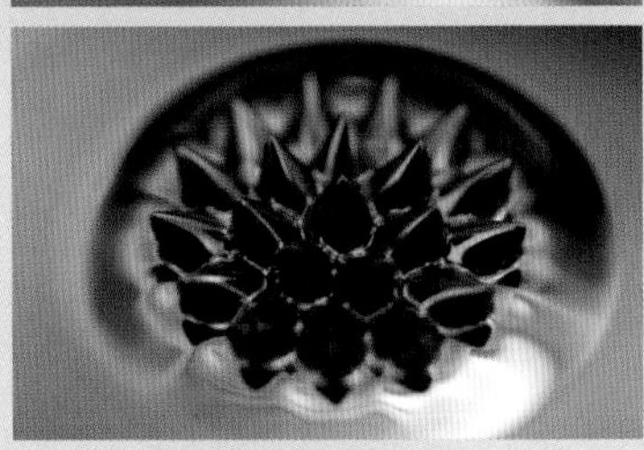

168

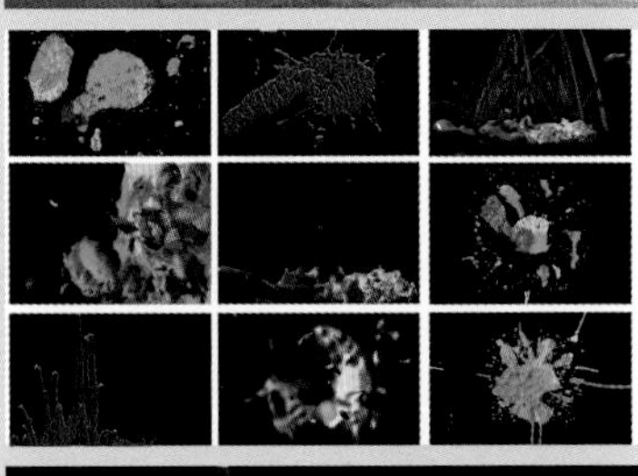

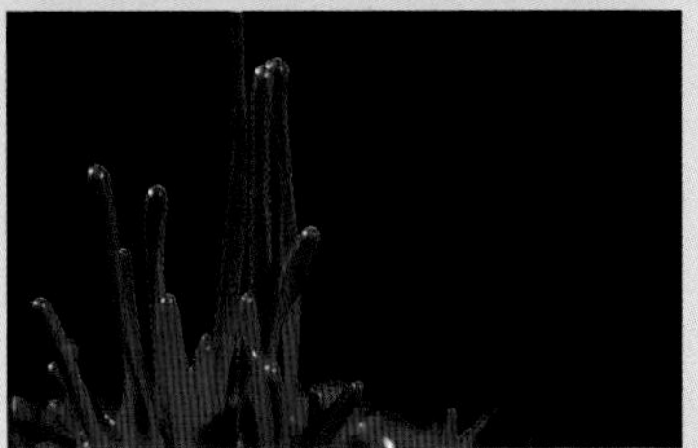

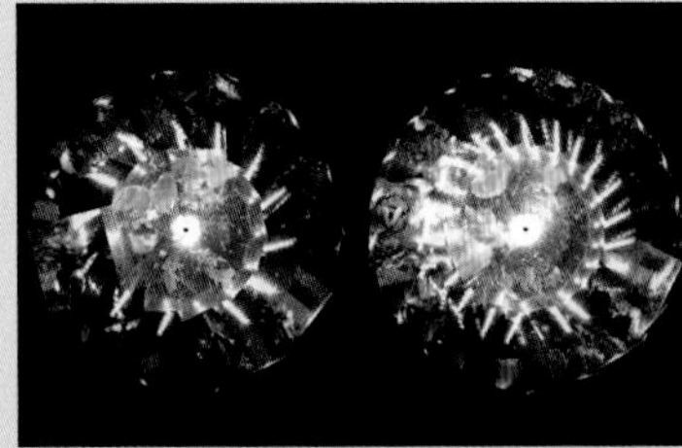

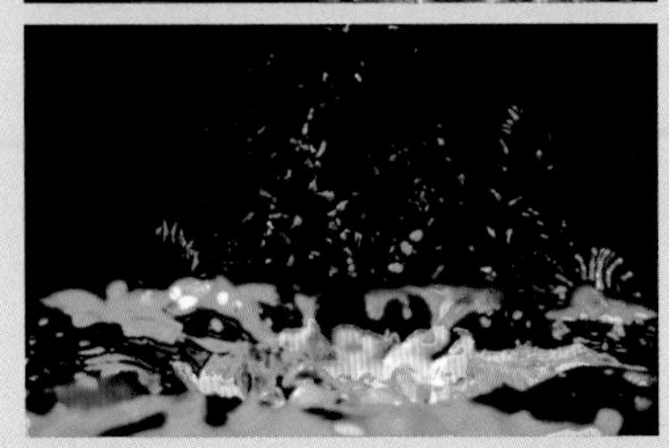

2.18 OBJECT ANIMATION

Instructor: Devyn Weiser
TA: Uriel Alexander Lopez
Robot House: Jake Newsum, Curime Batliner
Seminar: SCI-Arc 2015
Credits: Mary Franck, Tanveer Harun, Carlos Navarro, Dai Sen, Stefan Svedberg; Matthew Momberger, David Park, Todd Swanson, Evelyn Tring, Jacob Zindroski

A new medium is emerging that combines post-photographic cinematic techniques and real-time physical animation. Object Animation, a project series led by Devyn Weiser, is just beginning to explore the contours of this physical/cinematic form and its implications for architectural representation and design. Blending analog and digital, as well as architectural and cinematic techniques, this research program embodies a speculative approach to modeling and animating with application to the generation, representation, and simulation of the architectural assemblage. Working with existing, invented, and found objects, with movable and repositionable parts, design research makes extensive use of robotics and techniques of object animation both to physically test designs developed in the computer and as a generative design toolset collapsing representation and design processes.

Object Animation introduces workflows that advance a new conceptual and practical framework for animation. The work combines keyframe animation with robotic motion control to create *robotic stop motion.* The introduction of a purpose-built robotic stage creates opportunities in photographing stop motion sequences combining and compositing slices, sweeps, and panoramas in post-production. The robotic stage supports multiple-camera setups with a single camera. For example, each assembly step may have thirty-six camera positions, every 10 degrees around the object. Any number of editing techniques may be used, such as match cut (raccord), by which two different objects or two different spaces graphically match; a jump cut, in which two sequential shots of the same subject are taken from camera positions that vary only slightly; and shot reverse shot cutting, which alternates between front and back of objects. Objects may be multiplied, mirrored, or aggregated in an additive or subtractive sequence. Frame rates range from real-time to faster, slower, or any combination. Consideration is given to the lighting of objects in space versus rendered objects in the computer and altering color of physical objects for effects such as drop shadow and gradient fills.

67, 199

Central to this approach is the design of *mise-en-scène* on a six-axis robotic motion stage that supports real-time match moving and chroma keying. The innovative workflow includes pre-production to simulate camera positions in Grasshopper and Maya; robotic production to manipulate physical objects and capture motion sequences; and post-production to combine, configure, and composite images into a unique blend of CG and stop motion. This research program opens up ways of thinking, designing, modeling, and making *in medias res* "constructions." Object Animation anticipates the next generation of CGI emerging in the most advanced Hollywood animation studios but may also find application in cutting-edge architectural design, simulation, and imaging emerging within speculative architectural practices.

94, 194, 195, 196, 198, 200

Digital/Physical Interfaces
Animated Motion Control
Object-Oriented Programming
Visual Programming

Synchronous Robotics
Multi-Robot Choreography
Real-Time
Rigging and Kinematics

Effectors
End Effectors
Physical Computing

Imaging
Image Processing
Machine Vision

Fictioning
Object Animation
Physical Rendering
Robotic Cinematography

Augmented Fabrication
Free-Form Fabrication
Image-Based Fabrication
Multiresolution Fabrication

Computational Materials
Scaffolds and Templates
Transitive Materials

Digital/Physical Interfaces
Animated Motion Control
Object-Oriented Programming
Visual Programming

Synchronous Robotics
Multi-Robot Choreography
Real-Time
Rigging and Kinematics

Effectors
End Effectors
Physical Computing

Imaging
Image Processing
Machine Vision

Fictioning
Object Animation
Physical Rendering
Robotic Cinematography

Augmented Fabrication Free-Form Fabrication
Image-Based Fabrication
Multiresolution Fabrication

Computational Materials
Scaffolds and Templates
Transitive Materials

2.19 SPITTING IMAGES

Instructor: Peter Testa
TA: Uriel Alexander Lopez
Robot House: Jake Newsum
Studio: SCI-Arc 2014–15
Credits: Lucrecia Eudave-Acevedo, Tanveer Harun, Dong Kwak; Mary Franck, Sierra Ruth Helvey, Yuan Mu, Nina Soltani; Rishabh Khurana, Daniela Valladares, Ana Zapata, Sijia Zhu; Chuck Thoi Diep, Dai Sen, Per Stefan Svedberg, Pingting Wei; Lee Chi Hung, Jaehwa Leung, Haoran Wang, Peiyan Zhang

In contemporary software-driven workflows, the image is displacing conventional geometry and 3D modeling as the operational basis of the architectural project—ZBrush, Blender, projection mapping and rendering engines. In this project sequence, the "standard model" of digital design, based on 3D modeling in the computer, is displaced by an original workflow focused on an image-driven toolpath and multiresolution fabrication processes.

The toolpath is applied to conventional architectural representations (i.e. plan, elevation, section), exposing these protocols to new procedures that collapse drawing, imaging, and fabrication. This real-time, contingent methodology does not simply replace conventional design methods but operates in parallel, or in superposition, as a speculative enterprise and the beginnings of an alternative or non-standard model. This design, imaging, and fabrication paradigm aims to advance an abstract, nonrepresentational idea of architecture freed from geometrization.

Spitting Images' design processes use a layered, multitrack technique combining low- and high-resolution images and models; robotic scanning and drawing; and six-axis 3D printing. Particular attention is given to encoding and transcoding resolution and relevant design information across a full range of media. Designing with a purpose-built six-axis material extrusion technique, projects exploit the lacunae and opportunities hidden within shifts from 2D to 3D—privileging image over geometry in the definition of form. Six-axis filament printing is combined with robot-driven photo-scanning and mixed-resolution retopologizing of image information to create a continuous feedback between image and object. The resulting work breaks new ground in advancing mixed-resolution imaging into the analog world of material production and objects that exhibit new properties that are not obtainable via layer-based 3D printing or conventional industrial processes and geometry.

247, 248, 252

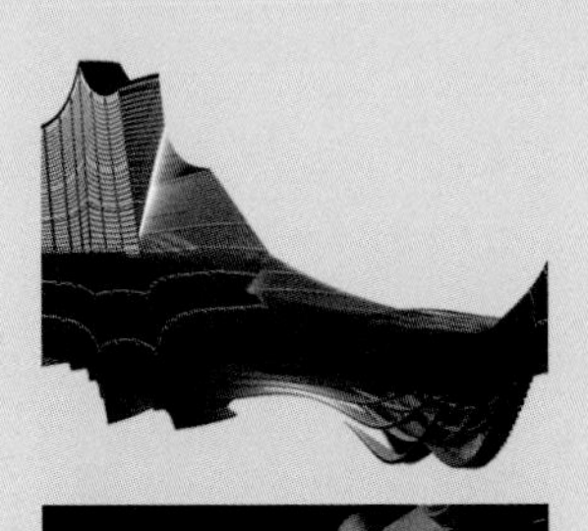

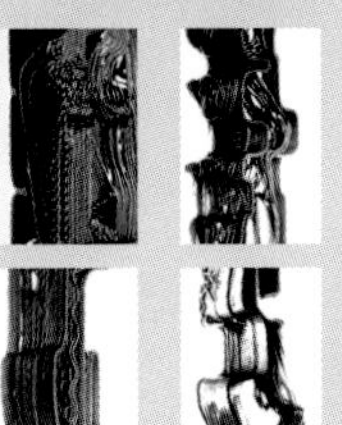

250, 251

249

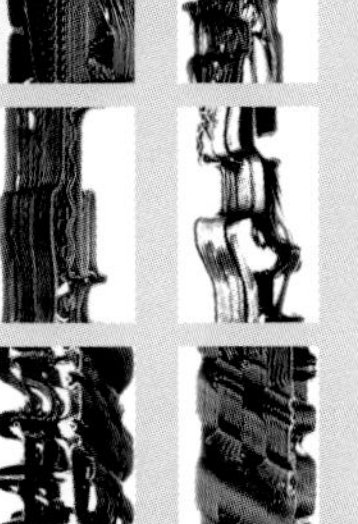

168, 169, 252, 253

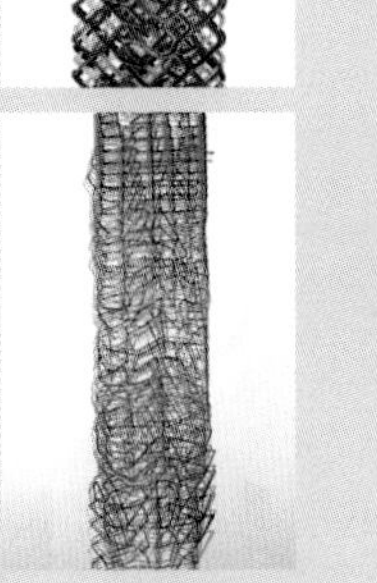

250

250

238, 239

248

168, 239, 265

249

198

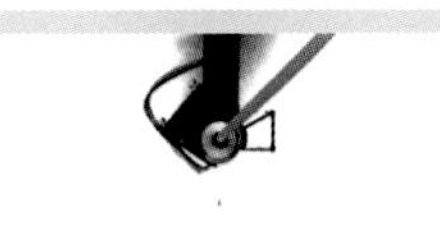

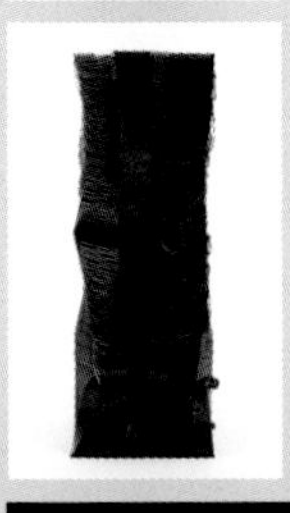

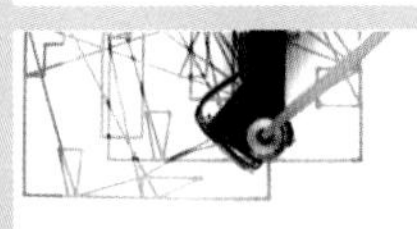

243

196, 197

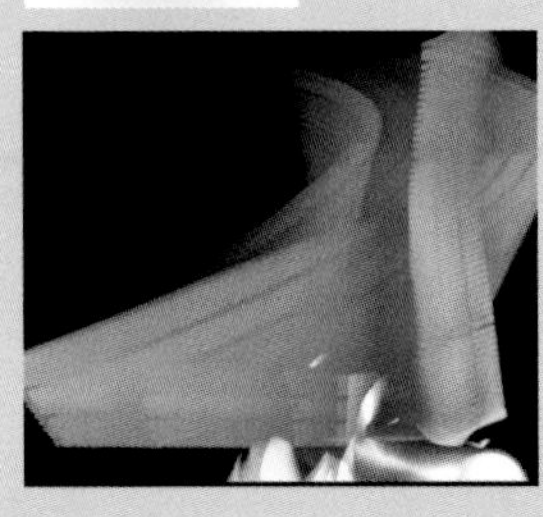

243, 247, 248

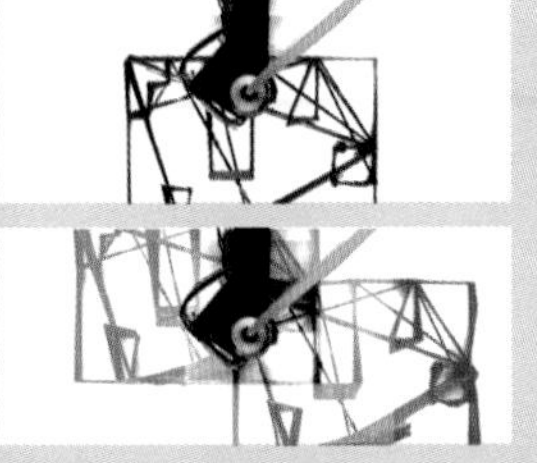

2.20 HARD COPY

Instructor: Peter Testa
Robot House: Jake Newsum
Seminar: SCI-Arc 2015–16
Credits: Andrew Adzemovic, Adrian Cortez, Stefan Svedberg, Yunyou Zhang; Agustina Alaines, Oren Harris, Galileo Morandi, Anthony Rosales; Daniel Hapton, Anthony Rossetto Jr., Feiran Wang, Aaron Young, Elias Darham, Jacob Falk, Patrick Geske, Stefan von Hallberg, Karin Hedlund

Hard Copy explores the aesthetics and contours of a contemporary "post-digital" formalism that turns from "relationism" to reassess the autonomy of the object. With extensive use of machine vision, work advances via real-time workflows across digital and physical media. Eschewing the default protocols of digital modeling and rendering, this project series begins with a subversion of early computer graphics experiments based on the Cornell Box, the 1980s litmus test originally aimed at correlating digital and physical scenes. Where the Cornell Box sought photorealism, Hard Copy operates across non-correlated or cloned digital and physical workspaces in parallel, in series, and in superposition rather than synthesis. The sensibility aims to play with the increasing overlap in post-digital culture between the fictive and the actual and what is generated by software and rendered in physical form.

The series uses machine vision protocols to transform conventions of projective drawing and modeling. Projects seek to articulate a specific way of looking at objects (in this case, classical and baroque sculpture) in relation to historical examples and conventions of representation, and tie these to ways of seeing. Projects begin within what can be understood as a conventional domain of mimetic representation, only to develop a more complex exchange between the mimetic and the generative and then to produce new formal logics and images out of a multiplicity of points of view.

No longer concerned with realism, images are understood from an altogether different vantage point. Digital imaging tends towards a realist projection that seeks to perfectly match pixel screen images to raster layer-based 3D modeling images generated and modeled in the computer. In this "standard model," translation from pixel to raster output, from computer graphics to physical media, is automated rather than design directed. In Hard Copy, projects examine discrepancies between perception and the perceived, between sight and the physical object, and how the controlled overlay of the two produces opportunities both analytical and generative. By capturing specific lighting conditions on the physical object, and projecting those onto the virtual synthetic object, specific conditions emerge to produce different objects. Those discrepancies are isolated by color and volumized according to the parameters of a range of colored light values. Objects produce objects—each new object is a recompletion of the original. Each instance produces a new object; it uses ways of seeing to produce new wholes.

203, 204, 205

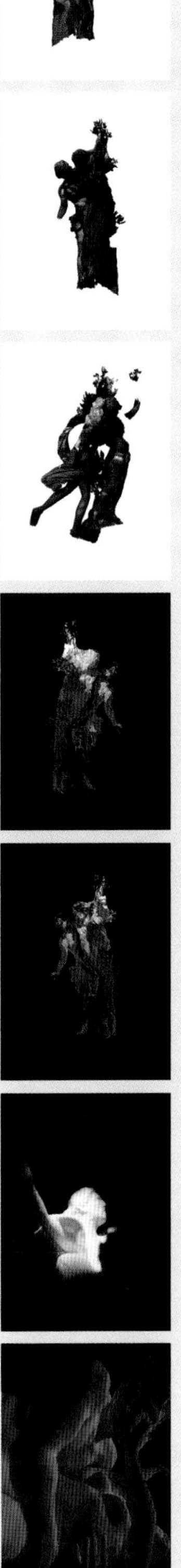

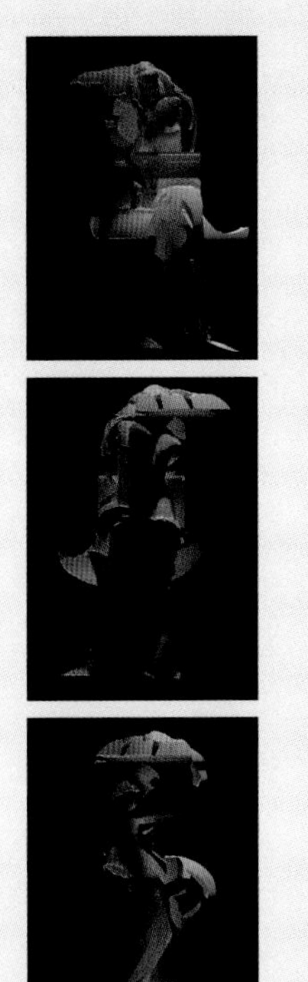

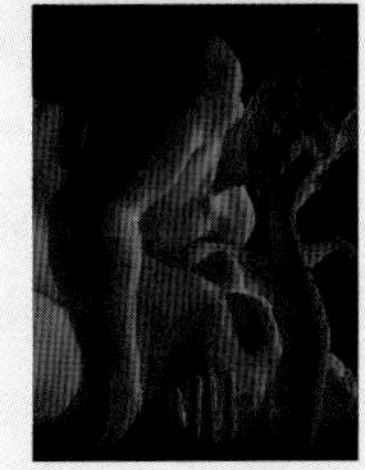

2.21 IMPOSTURES & IMPOSITIONS

Instructor: Peter Testa
TA: Anass Benhachmi
Robot House: Jake Newsum
Studio: SCI-Arc 2015
Credits: Laura Crosskey, Ayuna Mitupova, Stefan Von Hallberg, Sven Winkler; Hong Yang Lin, Xiangtai Sun, Ruizi Qin; Min Duan, Yichao Li, Menting Liu, Shilpa Sushil; Alaines Augusta, Oren Harris, Galileo Morandi, Anthony Rosales

Impostures & Impositions investigates a "deep digitality" that aims to invent a new mode of vision out of the collapse of earlier visual and representational schema in architecture. Pioneering a new understanding of machine vision tied to robotics, multiple points of view and matrices of vision are created. The project series originates in the construction of parallel, non-correlated or cloned digital and physical workspaces. This image discourse is on one hand closer to earlier instrumentation in the discipline (Dürer's drawing machines, panoramas, and so on) but it also runs parallel to cutting-edge film and video studios that move seamlessly back and forth across the digital/physical interface in real-time.

Starting with found or proxy objects (models), in this case three tenth- to fourteenth-century canonical buildings that make up the Piazza del Duomo in Pisa, design begins within a conventional domain of mimetic representation, only to develop a more complex exchange between the mimetic and the generative to produce new formal logics and images. Work seeks to articulate a specific way of looking at architectural objects in relation to historical conventions of representation and tie these to ways of seeing. Careful consideration is given to the particular typological, morphological, and syntactic elements that make up each object and how they may be mobilized in the creation of "super-objects," made up of nested objects—rendered as simultaneous possibilities or as a form of superposition. Sets of re-imaging strategies are established following the geometric characteristics of the architectural elements. These specific points of view are inherent in the object rather than established externally. Work incorporates animation, simulation, and emulation techniques that overlay digital and physical, actual and virtual representations to achieve specific architectural effects and shifts in resolution and scale.

This discourse and project series critically engages machine vision to expose new possibilities in which digitality and analogicity are addressed together as two modal conditions in parallel feedback and feedforward loops. Work investigates mediated vision and the gap between human and machine representation as a space for a new kind of modeling and drawing via multiple and simultaneous projections. The confrontation between "old" and "new" media produces in the work traces of disruption antithetical to any precise computer-generated genesis while simultaneously challenging a human-centered viewpoint that continues to dominate design thinking.

178

201, 203

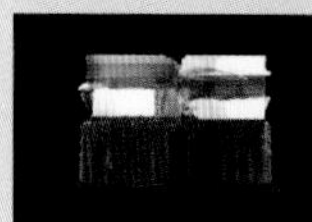

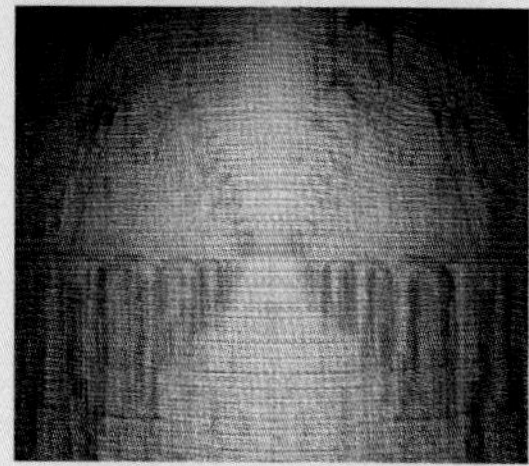

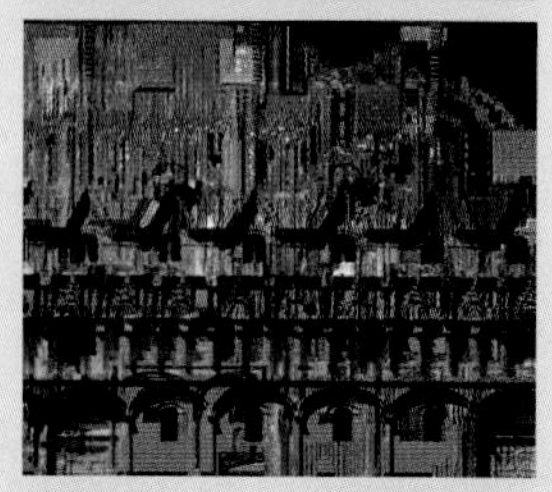

248, 249

2.22 DRAWING FROM THE DIGITAL, RENDERING OUT THE ANALOG

Instructor: Devyn Weiser
TA: Daniel Hapton
Robot House: Jake Newsum
Seminar: SCI-Arc 2016
Credits: Aaron Young Choi, ChienHan Ashley Hsu, Jiahao Yu, Huijin Zheng; Alaines Augustina, Andrea Baena, Eric Eisenhut, Hsien-Yang Kuo; Kevin Finch, Anthony Rossetto, Vincent Ngu To, Ganna Grininger; Rachel Burke, Eyad Kalaji, Kazuhiro Okamoto, Sasha Tillmann; Justin Kim, Vaishali Shah, Thao Trinh

"With the profusion of reproduction techniques, things become flatter. At any rate the vast majority of projections work that way, since two-dimensional information is so much easier to handle than three-dimensional things. In practice, projection has become thoroughly directional because of the availability of certain instruments and machines for making pictures."
—Robin Evans, *Architectural Projection*, 1989

Since Evans's essay, drawing and rendering in architecture have become increasingly automated through computer graphics procedures—directional projection, clipping planes, photorealistic rendering, and so on. Questioning the sufficiency of digitality, this project series introduces and explores techniques of representation that shift established hierarchies between the geometric and the stereometric, the image and the object. With reference to contemporary painters who are taking digital effects back into painting (keystrokes to brushstrokes), a vector-based drawing project appropriates two-dimensional effects (lines, strokes, fills, gradients) in the three-dimensional environment of Rhino using purpose-written Grasshopper scripts. This line work is made physical as a raster-based rendering project produced within a hybrid analog/digital setup. The earliest form of color photography, three-color process, is coupled with machine vision via robotically controlled camera paths in Robot House. Images are mapped back to digital models using Grasshopper scripts that exploit discrepancies in resolution and registration. Heinrich Kühn's autochromes, David Salle's "Ghost Paintings," and Andy Warhol's screen prints are antecedents to this post-photography aesthetic that oscillates between vector and raster effects to yield a new form of image- and object-making.

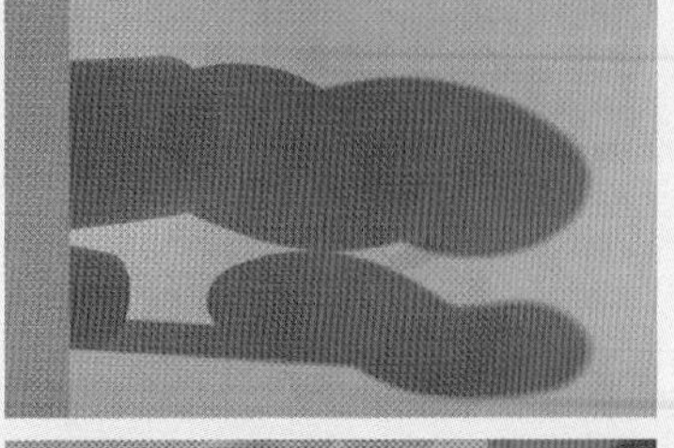

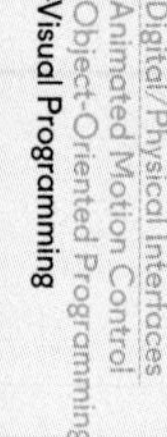

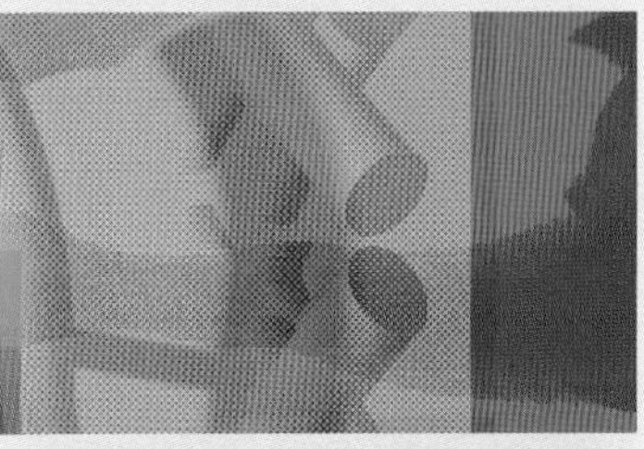

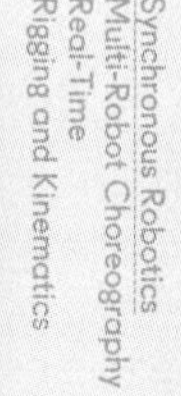

171, 206

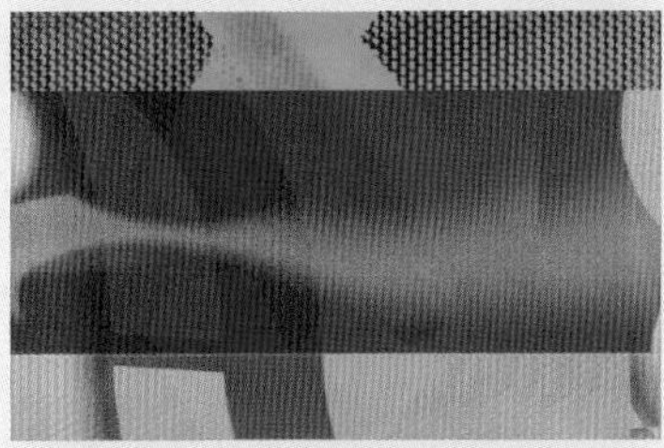

Effectors
End Effectors
Physical Computing

Imaging
Image Processing
Machine Vision

206

Fictioning
Object Animation
Physical Rendering
Robotic Cinematography

201, 202

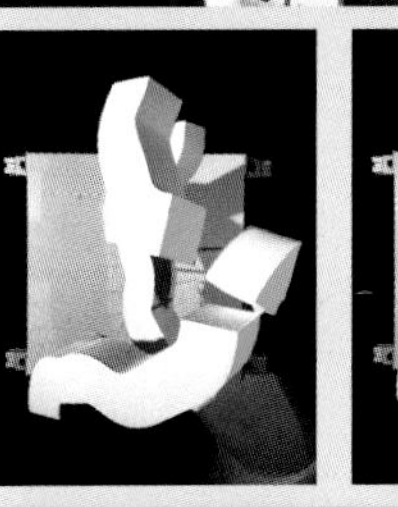

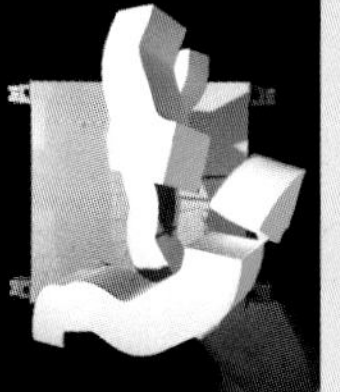

Augmented Fabrication
Free-Form Fabrication
Image-Based Fabrication
Multiresolution Fabrication

206

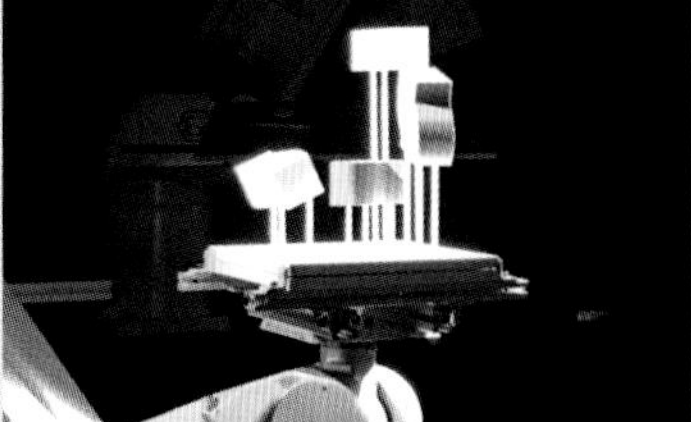

Computational Materials
Scaffolds and Templates
Transitive Materials

Glossary

Words in *italics* cross-refer to individual entries in the glossary.

actuator
A motor that translates control signals into mechanical movement. The control signals may be electrical, pneumatic, or hydraulic, just as the power supply may be any of these.

anisotropic
A property of an object or material that is directional-dependent, which implies different properties in different directions (as opposed to isotropy). An example of an anisotropic material is fiber-based composites, such as carbon fiber, which is stronger along the grain than across it.

Arduino
An open-source hardware and software system and microcontroller-based kits used to build *end effectors* and interactive objects that can sense and control physical devices.

artificial intelligence (AI)
The science and engineering of making intelligent computer programs and machines. These machine learning techniques and algorithms have wide application to robotics including image processing, pattern recognition, computer vision, and *real-time motion control*.

asynchronous See synchronous.

Autodesk Maya
A 3D computer animation software used for robotic simulation, emulation, and *motion control*. The joints of the robot are rigged as an articulated structure or skeleton in Maya and a rendering camera is directly linked to a physical camera attached to the end of an actual robot arm, offering endless possibilities across the digital/physical interface.

cloned (workspace)
The creation of cloned digital and physical workspaces involves more than simply mirroring or copying, as they are constructed in parallel taking into account the specific attributes of each medium or domain. In computing, the clone copies the structure of data and not the data itself. Dynamic clones continuously map changes to the original object onto the cloned object.

cloud robotics
The process of endowing robot systems with more capacity and intelligence from the cloud. This new paradigm extends the concept of *synchronous* and collaborative robotics to emerging research in cloud computing, machine learning, big data, open-source software, and the Internet of Things.

contingent
In 1936, Alan Turing showed that some functions cannot be computed, and thereby described the limits of computing machines. Incompleteness and incomputability—that is, contingency—can be used as conceptual tools in the aesthetic investigation of computation and robotics.

degrees of freedom
The number of values in a system that are free to vary expressed in terms of Cartesian coordinates (x, y, and z) and angular movements (yaw, pitch, and roll). A robotic joint is equal to one degree of freedom.

end effector
The device at the end of a robotic arm, designed to interact with materials and the environment. Sensing and actuation can be incorporated into tooling to support quasi-autonomous *feedback* and *feedforward* modalities.

feedback
A signal from the robot equipment about conditions as they actually exist, rather than as the computer has directed them to exist.

feedforward
A feedforward system is an open system that does not have any *feedback* loop for control or operation. Feedforward requires a mathematical model of the process and machine being controlled and any inputs of feedback the system might receive.

forward kinematics (FK)
The use of *kinematic* equations of a robot to compute the position of the end effector from specified values of joint parameters. Motion of the model is defined by the animator as no account is made of physical laws such as gravity or collision.

free-form fabrication (robotic)
An approach to fabrication that produces complex forms without the use of molds, and includes, but is not limited to, additive manufacturing technologies such as 3D printing.

generative
A computational model often involving the use of programming environments (Processing, Vvv) or scripting (Grasshopper in Rhinoceros 3D) that allows designers to explore a greater number of design possibilities with modifiable constraints with or without design evaluation routines.

inverse kinematics (IK)
The process of calculating joint angles of a multiple-degree-of-freedom robot based on the coordinates of the *end effector*.

improvisational robotics
A non-linear approach to interactive robotics systems that can respond to a changing environment and does not rely on pre-programmed motion paths. This paradigm generally requires *real-time* interaction with human users and various levels of sensing and *artificial intelligence* (AI).

industrial robot
Industrial robots have various configurations (Cartesian, cylindrical, polar, revolute, and SCARA are the most commonly used). The majority of articulated robots feature six axes, also called six degrees of freedom, allowing the arm to move to any point within a *working envelope* or work sphere. The robot consists of two units: the robotic arm, and the controller, a computer control system that relays signals to and from the robotic arm. Six-axis robots allow for greater flexibility and can perform a wider range of applications than robots with fewer axes.

kinematics
The study of all possible motions of a robot including the design of linkages to perform motion; also their planning, such as choosing a sequence of movements to achieve a broader task. Having a visual understanding of robot kinematics is necessary for effective use of the *work sphere*.

Leap Motion
A proprietory computer hardware sensor and input device that uses hand and gestural tracking to control a multiple-degree-of-freedom robot.

machine vision
Technology and methods that allow a computer or robot to "see" using 2D or 3D images and digital signal processing. After an image is acquired it is processed. A range of image processing methods includes stitching/registration, filtering, segmentation, edge detection, color analysis, pattern recognition, and metrology or measurement.

match moving
A cinematic technique that cuts across the digital/physical divide allowing for the insertion of computer graphics into live-action footage, and to match robotic camera movements in 3D computer animations.

material agency
Notions of non-anthropocentric "material" agency are gaining currency in art, design, and related disciplines to account for a more active role of matter and artifacts in shaping material culture. Within an expanded technological environment this idea may extend to challenging conventions of the real and the fake, the digital and the natural.

motion capture
The process of recoding the movement of objects involving measuring an object's position and orientation in physical space and recording that information in a digital format.

motion control
The position and velocity of robotic manipulators are controlled by electrical servo motors. The interface between the motion controller and the robot must provide coherent synchronization. Control functions include velocity, position, pressure, and impedance.

multiresolution fabrication
A design to fabrication process that applies multiresolution meshes and image processing from computer graphics to 3D printing and the fabrication of multimaterial parts. This image-driven technique affords the possibility of material change-out during part fabrication.

non-correlation
Where earlier forms of representation and graphical user interfaces sought a one-to-one correlation between the image (in the render window) and the object (in the physical world) this model creatively exploits discrepancies and slippage between these various workspaces and models of representation.

object-oriented programming (OOP)
A programming paradigm based on the concept of objects rather than actions and data. RhinoScript and Python are examples of OOP that involve the design of modular code for extensibility and reuse.

photogrammetry
The integration of image processing hardware including photography and scanning is used to recover exact positioning of surface points on captured objects as well as motion pathways. This information can be mapped back onto 3D digital models and animations.

physical computing
A computational paradigm focused on building interactive interfaces and physical systems. Sensors and microcontrollers translate analog input to a software system and electromechanical devices. Haptic interfaces (giving tactile feedback to the user) are also an example of physical computing, involving motion capture and gesture recognition.

Python
A high-level interactive and objected-oriented scripting language, Python is used to translate animated character rigs (articulated structures or skeletons) developed in *Autodesk Maya* to motion paths for Stäubli six-axis robot arms that operate under the *VAL3* programming language. There is also an additional Python component to manage the robot-to-robot communication (¡charla!).

real-time
This control model implies the robot reacts directly to inputs from the outside, and allows material processes, video projections, sound, and robot movements to be synchronized. The robot is equipped with an interactive control system that enables it to react to commands "on the fly."

repeatability
The variability of the *end effector*'s position and orientation as the robot arm makes the same motion paths under the same external conditions.

robot simulation
A model of a robot system constructed to create, imitate, and observe processes offline. A virtual robot in a 3D modeling and rendering environment (e.g. Autodesk Maya) is capable of emulating the motion of the actual robot or multiple robots with single or intersecting *work spheres*.

singularity
Kinematic singularities, a point in the robot's movement when the joints become redundant, are caused by the *inverse kinematics* of the robot. The more axes a robot has the more possibilities of singularities as there are more axes that can line up with each other. Singularities can be circumvented by programming and positioning.

superposition
In the quantum phenomenon known as superposition of states, particles are thought of as existing across all possible states at the same time. This weird situation may offer a model to conceptualize continuity of digitality and analogicity.

synchronous (robotics)
Synchronous robotics implies that robots must be aware of one another and must execute in some way that is dependent on the other(s). Asynchronous means they are totally independent and neither one must consider the other either in initiation or in execution. Multi-arm, synchronous robotics offers networked and distributed control and choreography of synchronous and asynchronous motion sequences. These systems are far more complex than single, task-specific, and pre-programmed industrial robots. Synchronous systems extend to and make possible a wide range of interactions among robot systems, with material processes and collaboration with human users.

teach mode
The control state that allows the generation and storage of positional data points effected by moving the robot arm through a path of intended motions and sequences. Robot arms and controllers are accessed from a teach pendant interface.

tomography
A type of volume imaging by virtual sectioning of a scanned object to produce three-dimensional images of the internal structure of a solid body.

toolpath
To generate a toolpath for a six-axis robotic arm, traditionally the robot toolpath is taught or programmed manually. Coupling robotics with machine vision and sensing allows for toolpaths to be un-programmed and driven in response to material agency, environmental factors, or other forms of *contingent* computing.

transitive materials

Materials are becoming smarter, with programmed, computational and robotic-driven behaviors. Emerging materials are capable of input/output, feedback and feedforward, computation and interactivity. These smart materials can alter their physical properties in response to external inputs, or in the case of composite materials laminate or weave together distinct materials to achieve specific behaviors.

VAL3 language

Robot software is the set of coded instructions that tell a robot what tasks to perform. Stäubli robot systems operate with a dedicated robotics language, VAL3. A flexible, modular approach makes it possible to reuse code for multiple motion sequences and scenarios.

virtualization

Refers to creating a virtual (rather than actual) version of a robotic platform, workflow, and operating system. Allows the simulation of hardware components with concurrent operating systems before actually building the hardware prototype.

visual programming

User-friendly visual programming tools abstract away functions, variables, and syntax rules of the underlying code and allow users to create programs by manipulating program elements graphically. Grasshopper is a visual programming language that runs within Rhinoceros 3D, a CAD application used to program and control robot systems.

working envelope, work sphere

In robotics the working envelope, or work sphere, is the volume that can be reached by the end of the robot arm. It is usually defined by the center of the *end effector* mounting plate and excludes tools or workpieces the end effector may hold. Not all points within the work sphere are equally accessible and there are "dead zones" that cannot be reached by the end of the robot arm.

Bibliography

Bishop, Christopher M. *Pattern Recognition and Machine Learning*. Vienna: Springer, 2007.

Blau, Eve and Kaufman, Edward, eds. *Architecture and Its Image: Four Centuries of Architectural Representation*. Cambridge: Canadian Centre for Architecture and MIT Press, 1989.

Bratton, Benjamin. *The Stack, On Software and Sovereignty*. Cambridge: MIT Press, 2015.

Carpo, Mario and Lemerle, Frederique, eds. *Perspective, Projections and Design: Technologies of Architectural Representation*. London: Routledge, 2007.

Carpo, Mario. *The Alphabet and the Algorithm*. Cambridge: MIT Press, 2011.

Coopmans, Catelijne et al. *Representation in Scientific Practice Revisited*. Cambridge: MIT Press, 2014.

Daston, Lorraine J. and Galison, Peter. *Objectivity*. Zone Books, 2010.

Davies, E.R. *Computer and Machine Vision: Fourth Edition: Theory, Algorithms, Practicalities*. London: Academic Press, 4th edn, 2012.

Evans, Robin. *Translations from Drawing to Building and Other Essays*. Cambridge: MIT Press, 1997.

Evans, Robin. *The Projective Cast: Architecture and Its Three Geometries*. Cambridge: MIT Press, 2000.

Flusser, Vilém. *Into the Universe of Technical Images*. Minneapolis: University of Minnesota Press, 2011.

Galloway, Alexander R. *Protocol: How Control Exists after Decentralization*. Cambridge: MIT Press 2004.

Galloway, Alexander R. *The Interface Effect*. Polity, 2012.

Gibson, James J. The *Ecological Approach to Visual Perception*. Routledge, 2014.

Gramazio, Fabio; Kohler, Matthias; and Willmann, Jan. *The Robotic Touch: How Robots Change Architecture*. Park Books, 2014.

Halpern, Orit. *Beautiful Data: A History of Vision and Reason since 1945*. Duke University Press Books, 2015.

Hughes, John F., et al. *Computer Graphics: Principles and Practice*. Addison-Wesley Professional, 2013.

Jordan, John, M. *Robots*. Cambridge: MIT Press, 2016.

Lefèvre, Wolfgang, ed. *Picturing Machines 1400–1700*. Cambridge: MIT Press, 2004.

Lynch, Michael and Wool, Steve, eds. *Representation in Scientific Practice*. Cambridge: MIT Press, 1990.

Manovich, Lev. "Automation of Sight—From Photography to Computer Vision," in *Electronic Culture: Technology and Visual Representation*, Timothy Druckery, ed., 229–40. New York: Aperture, 1996.

Manovich, Lev. *Software Takes Command*. London: Bloomsbury Academic, 2013.

Mataric, Maja. *The Robotics Primer*. Cambridge: MIT Press 2007.

Menges, Achim and Ahlquist, Sean, eds. *Computational Design Thinking*. London: Wiley, 2011.

Picon, Antoine. *Digital Culture in Architecture*. Birkhäuser Architecture, 2010.

Rancière, Jacques. *The Future of the Image*. London: Verso, 2007.

Reinhardt, Dagmar, Saunders, Rob, and Burry, Jane, eds. *Robotic Fabrication in Architecture, Art and Design*. Vienna: Springer, 2016.

Schröter, Jens. *3D: History, Theory and Aesthetics of the Transplane Image*. London: Bloomsbury, 2014.

Testa, Peter. "Collaboration Machines." Aalto Digital Design Laboratory, Add Thought, Lecture 9 (Helsinki, Oct 11, 2012). http://vimeo.com/532607.

Testa, Peter. "Autonomous Translations," in *Fabrication and Fabrication*, Amit Wolf, ed. Los Angeles: SCI-Arc Press, 2014.

Testa, Peter. "Black Box." Archeology of the Digital, Canadian Centre for Architecture, Toolkit 2013. https://www.youtube.com/watch?v=fl6gIV6PbFQ.

Testa, Peter and Lynn, Greg. "Machine Vision: Seeing Eye to Eye." SCI-Arc Media Archive, streamed Feburary 24, 2016.

Winsberg, Eric. *Science in the Age of Computer Simulation*. Chicago: University of Chicago Press, 2010.

Witt, Andrew J. "A Machine Epistemology in Architecture." *Candide, Journal of Architectural Knowledge* 03 (12/2010): 37–88.

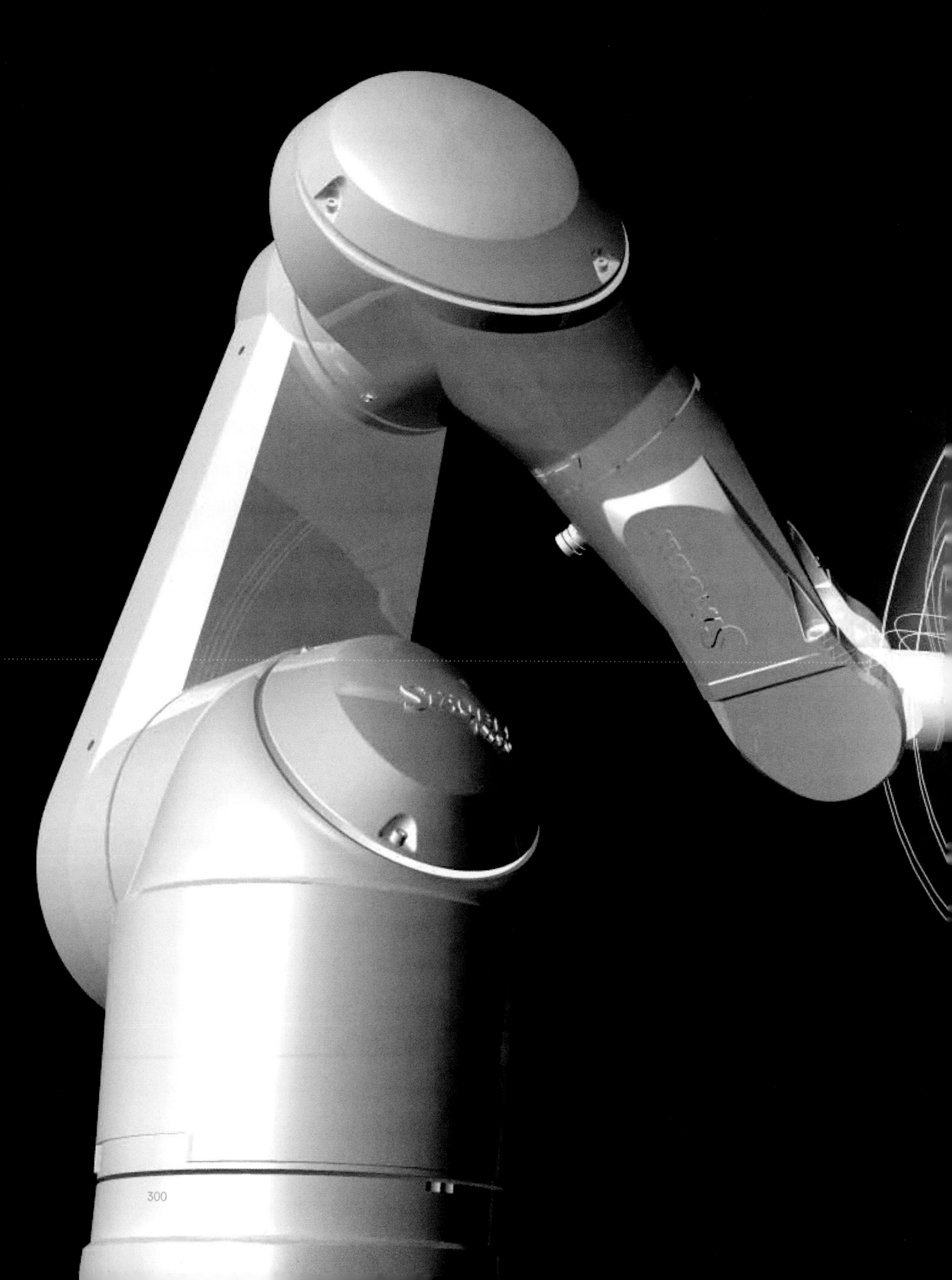

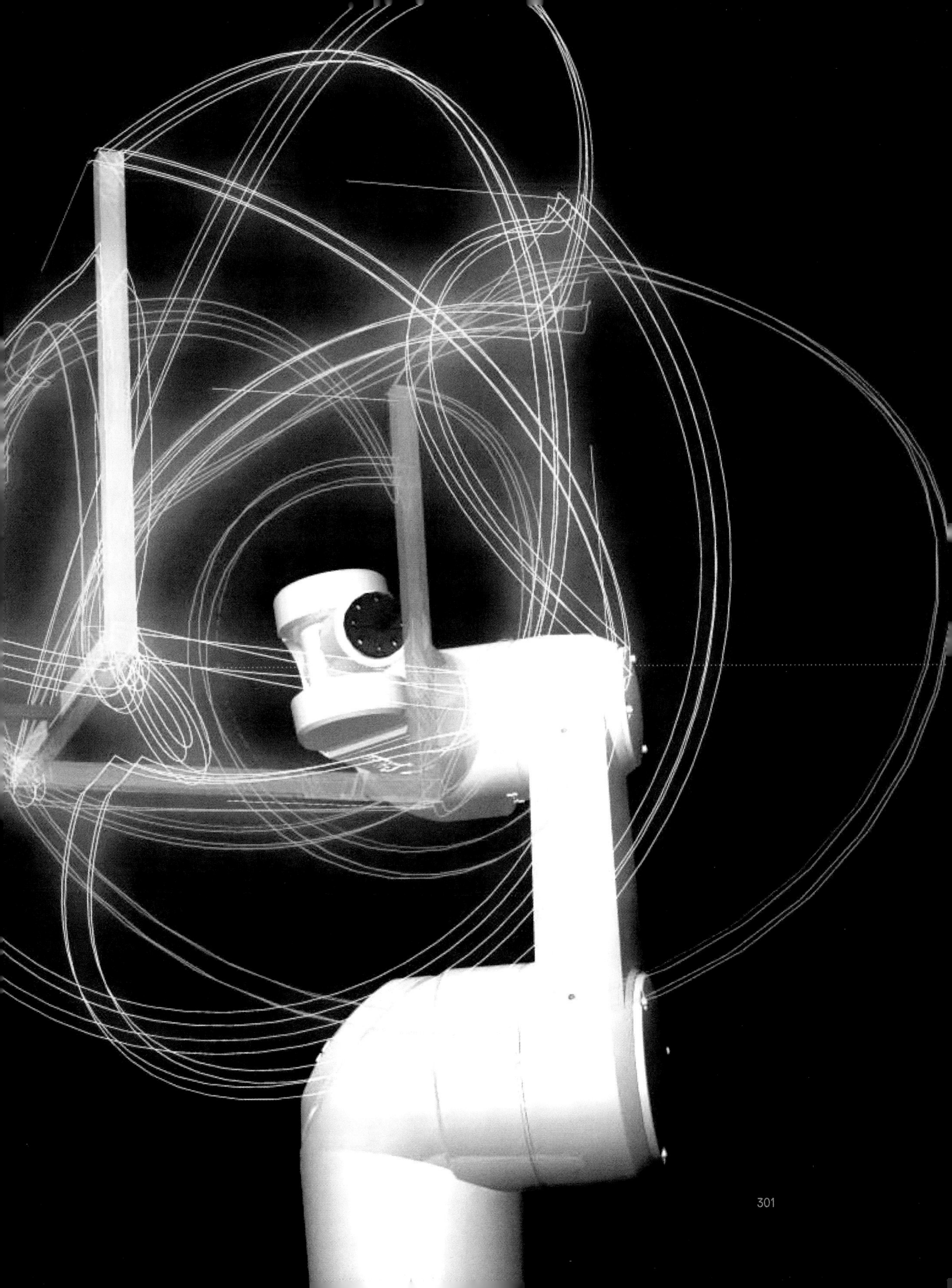

3—
PLAT-
FORM

POLY-SPHERICAL ARCHI-TECTURE

PETER TESTA

Industrial robots are not new, but have been in existence since the 1954 Unimate, and the 1969 six-axis Stanford arm with computer-controlled electronic movement.[1] While the hardware has evolved, control models and interfaces generally remain tied to automation of repetitive pre-programmed tasks. What is new is the introduction of a synchronous, multi-robot control model that breaks the industrial robot away from its role in linear production. With a more abstract work sphere, the Stäubli Unimate industrial robot arms support this improvisational paradigm.[2] Where previously industrial robots excluded contingency and real-time interaction with humans, other objects, and the environment, in Robot House this industrial logic is undone.

ROBOT HOUSE

At once speculative design and animation studio, imaging and simulation lab, movement and prototyping platform, Robot House occupies two industrial bays, between studios and fabrication shops, within SCI-Arc's downtown Los Angeles campus. The architecture of Robot House is delineated by the selection and placement of six Stäubli robot systems: one mobile TX40L with a 515 mm reach, two pedestal-mounted TX90s with a 1000 mm reach, one catwalk-mounted TX90L with a 1200 mm reach, and two RX160s with a 1710 mm reach. With a fully spherical range of motion, these small- to medium-payload robots combine to form a complex shaping environment with real-time interaction. Just placing multiple robots next to each other and treating them as individual parts of a larger story impinges on their individual statuses. Open to continual reorganization, a total of thirty-one combinations of six-axis robots is possible as designers choreograph their synchronous and asynchronous motion.

WORK SPHERES

The polyspherical architecture of intersecting work spheres characteristic of Robot House challenges assumptions of Cartesian and Euclidean models of geometrical space.[3] Rather than a network that lacks a spatial metaphor, the motion space is conceptualized as spheres of different sizes and forms that possess relational capacity. Work spheres are not idealized homogeneous spaces but are constrained by proxemics and singularities. The configuration space of these robotic systems is curved, and this plays a large role in the dynamic behavior of the system as it links robotics to new geometries from topological manifolds and mappings to morphisms.[4]

DIGITAL/PHYSICAL INTERFACES

Robot House aims to expand design-focused, improvisational control models, interfaces, and workflows. Built specifically for architects, artists, and designers, software tools are scalable and portable with application to any number of design, visualization, simulation, emulation, virtualization, and fabrication scenario. Using visual programming and animation-based motion control interfaces, designers can program robot systems and toolpaths using familiar off-the shelf computer modeling, design, and animation software. Three key interfaces have been developed, including the Autodesk Maya plug-in esperant.0/charla; the Rhino Grasshopper plug-in CRANE; and Quad, a platform-independent toolset.

ESPERANT.0

The first-generation interface esperant.0 is a plug-in for Autodesk Maya that is original in combining robotic motion control with animation techniques from keyframing to match moving. As software designers Brandon Kruysman and Jonathan Proto note, the core technique of esperant.0 is character rigging, typically found in the animation and film industry. This approach opens up the potential of animating the physical world, where designers have the unique ability to experiment with materials in motion, rather than only executing fabrication-related tasks.[5] esperant.0 supports invention of new workflows, including the creation of digital simulations linking both forward and inverse kinematic modeling to tie simulations to actual robotic motion in real-time. New control models, based on transcoding from Maya's 3D modeling program to Python and into Stäubli's robot language VAL3, support multi-robot synchronous motion control. Additionally, end effectors are fully integrated into the esperant.0 model and robot controller, or are externally controlled by users.

The basic concept behind the platform is to "rig" a skeleton for a physical machine. Custom character rigs are constructed for each robot using Autodesk Maya. In place of typical joint constructions for skeletons, more accurate and precise expression-based character rigs offer a computationally efficient solution to having multiple six-axis robots moving in a single digital model. Using Python scripting, the animated rigs are translated to the native robot language (VAL3) with its corresponding speed, I/O (input/output) for tooling (pneumatic or digital), and synchronization information for multi-robot applications. This exchange from digital simulation to physical motion is central to the esperant.0 platform.

Robots are rigged in a number of ways, depending on the type of motion being designed. In addition to more conventional forward kinematics (FK) and inverse kinematics (IK), hybrid rigs have been developed that, for example, combine forward and inverse kinematics. Experimental projects on the esperant.0 platform have included a single skeleton that rigs three robots conceptually as one machine. End effectors act as an additional rig attached to the robot arm, animated and translated to inputs/outputs for the robot. These unique methods of control extend the range of motion in ways previously unachievable using industrial robots. For the designer, this platform has the unique ability to design motion but also to program, simulate, and speculate all at the same time. In esperant.0, Maya's physics engine, kinematic solvers, and animation tools become part of a real-time robotic interface with endless possibilities of virtualization, image capture, and real-time motion control. esperant.0 combines with Robot House's polyspherical architecture to create a robotic extension of the digital—a speculative design platform that bridges the digital and physical without synthesis or reducing one to the other.

¡CHARLA!

Adding functionality to esperant.0, ¡charla! introduces a protocol for synchronous and asynchronous multi-agent systems with real-time adjustment.[6] The primary unit of representation in this system is the keyframe, just as a precise understanding of time is essential to synchronous motion control. Each individual object in the robot cell has its own timeframe, and choreography is based on "cueing," such that synchronization is both time-based and event-based. In this feedback system, multi-robot scenarios can react to disruptions and changes in the actual environment. Synchronous real-time robotics presents many opportunities and challenges as joint positions, multi-axial rotational speeds, and changeable end effectors must all be updated and coordinated in real-time. To achieve fully real-time coordination, the next-generation synchronous robotics control platform integrates hardware in the form of a Programmable Logic Controller (PLC) for automation of electromechanical processes.

CRANE

Where esperant.0 focuses on the visual and spatial, CRANE, a robot motion control interface for Grasshopper (the parametric modeling plug-in for Rhino), shifts attention to objects, surfaces, and patterning. CRANE provides custom Inverse Kinematic solving, visualization, diagnostic information, and one-click file generation for the VAL3 language underlying Stäubli robot systems.[7] CRANE can access all of Rhino's functionality as a CAD/CAM toolset now extended to include six-axis robots and custom-built tooling and fixtures. Multiple types of inputs and options allow users to create highly customizable and editable motion paths, control logics and process sequences without changing the underlying code. CRANE takes advantage of the advanced logic and data matching methods built into Grasshopper to parametrically assign simulation and control settings. For example, this functionality extends to the capacity to trigger electrical and pneumatic outputs on end effectors based on changing parameters in the simulation. Over time this open source approach to robotics is continuously updated, modified, and extended, just as designers share motion and tool libraries.

GESTURAL INTERFACES

In addition to the core Robot User Interfaces (RUI), a series of experimental gestural interfaces are developed in relation to specific project objectives seeking high levels of interactivity and multiple-user involvement. For example, Gesture+Form, developed by Brian Harms and Uriel Lopez, interlaces a range of existing tools to create innovative operating systems. Behind these intuitive interfaces, a range of software tools—Leap Motion, Firefly, Touch Designer—combines with machine vision and sensing to provide a real-time or near real-time interactive design platform. Using gestural and/or tablet-based touch-screen inputs, this approach circumvents mediation of inputs by traditional robot teach pendants, or mouse and keyboard, allowing users greater freedom in interacting with robot systems in physical space. For example, Gesture+Form supports real-time intervention in toolpaths and 3D output. The apparatus can be expanded to incorporate designer-programmed motion and material libraries—expanding the ability of the designer to intuitively enter a convergent workspace that combines generative and procedural design approaches.

QUAD V

As a third-generation digital/physical interface, Quad V instantiates a multi-agent paradigm able to run and combine tools and process sequences from esperant.0/Maya and CRANE/Rhino and transcode them into VAL3 or other industrial robot system or machine tool languages. Built by Curime Batliner and Jake Newsum with the Quad V authoring system, this platform-independent approach integrates within a single interface all elements that make up a project, performance, or design scenario—the robot is just one element among others. By separating information gathering and information generation, Quad V offers a multitracked temporal- and event-based system that is endlessly recombinant. Real-time control allows the robot to react directly to external inputs—supporting integration of animation, real-time texture mapping, sound, and robot motion. This interactive control system enables the robot to react to commands "on the fly." All commands are sent via TCP/IP so that the robot can be actuated from any authoring system or combination of authoring systems. Once information is flowing to the robots in VAL3 then a number of feedback options may be realized—through analysis, diagnostics, and in real-time projecting information for shared interface or recording for later use.

Streaming directly to robot systems, the interface supports full real-time synchronous motion control. By integrating Stäubli's uniVAL tools for speed synchronization and a third-party PLC (Programmable Logic Controller), any number and type of machine- or sensor-based element can be integrated and hacked into the workspace and synchronized with robot movements.

With the addition of machine vision and sensing modalities, which may be embedded in materials and the environment, geometric parameters and logics are redistributed.

END EFFECTORS

Industrial robot arms become specific and further constrained through the addition of end effectors that interoperate between control mechanisms, designers, and material processes. In Robot House this specificity is mobilized with reference to the whole conceptual equipment before it is put to work. With the prospect of increasingly "intelligent" tooling, the design protocols associated with the idea of end effectors are both extensible and scalable. With technologies of feedback there is a reversal of flows of information in which new contingencies and forms of creativity can develop. Robot House interfaces such as esperant.0 are designed with this interactivity and feedback in mind, just as robot arms themselves are becoming wired and connected to real-time Ethernet. At the most immediate level the availability of inexpensive, open-source, and hackable technology is allowing for ingenious mash-ups and customized tooling. These new classes of end effectors interact with designers, machines, materials and their environment via electronic sensing, machine vision, and actuation. Going further, sensors and actuators operating from within tailored material systems shift the definition of tooling from a mechanical to a biochemical model—ultimately challenging previous definitions of tools and theories of technology.

1—The Stanford arm was designed in 1969 by Victor Scheinman in the Stanford Artificial Intelligence Lab (SAIL). With six degrees of freedom, this manipulator was one of the first "robots" designed exclusively for computer control. The kinematic configuration of the arm is non-anthropomorphic with six points (five revolute, one prismatic).

2—The typical industrial robot arm has a directional, "hammer head" work envelope inflected towards the industrial production line.

3—For example, the configuration space of a two-joint robot arm is a torus and not a plane.

4—The spherical "work sphere" geometry links to Henri Poincaré's foundations of topology and interest in the topological properties that characterize a sphere.

5—Brandon Kruysman and Jonathan Proto, "Augmented Fabrication," Rob/Arch 2012: Robotic Fabrication in Architecture, Art and Design (Berlin: Springer 2013), 74.

6—icharla! was developed and implemented by Brandon Kruysman, Jonathan Proto, and Diego Trujilio Pisanty.

7—CRANE was originally designed by Brian Harms and subsequently developed by Jake Newsum.

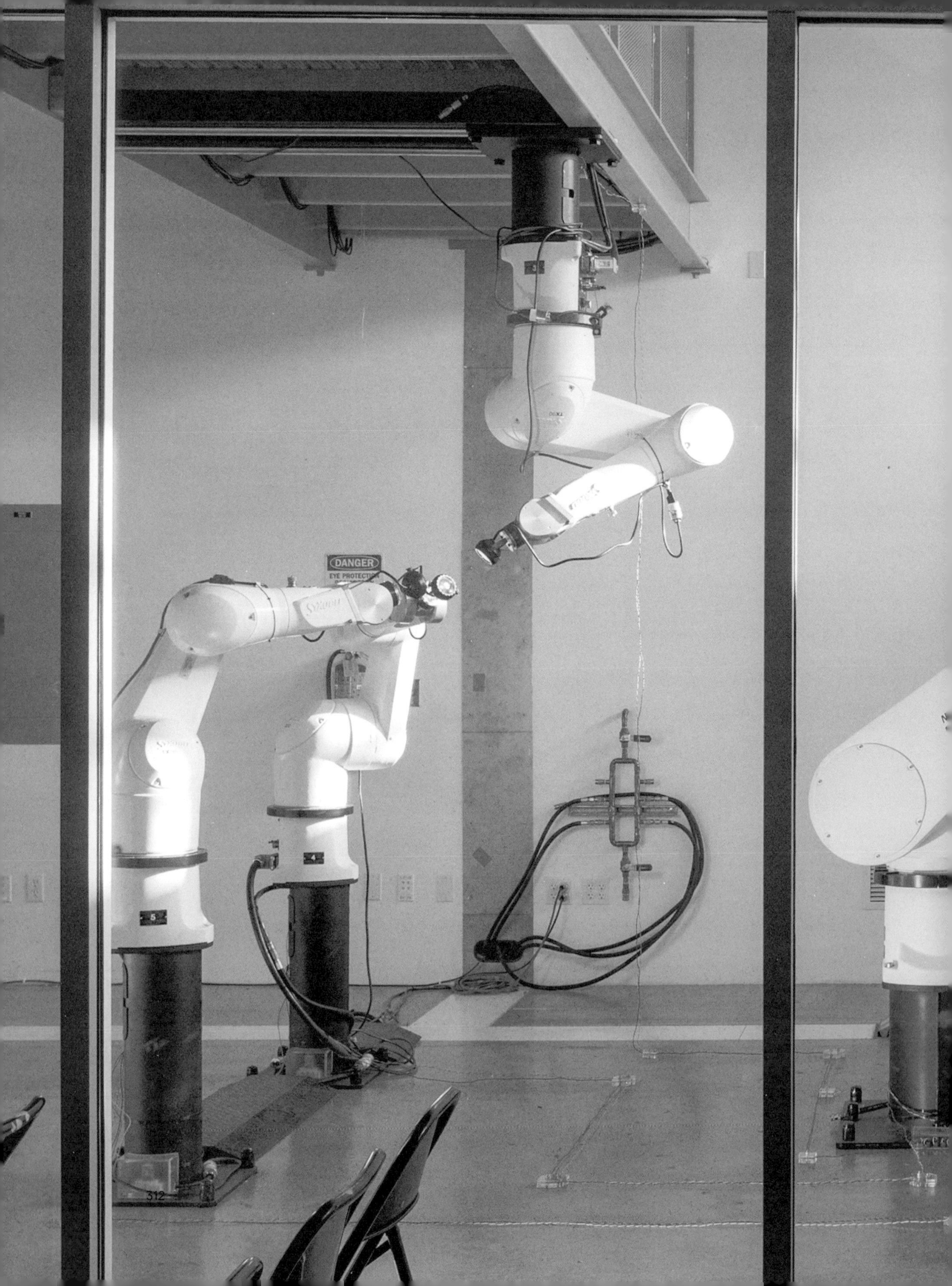
DANGER
EYE PROTECTION

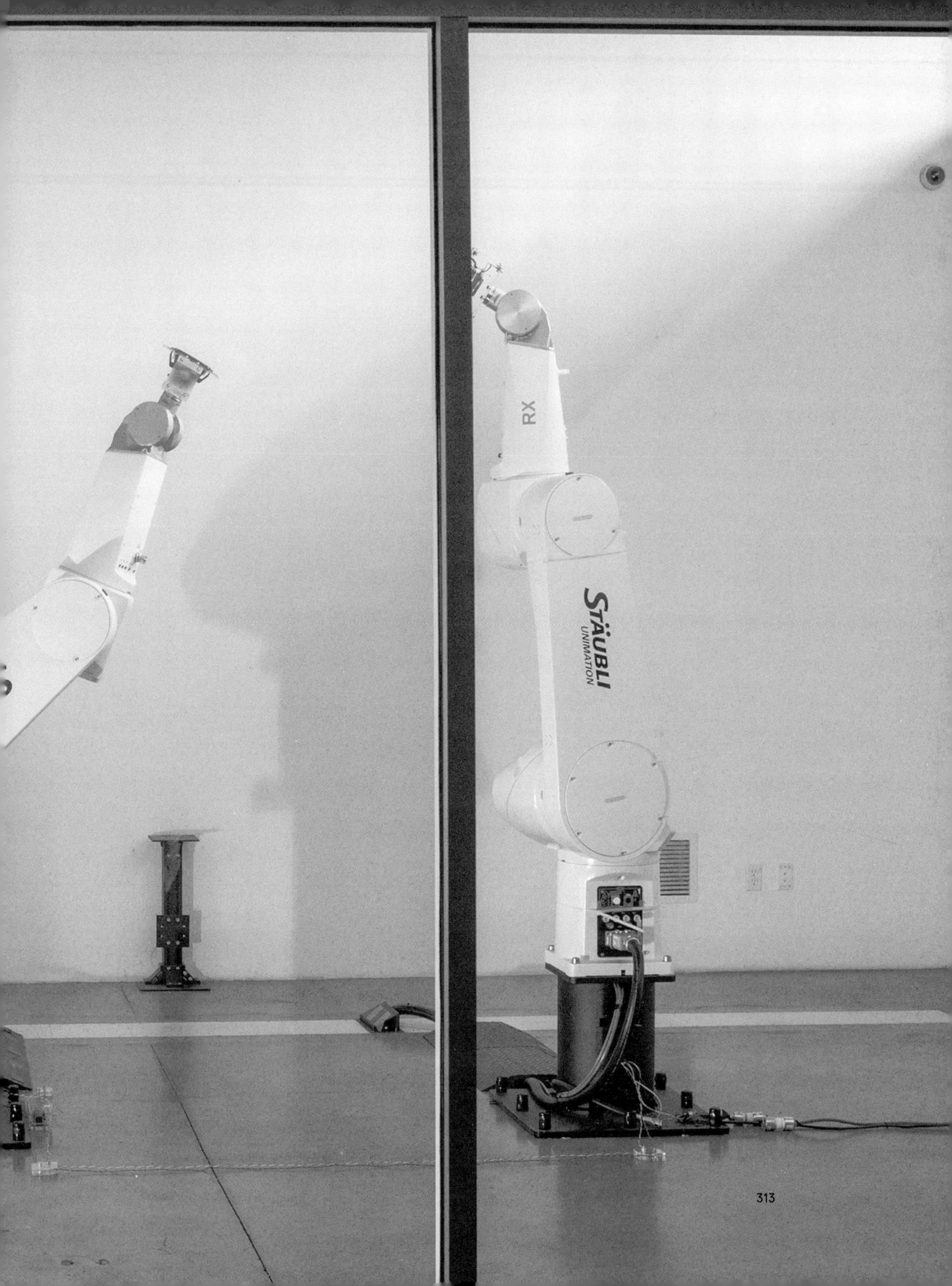
RX
STÄUBLI
UNIMATION

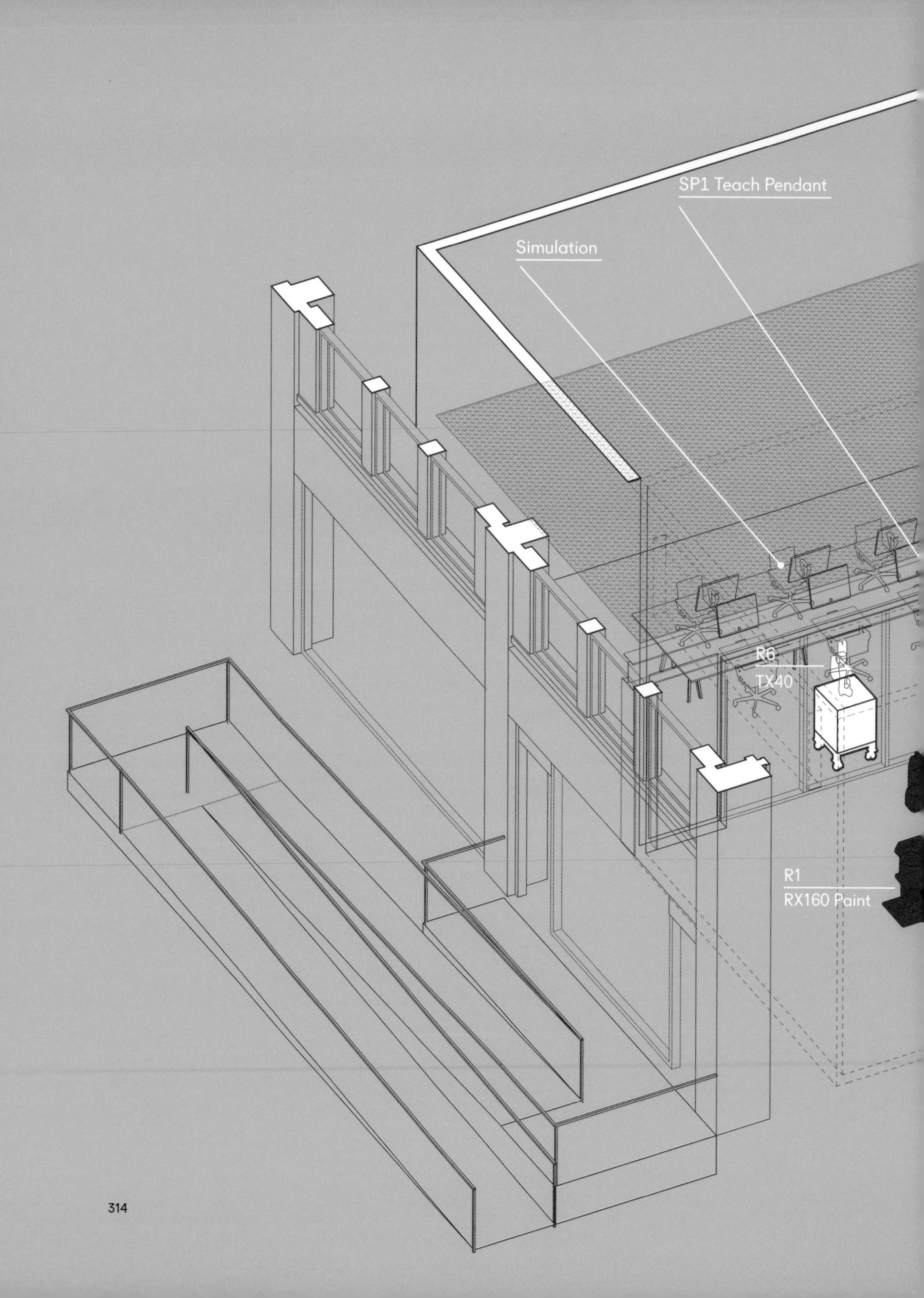

SP1 Teach Pendant
Simulation
R6
TX40
R1
RX160 Paint

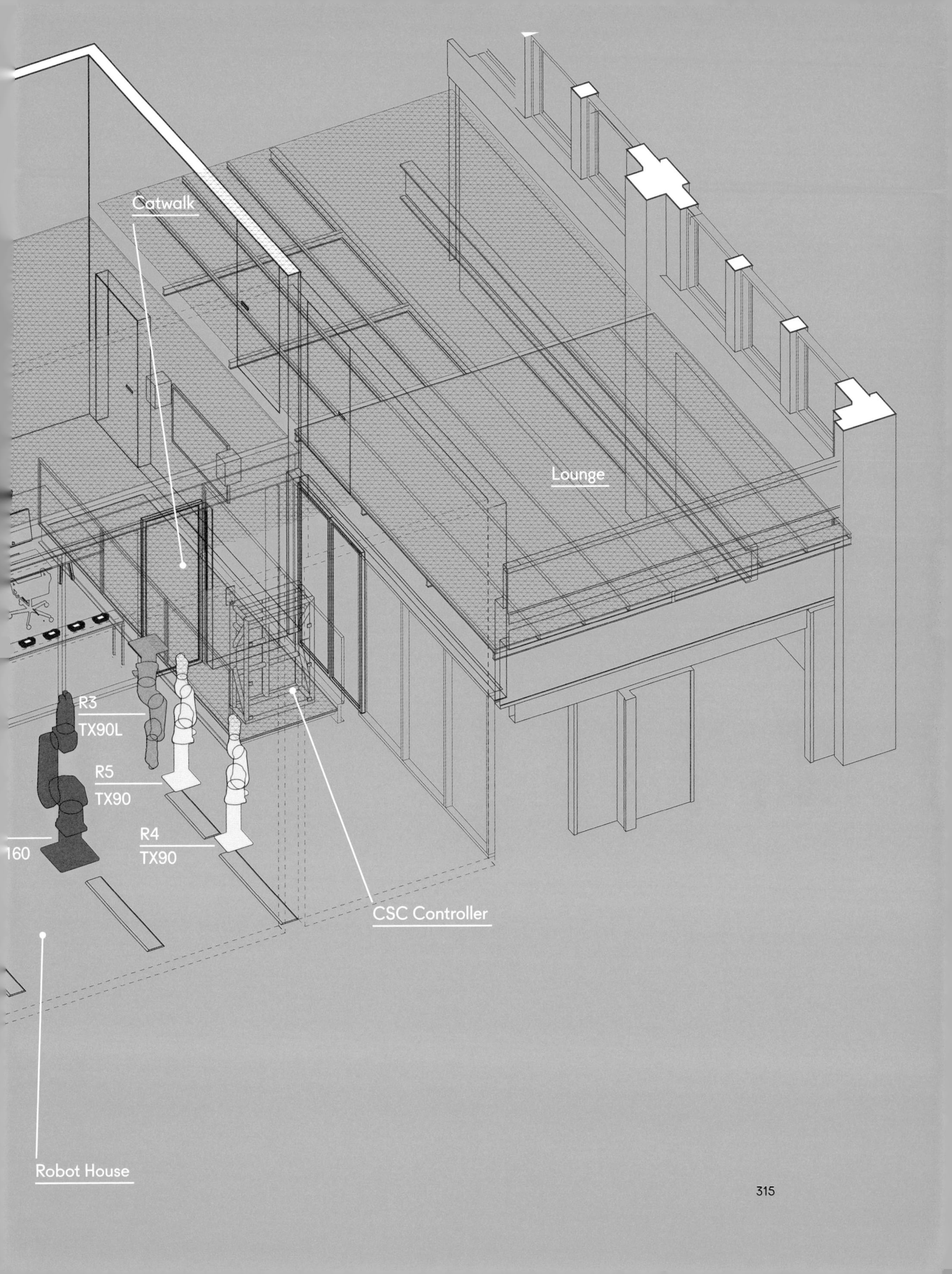
Catwalk
Lounge
R3
TX90L
R5
TX90
R4
TX90
160
CSC Controller
Robot House

Stäubli RX160

Reach	1710 mm
Maximum load	34 kg
Nominal load	20 kg
Degrees of freedom	6
Repeatability	+/- 0.05
Weight	248 kg
Maximum speed	10.3 m/s
Orientation	Pedestal

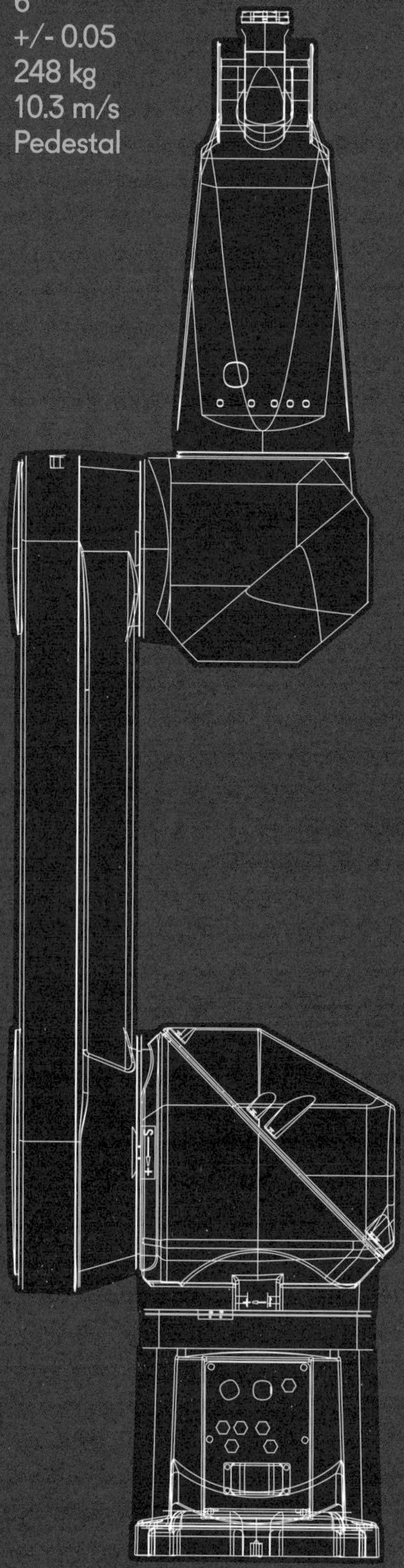

Stäubli TX90L

Reach	1200 mm
Maximum load	15 kg
Nominal load	6 kg
Degrees of freedom	6
Repeatability	+/- 0.035
Weight	111 kg
Maximum speed	10.54 m/s
Orientation	Catwalk

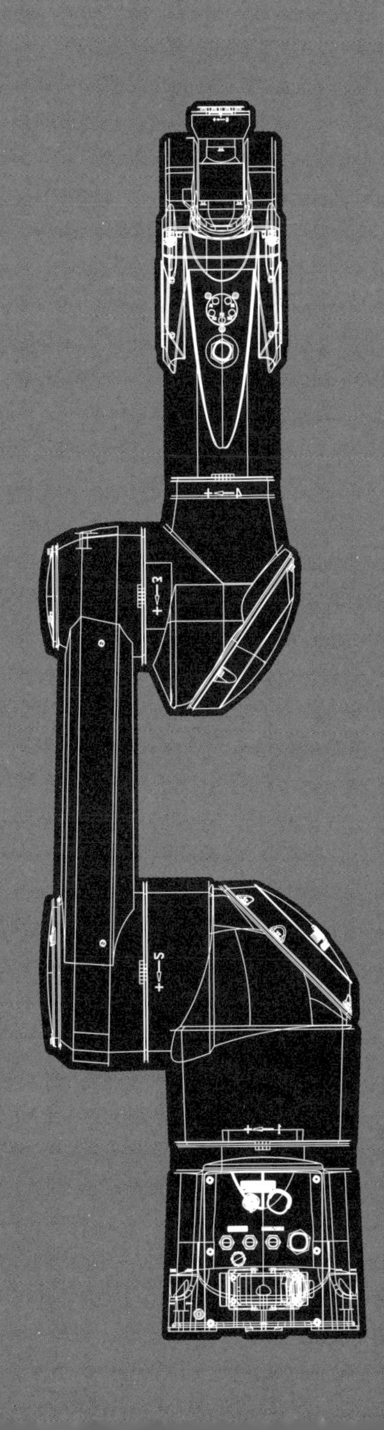

Stäubli TX90

Reach	1000 mm
Maximum load	20 kg
Nominal load	7 kg
Degrees of freedom	6
Repeatability	+/- 0.05
Weight	111 kg
Maximum speed	10.42 m/s
Orientation	Pedestal

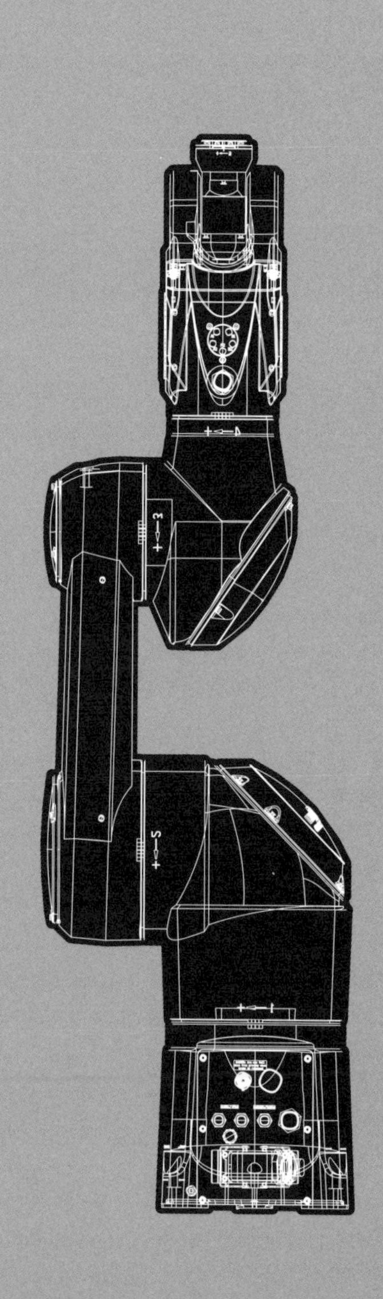

Stäubli TX40

Reach	450 mm
Maximum load	2.3 kg
Nominal load	1.7 kg
Degrees of freedom	6
Repeatability	+/- 0.02
Weight	27 kg
Maximum speed	8.2 m/s
Orientation	Mobile

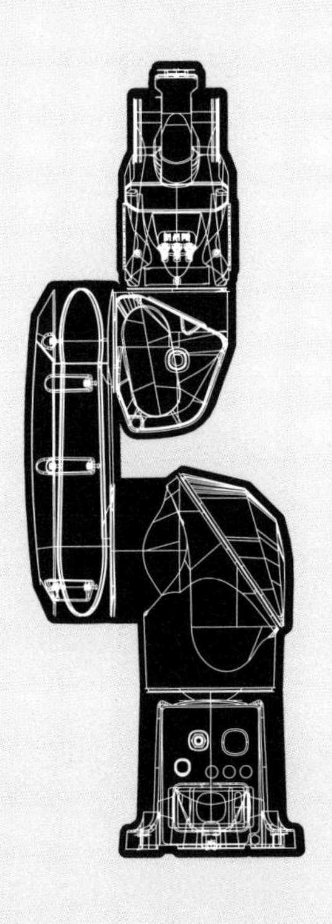

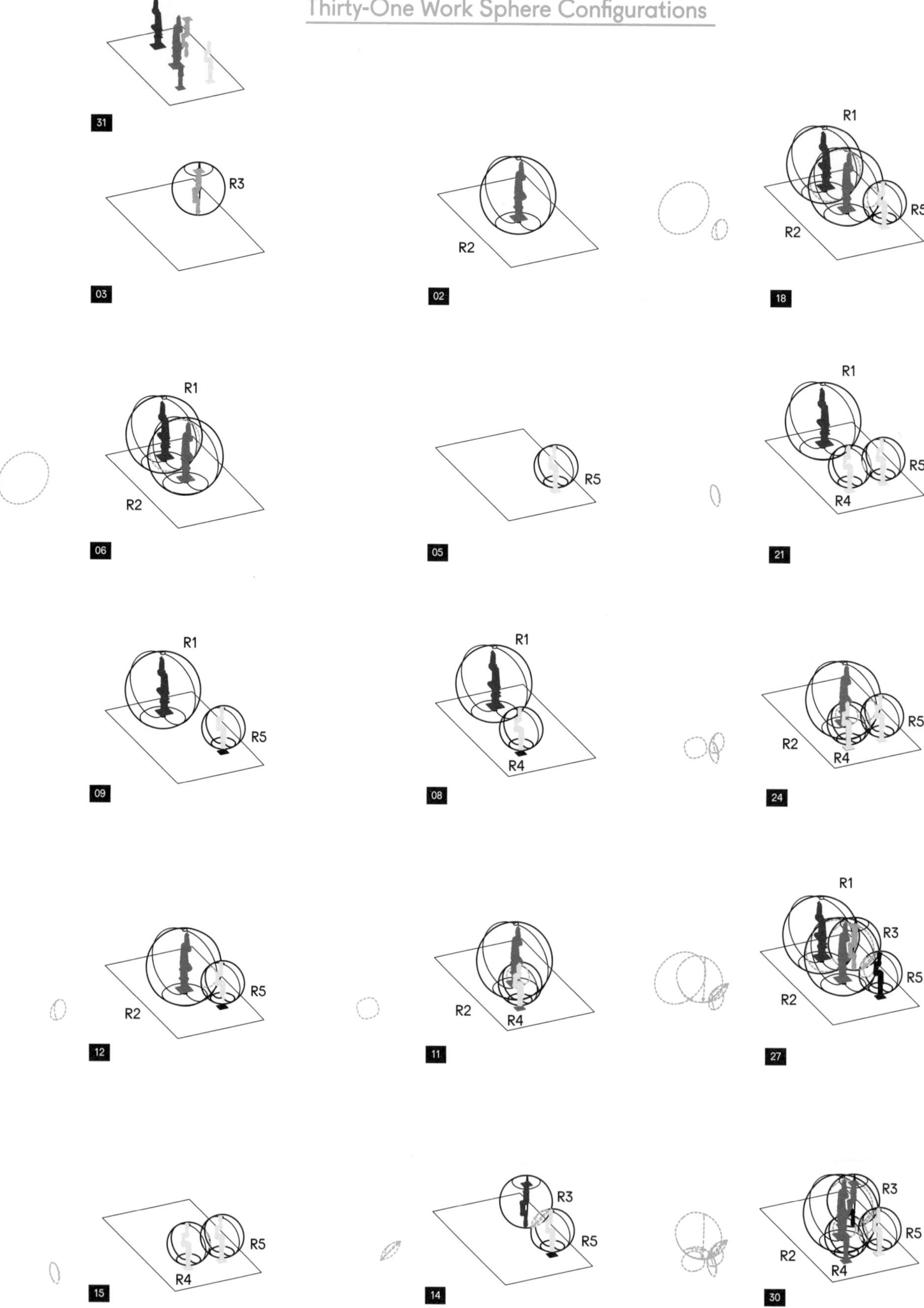
31
R3
03
R2
02
R1
R5
R2
18
R1
R2
06
R5
05
R1
R5
R4
21
R1
R5
09
R1
R4
08
R5
R2
R4
24
R5
R2
12
R2
R4
11
R1
R3
R5
R2
27
R5
R4
15
R3
R5
14
R3
R5
R2
R4
30

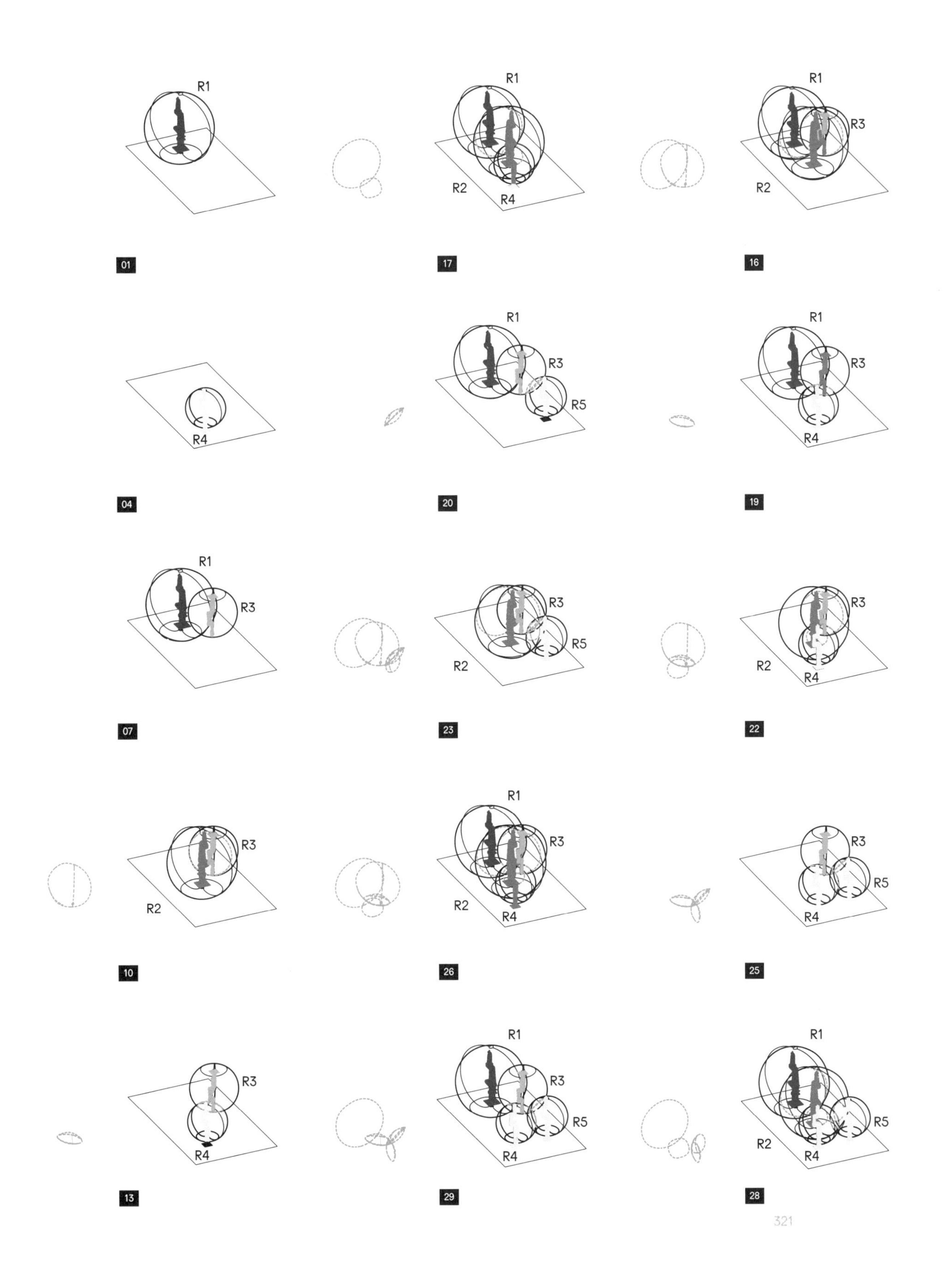
R1
01
R1
R2
R4
17
R1
R3
R2
16
R4
04
R1
R3
R5
20
R1
R3
R4
19
R1
R3
07
R3
R5
R2
23
R3
R2
R4
22
R3
R2
10
R1
R3
R2
R4
26
R3
R5
R4
25
R3
R4
13
R1
R3
R5
R4
29
R1
R5
R2
R4
28

Work Sphere Geometry

SCI-Arc's Robot House offers multiple configurations of work spheres. In most cases all five (or six) robots are not operated simultaneously. Configurations are project-specific, depending on reach, speed, and payload.

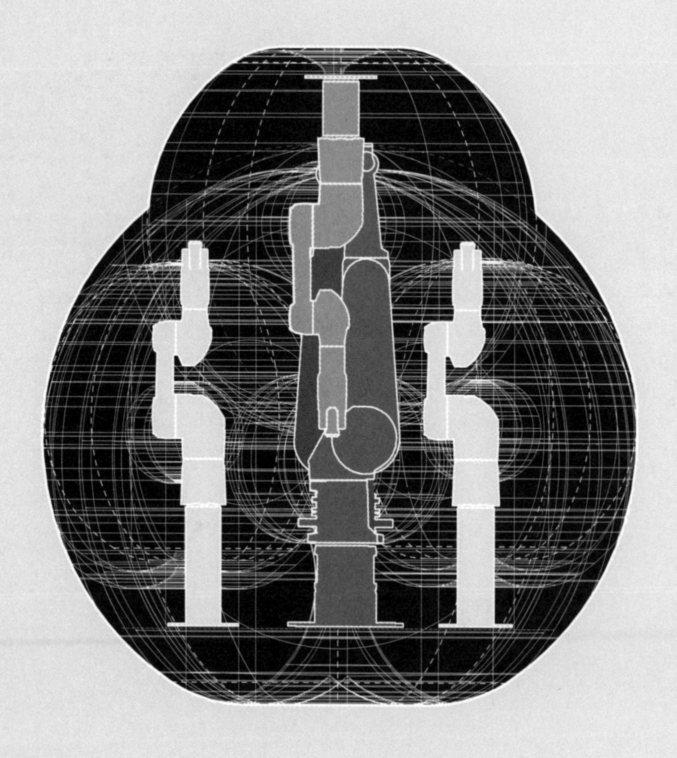

End Elevation

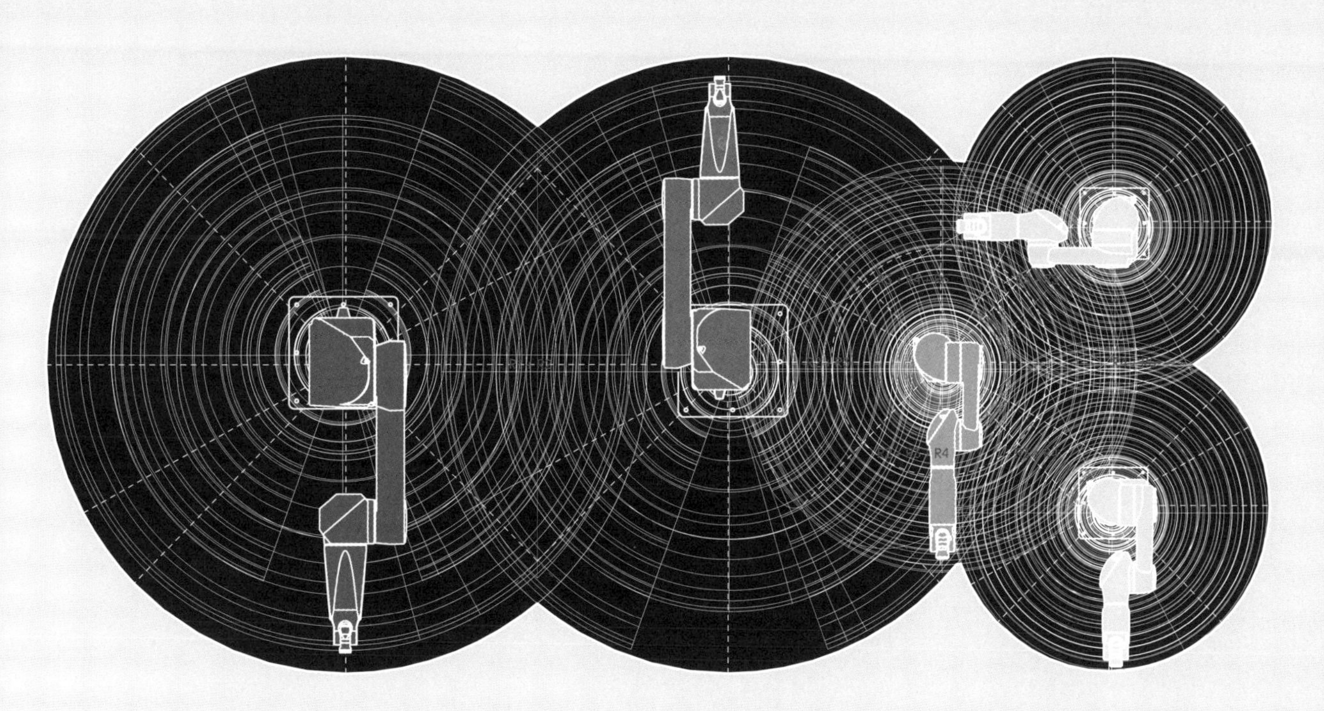

Top View

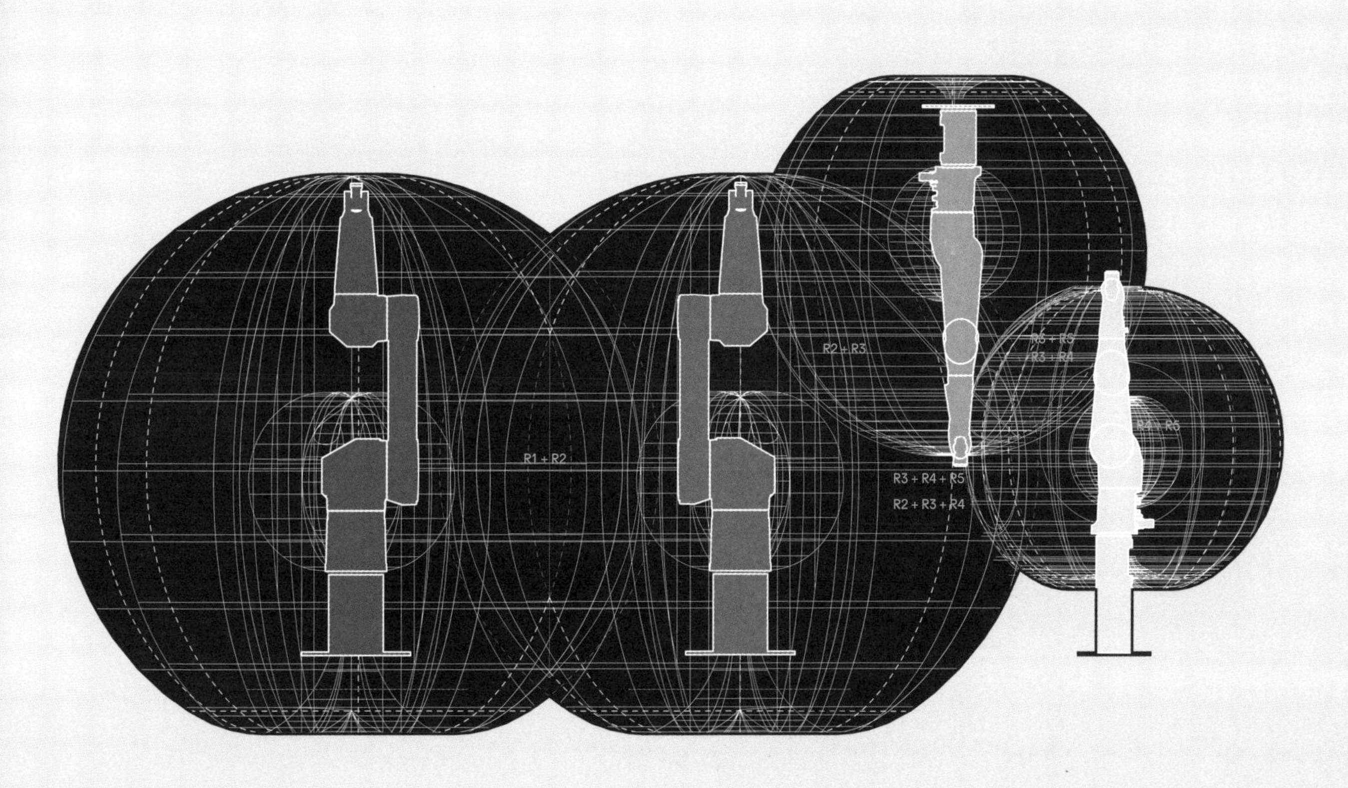

Side Elevation

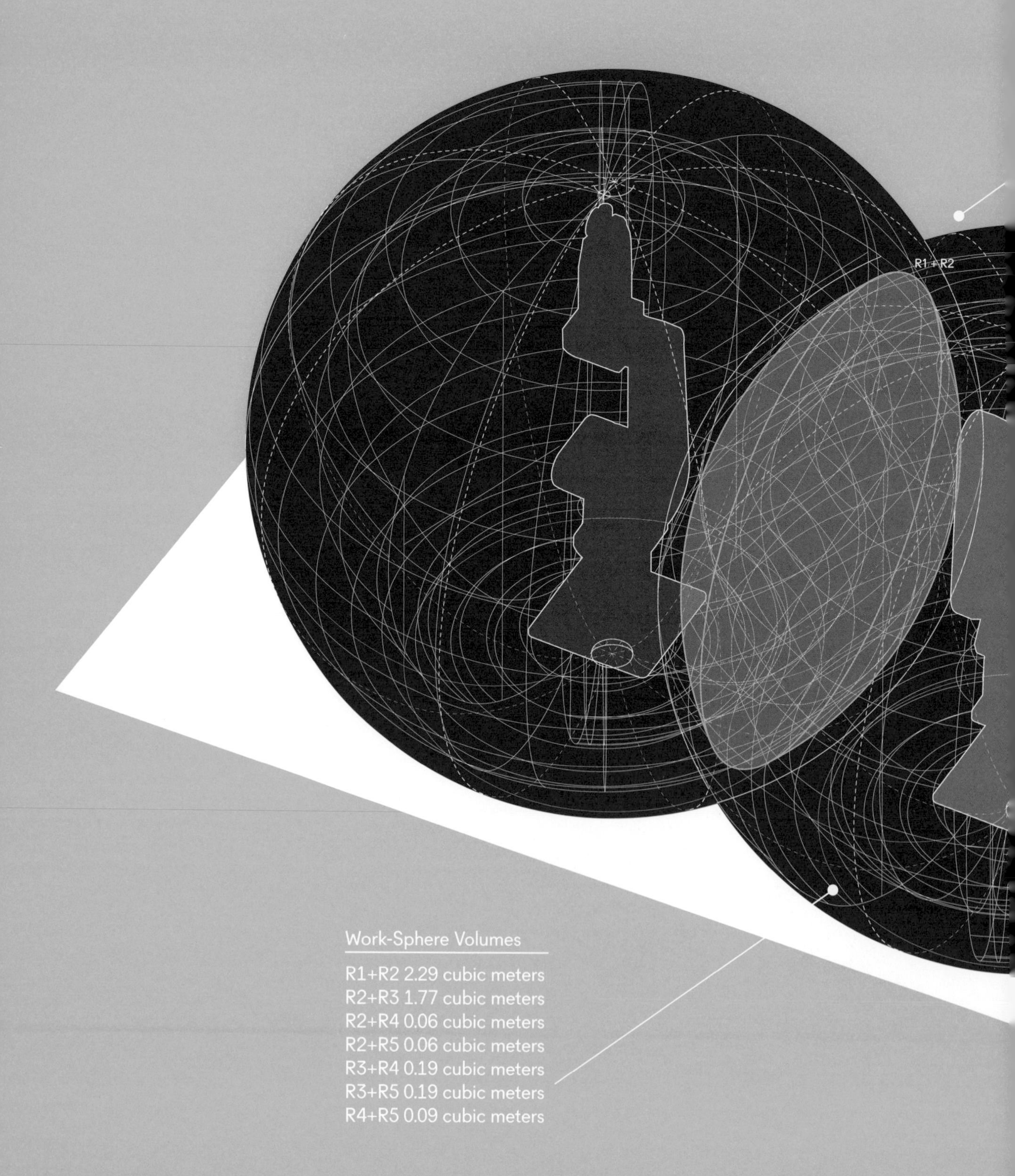
R1+R2
Work-Sphere Volumes
R1+R2 2.29 cubic meters
R2+R3 1.77 cubic meters
R2+R4 0.06 cubic meters
R2+R5 0.06 cubic meters
R3+R4 0.19 cubic meters
R3+R5 0.19 cubic meters
R4+R5 0.09 cubic meters

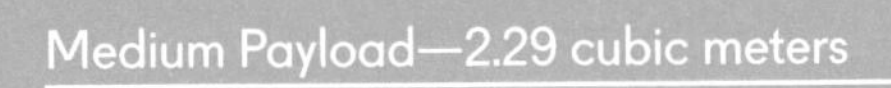

Medium Payload—2.29 cubic meters

The combined work spheres of the RX160 supports large-scale motion and assembly.

Intersecting Work Spheres—2.36 cubic meters

The intersection of R1, R2, R3, and R5 allows access to a diversity of robot types, including the catwalk-mounted TX90L.

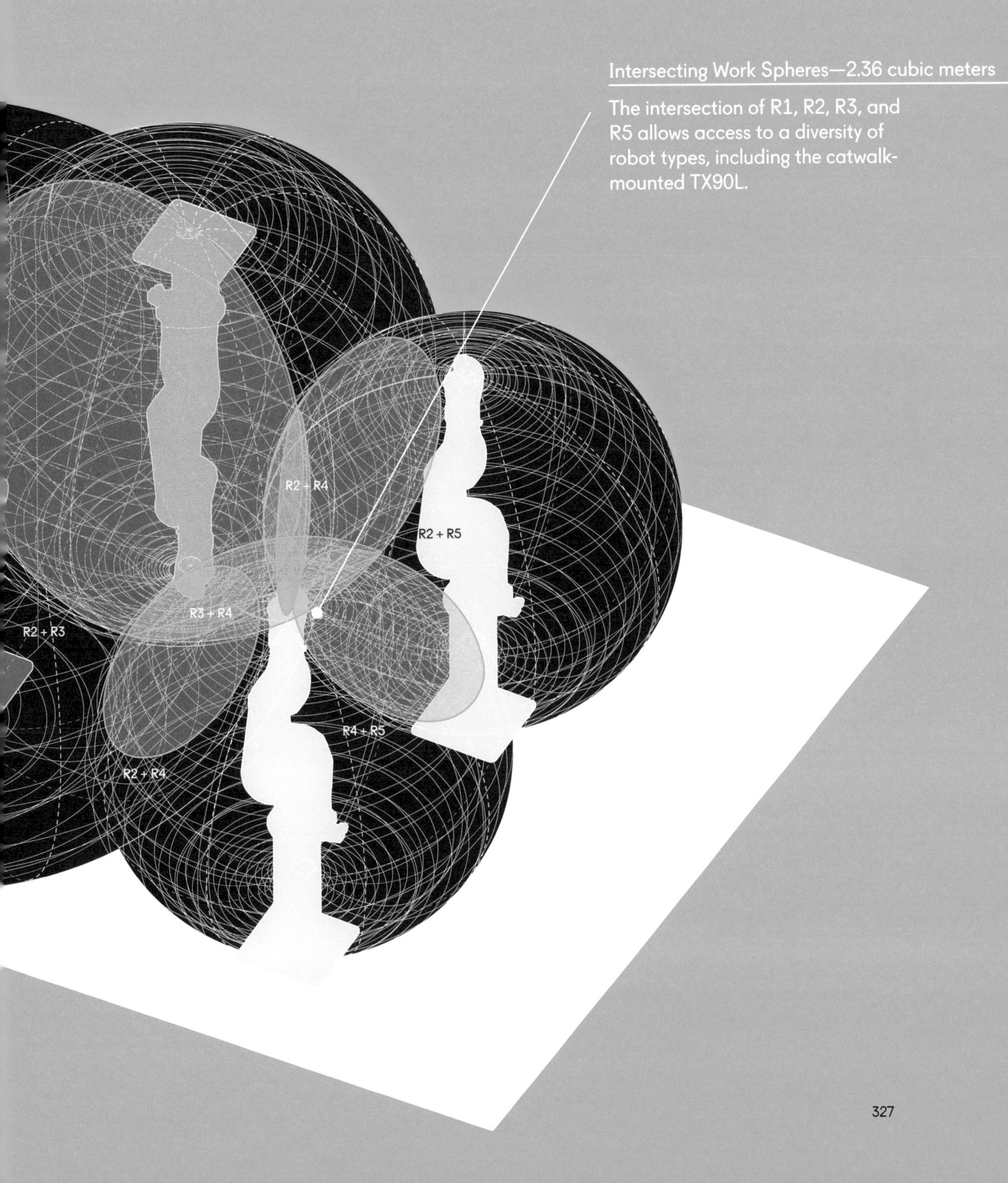

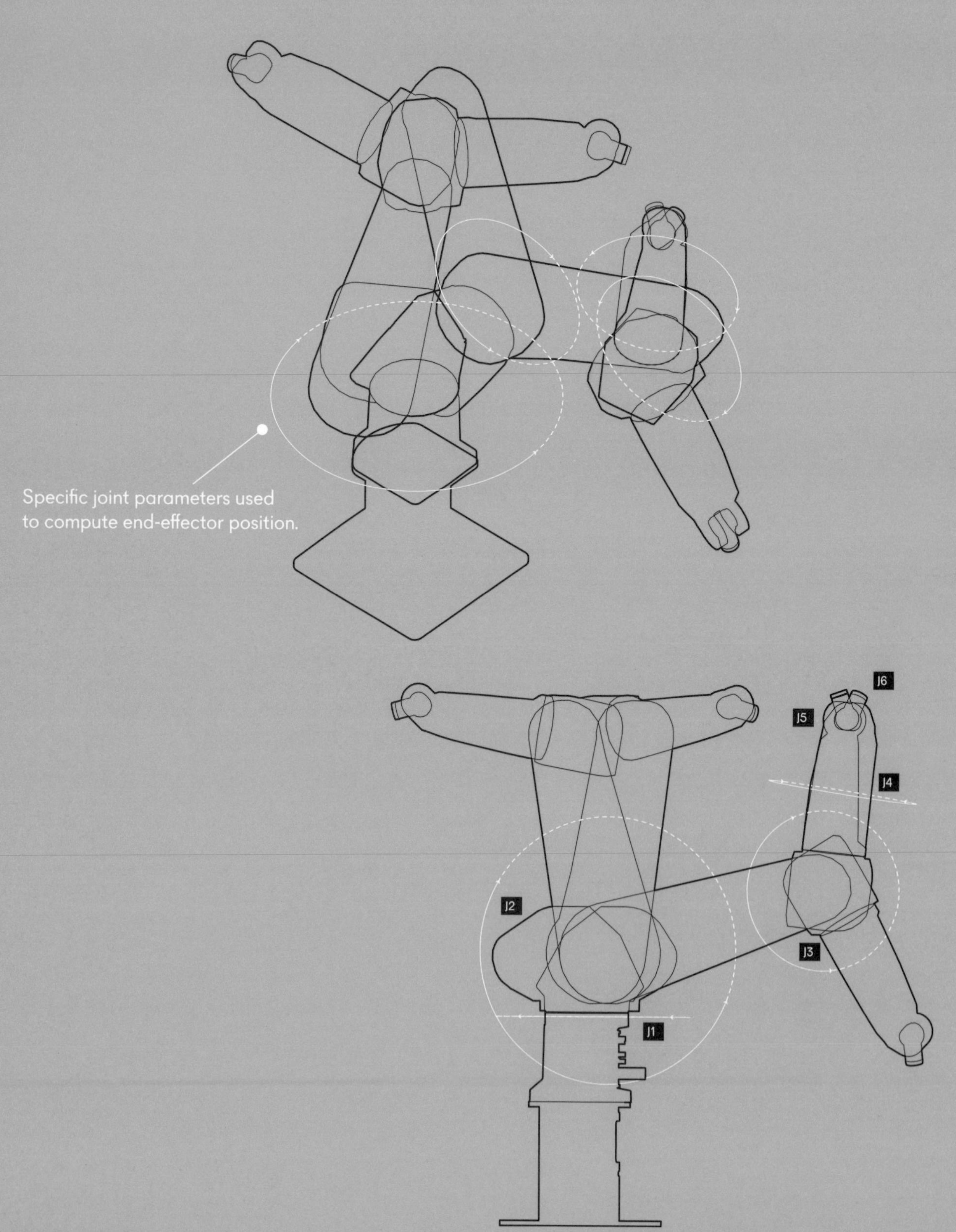

Specific joint parameters used to compute end-effector position.

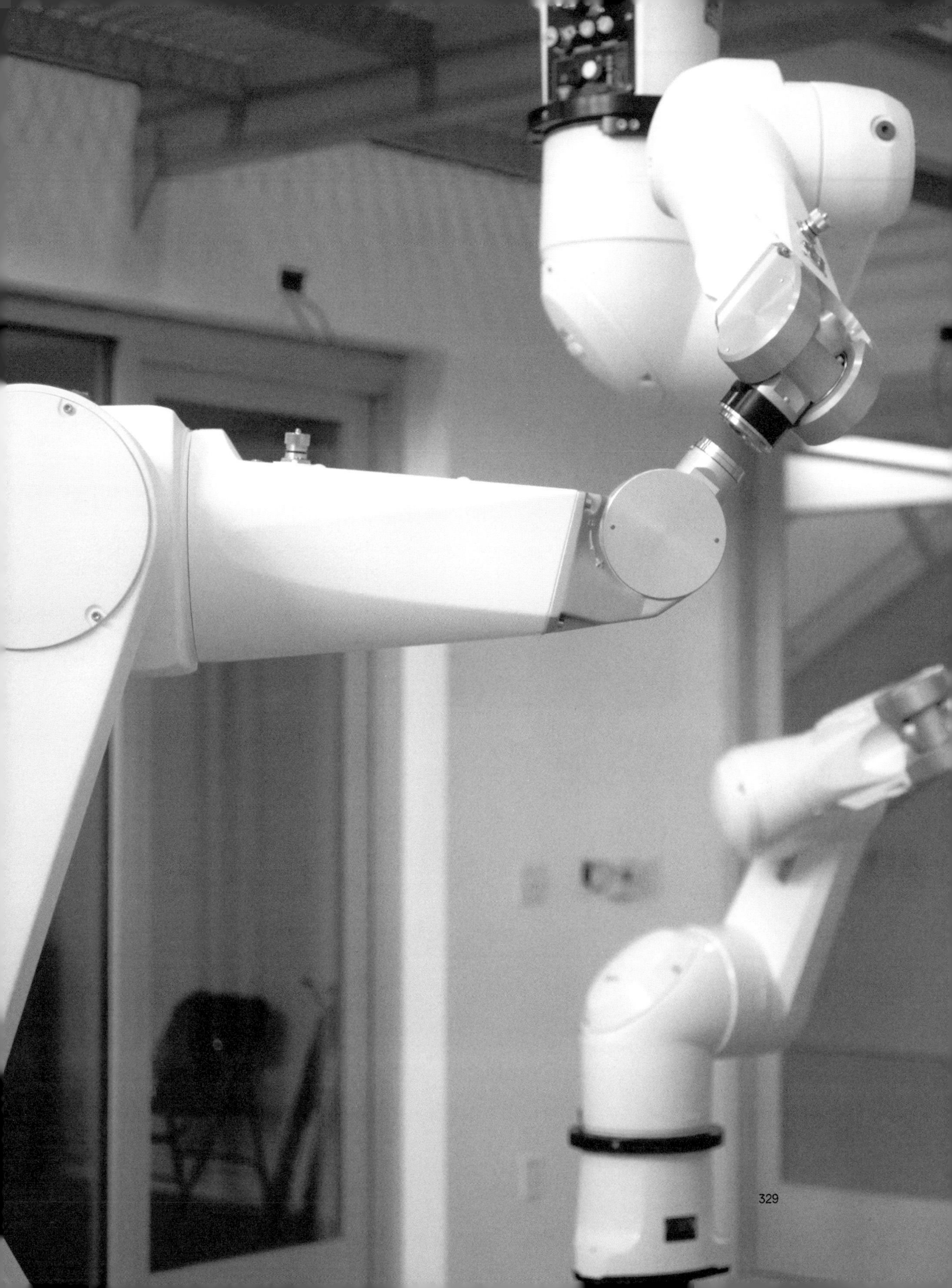

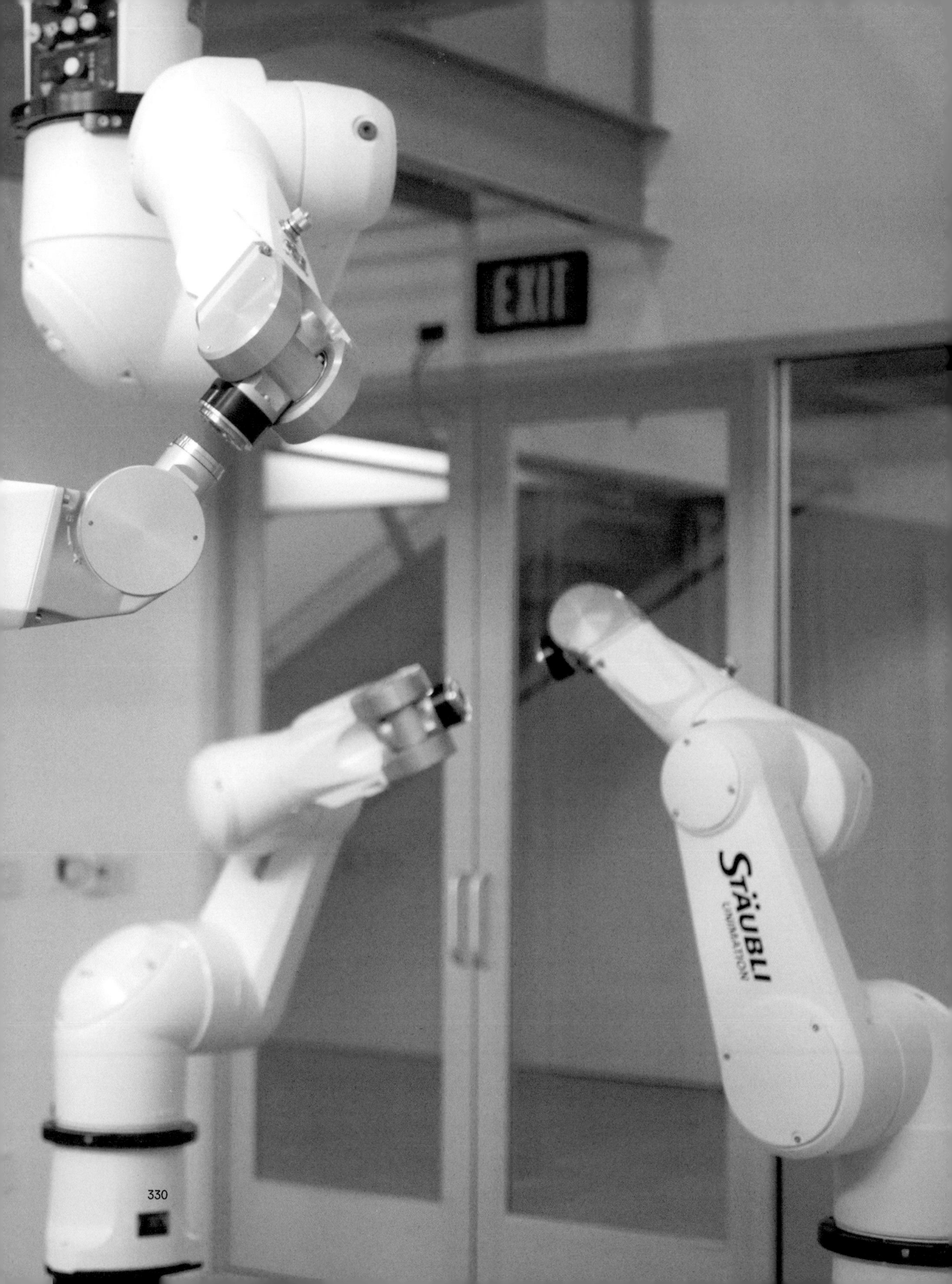
EXIT
STÄUBLI
UNIMATION

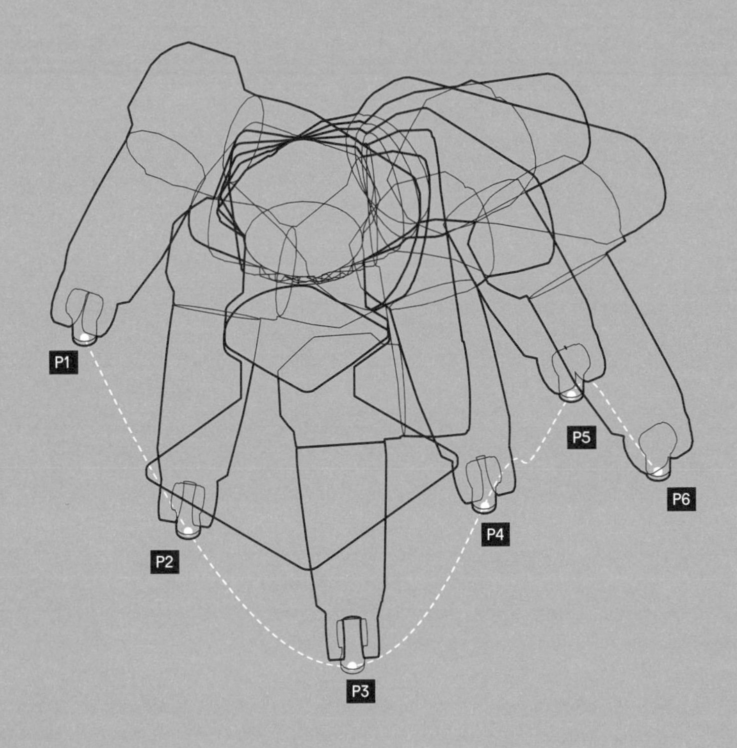
P1
P2
P3
P4
P5
P6

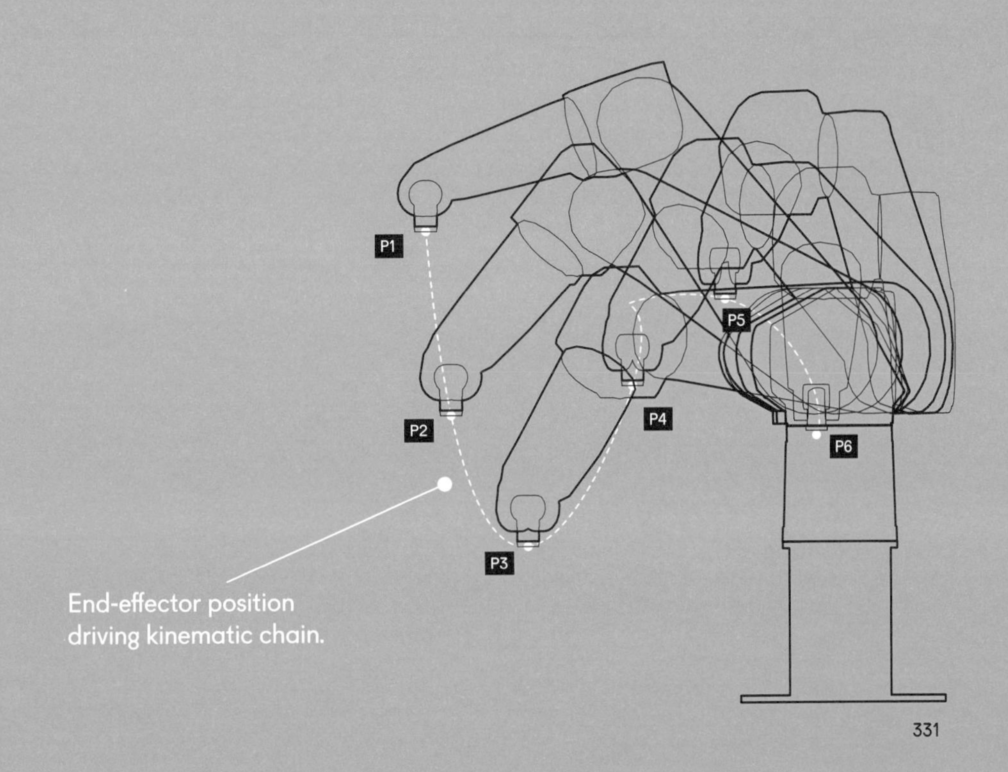
P1
P2
P3
P4
P5
P6
End-effector position
driving kinematic chain.

Acknowledgments

Robot House was initiated in December 2009 with the support of SCI-Arc's Leadership and Board of Trustees. This project was made possible with generous guidance and encouragement of Eric Moss, John Geresi, Rick Carter, Hsinming Fung, John Enright, and Bill Kramer. SCI-Arc Director/CEO Hernan Diaz Alonso has been essential in producing this volume and furthering the larger project.

Stäubli Robotics, the Fletcher Jones Foundation, and Ralph M. Parsons Foundation provided generous in-kind contributions and grants in support of the Robot House facility, research, and academic programs.

This book would not have been possible without the continuous encouragement and editorial vision of Lucas Dietrich, Architecture Editor at Thames & Hudson. Technical editor Kirsty Seymour-Ure was both patient and rigorous in editing the manuscript. The graphic design studio Omnivore—Alice Chung, Karen Hsu, and especially Julie Cho with the assistance of Jacqi Lee—made key contributions in every aspect of the conceptualization, design, and production of the book.

Writing for this book began in spring 2014 and concluded in fall 2016. The inspiration began sometime earlier when I conducted a series of design studios and seminars often in collaboration with Devyn Weiser, first at the Massachusetts Institute of Technology and subsequently at SCI-Arc.

I am especially grateful to a number of colleagues and students who have made extraordinary contributions to the realization and development of the work presented in this volume. In particular the early contributions of Brandon Kruysman, Jonathan Proto, and Curime Batliner. Brian Harms and Nazareth Ekmekjain were essential to making this 'impossible object' user friendly. Kyle and Liz Von Hasseln played a key role in demonstrating the potential of Robot House as a new type of design platform. I also wish to acknowledge the ongoing contribution of Jake Newsum, SCI-Arc Robotics Lab Coordinator. This list would not be complete without the original contributions of colleagues including Devyn Weiser, Marcelo Spina, Tom Wiscombe, Andrew Attwood, and Casey Rehm. I am particularly indebted to Assistant Teachers Patrick Shields, Jonathon Stahl, Peter Vikar, Uriel Lopez, and Anass Benhachmi; and a large group of extraordinary students in the studios, seminars and workshops at SCI-Arc that produced work documented in this book and credited in the Projects section. I benefited from two fine research assistants during preparation for the book, Emily Burton and Uriel Lopez.

I also wish to thank Greg Lynn and Andreas Froech for their early support and encouragement of the larger project.

My firm Testa & Weiser Inc. and in particular Devyn Weiser, Patrick Shields, and Jonathon Stahl were essential to the conceptual, and technical development of Robot House. For their work in executing this idea, and overseeing construction, and installation I wish to acknowledge and thank John Bencher AGA Architects and Trinity Automation.

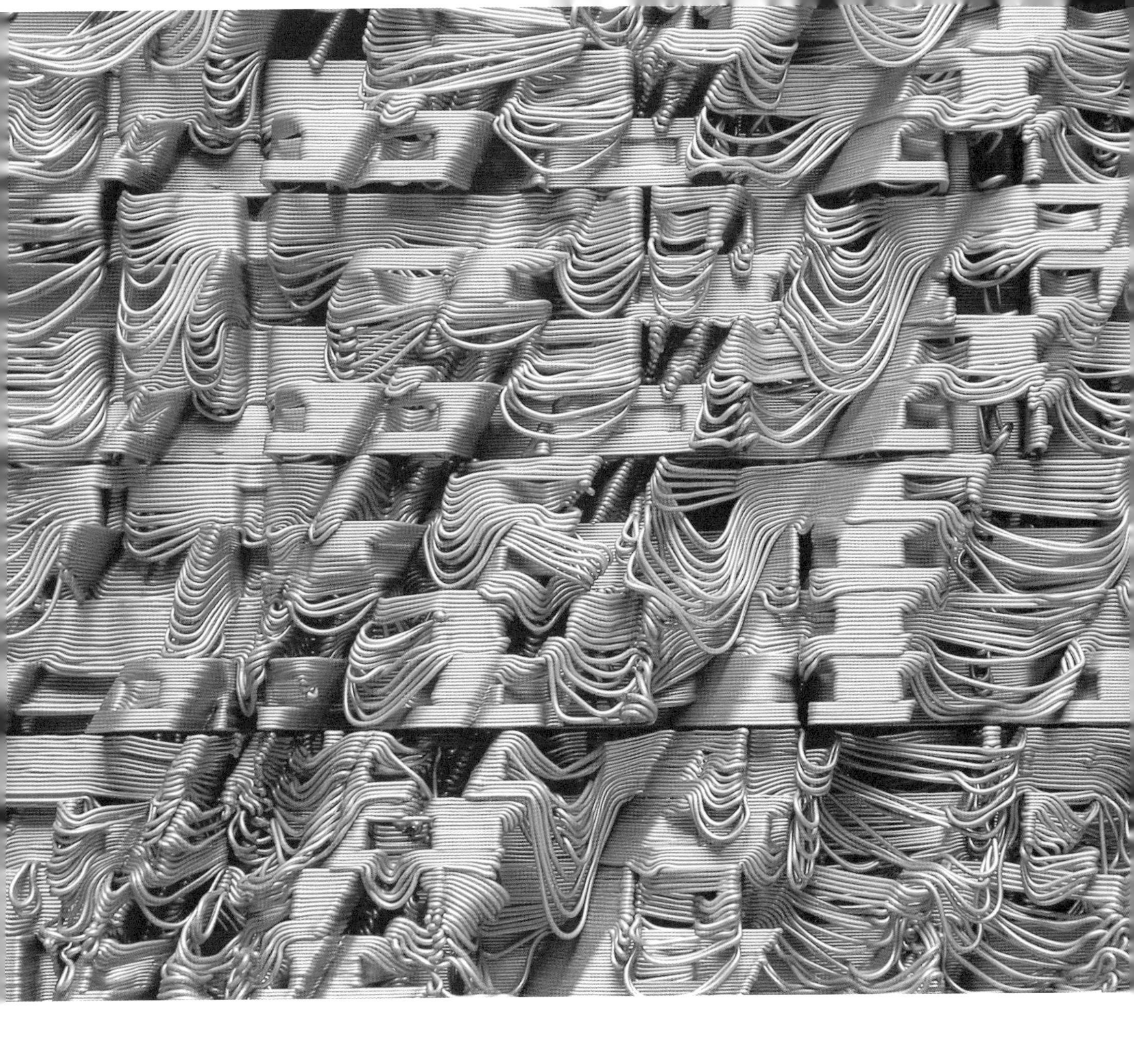